LIGHT

LIGHT

BY

F. BRAY, M.A. Oxon.

LATE SCIENCE MASTER AT CLIFTON COLLEGE

LONDON

EDWARD ARNOLD & CO.

First Published *1927*
Reprinted . . . *1928, 1930, 1934*
Second Edition *1938*
Reprinted *1939*
Reprinted *1942*
Reprinted *1944*
Reprinted *1946*
Reprinted *1948*

Printed in Great Britain by
J. W. ARROWSMITH LTD., BRISTOL.

PREFACE TO THE SECOND EDITION

The book has been completely revised for the purpose of introducing one of the sign conventions recommended by the Physical Society and also in order to meet the demand for more up-to-date instruction, mainly in Illumination, Diffraction and Spectra.

The Author has found that the most effective method of teaching geometrical optics is to regard real objects and real images as being formed in positive spaces and virtual objects and virtual images as being formed in negative spaces. This convention, although arbitrary, appeals to boys much more than one based on mathematical usage and has, therefore, been adopted.

Another convention adopted is to regard erect images as having positive magnification and inverted as having negative magnification. This appears to be a natural and consistent way of dealing with magnification in a lens system.

It is hoped that the method of treatment of a lens system will provide an easier approach to the study of thick lenses than the methods commonly used. The aim has been to provide a logical and easy introduction to more advanced optics.

Owing to the rapid advances in illumination engineering the chapter on Photometry has been rewritten and its position in the text changed. The subject, properly treated, is not easy for the beginner, and for this reason should not be attempted until the ordinary principles of reflection and refraction have been studied.

The chapter on Spectra has also been rewritten in order to meet the demands of the advanced student.

The Author has received numerous suggestions during the last ten years, so that it will be found that additional material has been included in every chapter.

A set of examples selected from Higher Certificate, Intermediate Science and Scholarship papers have been added at the end of the book. For these I am indebted to the Cambridge University Press and the Oxford and Cambridge Schools Examination Board.

My thanks are due to the many friends who have advised me on various points, to Mr. H. E. George, M.A., who has assisted me from time to time, and to Mr. J. W. Cottingham, B.Sc., for his ripple tank photographs. I am particularly grateful to Mr. F. Y. Poynton, M.Sc., who has given me considerable help both in the revision of the text and in the reading of the proofs.

F. B.

July, 1938.

CONTENTS

PART I

CHAPTER I

CONTENTS

CONTENTS

SEPARATE PLATES

TEXT PLATES

PART I

CHAPTER I

HISTORICAL INTRODUCTION

The earliest investigations of the nature and behaviour of light, as far as we know, seem to have been made by the Egyptians. Whether or not such investigations were carried out entirely for practical purposes and with no definite desire for knowledge will probably never be known. Certainly the periodic floodings of the Nile were responsible for the rise of surveying, and as the latter could more easily be carried out by observations on the rising and setting of stars we might find in this the " cause " which brings astronomy to the fore as one of our earliest sciences. The influence of the Egyptians on the well-known philosopher THALES OF MILETUS (640 B.C.) was such as to cause him to abandon trade and return to Miletus to devote the rest of his life to the study of the Egyptian Sciences. It is possible that Thales was responsible for the introduction of Science to the Greeks. Such philosophic people preferred to investigate nature by studying themselves rather than by recording observations and ascertaining whether their conjectures were verified by experiment. Many theories of light were put forward by these philosophers, but very few survived the test of experiment.

The first school of physical thought, that of EMPEDOCLES (444 B.C.), considered that the eye was endowed with the qualities of an octopus. The eye was supposed to project millions and millions of small tentacles which seized an object and caused it to be illuminated. PYTHAGORAS and the EPICUREANS (540 B.C.) held the opposite view. According to their theory images formed in the eye were emanations from objects ; in other words, the objects became the octopi.

1   B

PLATO (430 B.C.) tried to combine the two theories. He explained light as the phenomenon caused by the collision of the emanations from the eye and object—the " neutralisation " as it were of the two emanations, just as the sudden neutralisation of positive and negative electricity causes a spark.

Some historians credit Plato's school with the discoveries of two laws of light : (1) light travels in straight lines ; (2) light is reflected in such a way that the angle of incidence is equal to the angle of reflection (Chapter III). We are told that some of Plato's disciples broke away from their traditional habits and actually verified the laws experimentally. The method they adopted was to allow a small beam of light to pass through a narrow hole into a dark room so that the light impinged on a plane piece of polished metal. Then by observing the small particles of dust which were illuminated they concluded that the above laws of light were obeyed.

ARISTOTLE (384 B.C.) and his disciples were of the opinion that light possessed wonderful powers of its own of which it could make use whenever it felt the need was required. Thus, transparent bodies such as air, water and glass received their properties from the light and it was owing to the latter's gracious condescension during the day time that these bodies could possess the power of permitting other objects, placed behind them, to be seen. During night time this power was removed. It is remarkable to us that such a purely imaginary conception could find any adherents ; yet although it was not unanimously accepted by Aristotle's disciples, a great many admitted its possibility. All the followers of Aristotle considered that light and colour were the natural qualities of the luminous bodies and were of the same nature as the sensations they produced in the eye. This was in accord with their general principle " Nothing can be given out by a body unless it is of the same nature as the body."

After the conquest of Egypt by ALEXANDER THE GREAT, King of Macedonia, about 310 B.C. and the subsequent division of this empire among the more powerful generals when this great king died, a new school of philosophy was founded at Alexandria. One of the most illustrious members of this famous school was ARCHIMEDES (287 B.C.), sometimes called "The father of physics." He was not only a brilliant philosopher, but was also a gifted experimentalist, and although he contributed very little, as far as we know, to the study of optics, it is interesting to note that when the Romans attacked Syracuse in 212 B.C., Archimedes is said to have constructed huge mirrors for the purpose of concentrating the sun's rays on the hostile fleet lying inside the harbour.

When Egypt became a province of the Roman Empire the Alexandrian school received a serious set-back and for practically 300 years no scientific research was carried out by it. Fortunately, the Emperor MARCUS AURELIUS ANTONINUS, a lover of scientific learning, gave fresh impetus to the school and about A.D. 100, PTOLEMY, the celebrated Egyptian astronomer, tabulated a complete system of the heavenly bodies. In his work on astronomy he is supposed to have branched into the study of optics, for we find him cited as the author of a treatise on optics, of which there is a Latin translation from an Arabic version in the National Library of Paris. It is in this treatise that we first find refraction mentioned, that is the bending of light when it leaves one transparent medium and enters another.

The Romans, unfortunately, were not scientists, but they had mastered, to a certain extent, many of the Greek scientific works. NERO is supposed to have possessed an emerald monocle made in the form of a concave lens. Glass lenses were used to concentrate the sun's rays and so relight the sacred fires of ancient Rome. The cauterising of flesh was carried on in a similar manner. It would seem then that although the Romans produced no well-known scientists who were interested in optics, some of them had obtained sufficient knowledge for practical application.

During the time when the Romans were at the height of their power, scientific learning became almost extinct in Europe. Fortunately for science the MUSLIMS, who had conquered Byzantium and Persia (seventh century) and had succeeded in extending their Empire as far as Spain, were not only fighters but lovers of learning. Hundreds of books were translated from Greek into Arabic, for the Muslims were fully aware of the merit of Greek philosophy, and as the Arabs had acquired the Egyptian methods of observation and experiment we find for the first time a correlation of the theory of Greece with the practice of Egypt. As this is the true principle of scientific method it is not surprising that the Arabs became keen scientists. The study of optics does not appear to have been made during this period, and it was not until A.D. 1000, long after the overthrow of the Muslims in Spain by the Moors that ALHAZEN, a Moorish philosopher, revived its study. In his works on optics we find mentioned the phenomenon of refraction and also a knowledge of the properties of glass spheres.

From Spain the study of science spread rapidly over Europe, and the Europeans following the example set by the Arabs began to study Greek scientific philosophy. Unfortunately, many of the Greek speculations were accepted blindly as the truth and for many years it was considered heresy to seek for new knowledge or question ancient dogmas. Into this unprogressive age appeared ROGER BACON (A.D. 1214), our first well-known British scientist. He interested himself chiefly in astronomy, for like most men of his time he was a firm believer in Astrology or the influence of stars and planets on human existence. The study of astronomy naturally led him on to that of optics, and although it is doubtful whether or not he actually constructed a telescope, his book *Opus Majus* shows a clear knowledge of the properties of the burning glass (lens) and mirrors ; it also shows that he was acquainted with the possibilities of lens combinations such as are now used in microscopes and telescopes. Although astronomy was apparently merely the handmaiden of astrology, for the value of the former was always measured by the assistance it could give the latter, nevertheless astronomy rendered necessary the study of optics and, in consequence, we find such men as VITELLIO (A.D. 1270), COPERNICUS (A.D. 1473), GALILEO (A.D. 1564), and KEPLER (A.D. 1571) making slow but sure headway towards the true laws governing light. Galileo's telescope led Kepler in 1611 to put forward an interesting theory of the refraction of light, and although this was only an approximation to the truth it undoubtedly provided the necessary inspiration for the discovery of the exact law. This came in 1621, for in that year WILLIBROD SNELL first formulated the simple relation between the angles of incidence and refraction of light. Simultaneously with Snell's exposition came that of DESCARTES (1596–1650) the illustrious French philosopher, who also claimed the honour of this discovery. Much controversy has ensued over these rival claimants without any satisfactory conclusion having been reached. Following quickly on this discovery came the overthrow of the accepted theory of Descartes that light passed instantaneously through space. ROEMER, a Danish astronomer (1676), not only accounted for the discrepancies of the observed and calculated times of the rotation of the planet Jupiter's satellites but, by a brilliant piece of reasoning, succeeded in calculating the velocity of light. Although this created quite a sensation at the time it was not accepted until over fifty years afterwards (1729) when BRADLEY, Professor of Astronomy at Oxford University, accounted for the apparent shift of a star on the grounds that light had a definite velocity and, therefore, took a certain time to travel from the star to earth. Another flash of genius enabled him to calculate the velocity, giving a result very nearly the same as that obtained by Roemer. It is remarkable that the first two determinations agree very closely with those obtained by modern scientists who do not depend on astronomical observations for their calculations.

During the latter part of the seventeenth century and the beginning of the next, the greatest name in the history of optics is that of SIR ISAAC NEWTON (1642–1727). As the result of a famous and beautiful series of experiments he was led to the view that ordinary white light is really a mixture of rays of every variety and colour. He also developed the idea of, and himself made the first reflecting telescope, the first of that great series of such telescopes which, with ever-increasing power, have revealed to us the secrets of space. In addition to his experimental work, Newton gave a great deal of thought to the theoretical explanation of optical phenomena. Apart from the very early speculations it has always been agreed that vision is caused by something coming from the object seen and entering the eye. This "something" we call Light. What is it? This question has fascinated generation after generation of scientists. It seems as though we can only imagine two general answers, either

(1) it is some "substance" (not necessarily at all like ordinary matter) emitted from the luminous body in the form of a shower of particles. This is the basis of the *corpuscular theory of light*, or

(2) it is some form of wave motion set up by the luminous body and travelling outwards through space, as sound waves are produced by a vibrating body and ripples by a stick shaken in water. This is the fundamental idea of the *wave theory of light*.

Newton adopted the first of these alternatives as the basis of his theoretical work. No doubt his great researches on mechanics and gravitation influenced him in this choice; but, most of all, he was impressed by the sharpness of light shadows and this seemed to him inexplicable if light consisted of waves. Obstacles placed in the path of water ripples, or of sound which undoubtedly consists of waves in the air, do not give rise to sharp shadows; the waves spread round them. On the other hand, the corpuscular theory gives a very simple and immediate explanation of this straight-line propagation of light. It is only necessary to make the natural assumption that the light particles while travelling in a uniform medium are not subject to any force and hence, in accordance with Newton's first law of motion, they travel with a constant velocity in a straight line. Reflection and refraction can also be shown to follow from very simple assumptions with regard to the behaviour of the particles at the boundary between two media.

In the case of reflection (Fig. 1) Newton assumed that when the particle approaches very close to the surface it experiences a repulsive force which gradually diminishes and then reverses the component of the velocity perpendicular to the surface,

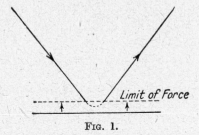

Fig. 1.

so that the particle moves away from the surface with the same speed as that at which it approached.

In the case of refraction at the surface of an optically denser medium (such as water) he assumed that an attractive force

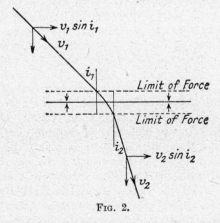

Fig. 2.

begins to operate very near to the surface (Fig. 2). The component of the velocity perpendicular to the surface is increased, but that parallel to the surface is unchanged. Hence, if v_1 and v_2 represent the velocities in the first and second medium respectively, and i_1 and i_2 the angles between the directions of the particle before and after refraction and the normal at the point of incidence, it follows that

$$v_1 \sin i_1 = v_2 \sin i_2$$

$$\text{or} \quad \frac{\sin i_1}{\sin i_2} = \frac{v_2}{v_1}.$$

That is, the ratio of the sines of the angle of incidence and refraction is a constant.

The alternative idea of the wave theory was first seriously treated in a scientific manner by a great contemporary of Newton, CHRISTIAN HUYGENS. He showed how on this theory it was possible to explain reflection and refraction as simply as on Newton's theory. His explanation of refraction led to the result

$$\frac{\sin i_1}{\sin i_2} = \frac{v_1}{v_2}$$

that is, he showed that on the wave theory as in the corpuscular theory, the ratio of the sines of the angles of incidence and refraction would be a constant. But whereas according to Newton the velocity is greater in the optically denser medium, according to the wave theory it is less. At the time no one knew how to measure the speed of light in empty space or any other medium and so it was not possible to decide this point experimentally. Thus, as far as known results went, the two explanations were equally satisfactory. Huygens realised the difficulty of explaining why light, if it is a wave motion, should travel in straight lines and his attempt to get round the difficulty was not very convincing as compared with the simplicity of Newton's explanation. On the other hand, the corpuscular theory also had its difficulties, one of which it is easy to appreciate. According to the ideas we have explained above, it seems clear that when light strikes a boundary it should *either* be reflected *or* transmitted, whereas actually some of the light is reflected and some transmitted. Newton tackled this difficulty with extraordinary ingenuity and it is interesting to note here that in his explanation he introduced some ideas of the wave theory, so that his more developed views presented a rather curious blending of wave and particle ideas.

The next century saw no great discoveries in optics and all the work that was done was dominated by Newton's corpuscular ideas. His prestige and authority drew attention away from the great work of Huygens and it was not until the beginning of the nineteenth century that a new impulse was given to the study of the wave theory by THOMAS YOUNG. He devised a very beautiful experiment to show that in certain circumstances two beams of light could annul one another and produce a region of darkness. This seems quite inexplicable on Newton's corpuscular theory, but Young showed that it was very simply explained in terms of waves. If at any place the waves of one beam always produce a " crest " at the moment those of the other beam produce a " trough " it is clear that the total effect would be zero. This is a simple example of the great Principle of Superposition of waves (or " interference " as it is often called), one of the most important ideas throughout physics. Stimulated by this work of Young, FRESNEL, a young French engineer, developed the wave theory with brilliant success. He showed how the existence of sharp shadows was easily explained by Huygen's method if this was combined with the principle of interference. He did more than this. He showed that light does in fact to some extent spread round obstacles, and that the minutest details of this spreading phenomena (called diffraction) could be predicted by the wave theory. In this way the greatest difficulty in the early development of the theory was converted into strong evidence in its favour. Fresnel also showed how by adopting the idea (first suggested much earlier by Hooke) that the light vibrations were transverse, that is, at right angles to the direction of travel, another great group of optical phenomena, called polarisation, could be very simply understood. Huygens and earlier workers knew of these facts, but they always thought of light vibrations as longitudinal, that is, along the direction of travel, and with this idea no interpretation of polarisation was possible. Fresnel's great work may be said to have completely turned the tables on the corpuscular theory and what seemed a very decisive blow was struck against it in 1850 when Foucault showed that light travelled slower in water than in air. As we have noted, this was what Huygens predicted and just the reverse of Newton's view. During the remainder of the century many workers contributed to build up the wave theory into an imposing structure. Perhaps the greatest of these contributions was made by CLERK MAXWELL. He put forward with very convincing argument the view that light waves were electric waves and he predicted the possibility of producing such waves of any wave length. Everyone knows how this wonderful prophecy was confirmed in the experiments of HERTZ, the great German physicist, who thus was the founder of wireless communication. In this way the study of light became a branch of electricity—a great example of the way in which our deepening knowledge shows the interrelatedness of things, however separate they may seem.

It is not to be wondered at that by the end of the nineteenth century the electrical wave theory of light had become a firmly established doctrine—almost a dogma. The physicists of the time were so impressed by the wonderful successes of its development that they did not doubt that it would be found capable of explaining all the facts about light. But their optimism was too great. At the end of the century a great series of new discoveries were made which—as every educated layman these days is expected to know !—have caused nothing less than a revolution in physics. Among these were some new and very unexpected facts about the behaviour of light, concerned particularly with the way it is emitted and absorbed by matter. Despite immense displays of skill it was found quite impossible to explain these new facts in terms of the wave theory. In this new and exciting situation, EINSTEIN —a great genius comparable to Newton—evolved a new form of corpuscular theory in terms of which he gave a very simple interpretation of these new discoveries. His theory was indeed very different in detail from Newton's, but it was none the less a corpuscular one. He regarded light as a shower of particles—now called " photons "—emitted by the luminous body. So we had the extraordinary situation of again having two theories about the nature of light, each explaining a certain part of the facts which was inexplicable by the other. Light seems to show a kind of twofold character and in trying to explain its behaviour we have sometimes to think of it as waves and at other times to regard it as particles. As Sir William Bragg once put it : " physicists use the wave theory on Mondays, Wednesdays, and Fridays, and the corpuscular theory on Tuesdays, Thursdays, and Saturdays."

It is true that this is a very unsatisfactory state of affairs ; but it is also a very exhilarating one. It is, indeed, very pleasing when a theory goes on steadily advancing from success to success, all its predictions being verified, and very troubling when it comes up against facts which it simply cannot explain. But it is in such times of crisis that great new discoveries are made. All that is needed then is some creative genius to point the way. We live in such a period, and the great difficulties are finding great men to grapple with them. Einstein, Bohr, Schroedinger, Heisenberg, Dirac, and others are making wonderful contributions towards an understanding of the enigma, and though it cannot yet be said that a solution has been found, it is certain that when it is, we shall have a far deeper understanding of this " Universe of Light."

PROPAGATION OF LIGHT

The Æther and Light Waves.—Since the idea that " light consists of small particles projected with great velocity by a luminous source " was found inadequate to account for experimental fact, it was assumed that something exists which can carry the light from the source to the eye. It is obvious that air is not the transmitting agent, for light can pass through a vacuum ; therefore, we must follow the example of Huygens and assume something exists which can carry luminous energy. That is, we must imagine a medium existing which can have the property of forming waves, very

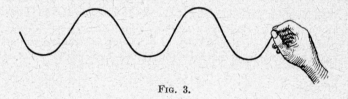

FIG. 3.

much in the same manner that water waves form when a stone is thrown into a pond. This medium is called the **Æther.**

According to the wave theory the way in which light is conveyed from a source to the eye is best understood by carrying out the following simple experiment :—

Fasten one end of a long piece of thick india-rubber band to any convenient fixed object such as a wall. Hold the other end in the hand and move away from the wall until the band is taut. Now jerk the band up and down sharply and a wave is seen to travel from the hand to the wall (Fig. 3). As the wave moves along the band, each portion of the band in turn moves up and down, that is at right angles to the direction of the wave. No rubber leaves the hand and pays a visit to the wall: only the wave or disturbance does this.

Applying this conception to light, the source provides the jerk, that is, it passes light energy to the layers of æther near it, and waves move away through the æther with tremendous velocity until they arrive at the wall, that is the eye. Just as each part of the rubber band moves up and down, so each part of the æther changes its condition periodically, whenever the waves travel through it. It is the disturbance which arrives at the eye and gives us our sensation of sight.

When a heavy stone is cast into a pond, waves spread out in all directions and may be seen sometimes to disturb small floating objects at a considerable distance from where the stone entered. The floating bodies, however, are not taken along with the waves, but gently vibrate up and down. Thus there is no need to imagine a medium which is continually rushing about through space in a state of perpetual storm. It would seem that the æther may be regarded as a gentle rippling " sea " with movement everywhere and yet with a certain calm.

We cannot see the æther and, therefore, we cannot see the waves. If the waves, however, collide with any material particles, these particles become visible because they scatter the vibrations in all directions. The portion received by the eye betrays the existence of the particles.

To realise this invisibility of light waves, compare the modern searchlight with that used to project photographs on to a screen in a picture theatre. The strong beam from the searchlight, instead of being clearly visible to an onlooker, has large gaps which appear to possess no light and it is not until an object such as an aeroplane enters these gaps that it shines out brightly illuminated. The much weaker source in the picture theatre, on the other hand, illuminates all the small particles of smoke and dust, which find their natural home in such places, with the result that the beam appears to possess enormous intensity. Pay a visit to the theatre in the early hours of the morning before the cleaners have disturbed these small particles which form our objects, and you will find that the beam is barely visible in the intervening medium between the source and screen.

All experimental phenomena of this type tend to show that the presence of material particles is necessary to betray the existence of light waves, unless of course the waves actually enter the eye direct from the source, in which case the small sensitive plate at the back of the eye is the brain's intelligence officer.

Rays.—We call the paths along which light travels, **rays.** These are obviously the directions in which the waves travel from the source to the eye. They do not exist in a physical sense any more than did the reflection of the bone in that well-known fable of Æsop. Æsop tells us how, one sunny day, the classical " Bonzo " with the habitual bone in his mouth was walking along a river bank when he chanced to notice in the water a reflection of himself. Thinking this reflection was another dog carrying a bone, the greedy Bonzo dropped his own bone which was real, and dived for the other. The dog was quite convinced he saw the other bone, just as most of us first imagined we actually saw rays. What we see are merely the small particles among which the beam pursues a straight course.

FERMAT (1608–68) enunciated the principle that " Nature could not be wasteful " and was bound for this reason to cause the rays of light to travel between two points in the shortest time possible. Accepting this, not necessarily because we believe nature to be so thrifty but because experience shows it to be true, we can define a ray as

" The path of shortest optical length."

It will simplify our mathematics considerably if we consider rays instead of waves as long as it is clearly understood that when we speak of rays of light we mean the paths along which waves are travelling.

Beams or Pencils of Light.—When we have a collection of rays proceeding from a source in some definite direction they are usually called a **beam or pencil of light.** This is again classified according to the direction of the rays in the beam : three types exist : Diverging, Converging and Parallel.

Diverging.—The eye sees a luminous point by means of all the light which can enter it. Thus rays diverge from the

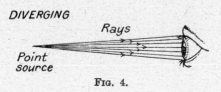

FIG. 4.

point to the eye and constitute a diverging beam of light (Fig. 4).

Converging.—Sometimes rays are made to converge to a point as is the case when a burning glass is held towards the sun and the rays from the sun are made to converge on to a piece of paper until it sets on fire (Fig. 5).

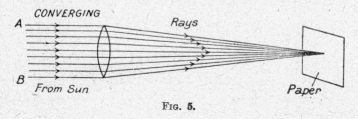

FIG. 5.

Parallel.—It will be noticed in Fig. 5 that the directions of the sun's rays are drawn parallel to one another. This follows from the fact that light which comes from a distance so great as 93 million miles can only reach us as a beam if the rays are parallel.

Rectilinear Propagation of Light.—This heading means simply " **Light travels in straight lines.**" A good illustration of the truth of this is to take a small source of light and three screens containing pinholes (Fig. 6). Adjust the three holes in a straight line by any means, such as by getting a stretched thread to pass through the three without being held in any particular way by the edges of the middle hole. On placing a small source of light at the point S the eye can receive light which has passed through the three holes.

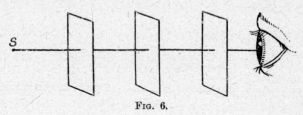

Fig. 6.

If, however, any one of the screens is displaced, the light is immediately cut off and the eye cannot perceive the source.

Shadows.—The formation of shadows is the natural consequence of the propagation of light in straight lines. The simplest way of understanding how shadows are produced is to consider all luminous bodies as made up of a great many

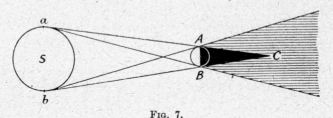

Fig. 7.

point sources. Then it will only be necessary to examine the rays from the two extreme points of the body.

The two extreme points of our luminous source are *a* and *b* (Fig. 7). Both of these cast shadows, but except for the cone ABC the shadow due to *a* is illuminated by that due to *b*. ABC is totally black and is called *umbra*. The partially illuminated shadow is called *penumbra*.

The student will easily see by means of a drawing that the

size of the umbra decreases as the source increases in size and the distance between the source and the object diminishes. If carried to extremes the shadow will lose outline and become a confused shadow of penumbra.

Eclipses.—These phenomena are perhaps our most interesting examples of shadows. Every illuminated body casts a shadow into space in the direction opposite to the source

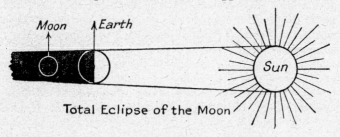

Total Eclipse of the Moon

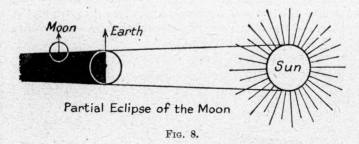

Partial Eclipse of the Moon

Fig. 8.

of illumination. Thus the Earth casts a shadow conical in shape, and the Moon casts a similar but smaller shadow. Mars, Jupiter, Saturn, Venus and the other planets cast shadows in the same way. But it is the shadows of the Earth and the Moon which cause the phenomena known to the Earth's inhabitants as eclipses of the Moon and eclipses of the Sun.

The Earth casts a shadow into space ; and when the Moon, the Earth and the Sun are in a line, with the Earth in the centre, the shadow of the Earth which extends beyond the Moon encloses the latter in its gloomy mantle. This is called a **Total Eclipse of the Moon.**

It is only occasionally that the Moon is completely immersed in the Earth's shadow : usually a *partial eclipse* takes place, a portion of the Moon's disc remaining outside the true shadow. A total eclipse, however, is a wonderful and striking phenomenon. As the Moon becomes more and more immersed in shadow, the illuminated portion becomes smaller and smaller until it completely disappears. Many stories have been related of how explorers have used this phenomenon to strike terror into the hearts of superstitious and ignorant savages, and by so doing, have avoided the horrible tortures and death which otherwise would have awaited them. COLUMBUS, according to SIR A. HELPS, used the same phenomenon to save the lives of himself and his followers from the Indian tribes when the latter refused to continue the supply of provisions to the Spaniards. The " killing of the Moon " caused such panic amongst the savages that when Columbus kindly offered to intercede for them and remove the terrible shadow, their gratitude was as deep as their previous terror.

The Sun's eclipse is even more striking than the Moon's ; it is also more useful, for it is only during the time the former

FIG. 9.

At A on the earth no sun is visible—total eclipse.   At B, lying in penumbra, a partial eclipse is seen.   At C all the sun is visible.

takes place that our astronomers can study the fainter and outlying portions of the Sun, those portions which give us such intimate knowledge of it.

The Pinhole Camera.—This is another of the many interesting examples of the rectilinear propagation of light. Consider the luminous source AB (Fig. 10). Every point on AB is giving out light in all directions. A narrow cone from the point A will pass through the small aperture O and will illuminate a screen at C. The base of the cone at C is the illumination received from the point A and the size of this patch will obviously depend on the distance of the screen from O and the size of the aperture O. Hence, if the aperture is very small, and the screen not very far away, a spot of light will appear on the screen corresponding to every point of AB. The spot from A will appear at the bottom and that from B at the top of C. Thus we obtain an inverted

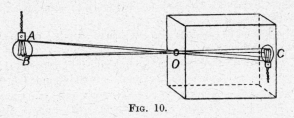

Fig. 10.

image of AB on the screen. The same quantity of light which falls on the small base of the cone from A when the screen is near, will fall on the larger base when the screen is far away, and consequently the brightness diminishes as we increase the distance of the screen from the aperture. Let us consider the aperture again. If it is extremely small we shall get so little light from the source AB that C will hardly be visible.[1] If, on the other hand, the aperture is very large, it will be equivalent to a large number of small holes and therefore many spots of light will fall on the screen to represent A. These small images will overlap with images of other points of our luminous source and consequently a blurred effect will be produced on the screen. This blurring is called "**lack of definition.**"

[1] Diffraction phenomena (Ch. XV) also occur which make it impossible to use too small an aperture.

Self-Luminous and Non-Luminous Bodies.—Every point of a self-luminous body emits light in all directions. The eye intercepts a cone of rays from each visible point, and the light received is registered by the nerves at the back of the eye. The nerves convey to the brain the sensation of sight.

When no self-luminous body is present, as for example in a dark room, no object can be seen. We infer from this that if a body is visible, light must be coming from it to the eye. If a body is non-luminous it may possess the power of transferring light, which falls on it, to other objects. This light on entering the eye makes the body visible. The more light a body absorbs the less there is to be transferred. We see then why polished metals always appear so very bright and why blackened surfaces which absorb light to a great extent appear so dull.

Non-luminous bodies are of three kinds—transparent, opaque, translucent.

Transparent.—Substances through which light freely passes. Examples : Air, glass, water, rock salt, diamond.

Opaque.—Substances which may reflect light but which do not allow light to pass through them. Examples : Metals, stone, wood.

Translucent.—Those substances which allow a portion of the light to pass through them and which scatter the rest.

Examples : Ground glass, greased paper, milky water, paraffin wax.

It must be clearly understood that the difference between opaque and transparent bodies is simply one of degree. In an opaque body a very small thickness of the substance is sufficient to prevent the light from being transmitted, whilst comparatively large thicknesses can be traversed in a transparent substance without much absorption. Some bodies which are opaque become transparent usually when extremely thin. A good example of this is gold leaf, which is quite transparent when held in front of a luminous body. Thin metallic films also are often transparent.

QUESTIONS. II.

1. Give a short account of light waves and explain their method of propagation.

2. What is a ray of light ? Explain the difference between rays and waves of light.

3. Define a pencil of light. How many kinds are there ? Illustrate your answer by examples.

4. What do you understand by the term " Rectilinear Propagation of Light " ? How would you show experimentally that light travels in straight lines ?

5. Explain the formation of shadows. Distinguish between umbra and penumbra.

6. What is an eclipse ? Account for the eclipses of the sun and moon.

7. Give a description of a pinhole camera and carefully explain its action.

8. Distinguish between self-luminous and non-luminous bodies. How are non-luminous bodies usually subdivided ? Give an example of each kind.

CHAPTER III

REFLECTION AT PLANE SURFACES

When light comes into collision with bodies, three effects in general, will be observed to take place.

(a) One portion of the incident light is turned back or reflected.

(b) A second portion is absorbed, that is, it is converted into some form of energy within the body.

(c) A third portion travels on and is bent or refracted into the medium of the body.

The amounts of each vary considerably with the nature of the body on which the light falls. Most of us have enjoyed the sight of the reflection of the moon in a pond or river. We owe this solely to the reflected light. The image of the moon never appears as bright as the moon itself since some of the light is transmitted and some absorbed. The transmitted light would easily be observed by a moonlight bather under water, and the blackness of a deep pond in daylight gives indication of the absorption of light. The shallower the pond the " clearer " it always appears to be.

The first effect, that of the reflection of light, is what we shall consider in this chapter, for this phenomenon was the cause of that scientific curiosity of the ancients which laid the foundation stone of our present knowledge of optics.

It will be a great help to beginners if we first explain the apparatus we shall employ and the technical terms which make scientific descriptions so concise.

Mirrors.—A mirror is any polished surface of regular geometrical form which is smooth enough to reflect light regularly. Two forms are most commonly used—plane and spherical. It is necessary, as will appear later, to ensure the highest degree of smoothness in mirrors if any accurate work is to be attempted. Polished metal surfaces were first used, but these have been almost entirely superseded by glass surfaces coated in front with silver. The ordinary plane mirrors used in school laboratories are made of plate glass, the back surface of which has deposited on it a thin layer of silver.

The *incident ray* to a surface is the direction in which the light travels before collision between the light and the surface takes place.

The *reflected ray* is the direction after collision.

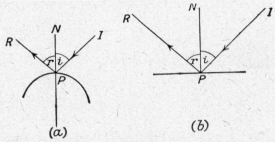

FIG. 11.

P is the point of incidence.   PN the normal.   IP, PR the incident and reflected rays respectively. *i*, *r* the angles of incidence and reflection respectively.

The *angle of incidence* is the angle the incident ray makes with the normal at the point of incidence.

The *angle of reflection* is the angle the reflected ray makes with the normal at the point of incidence.

The Laws of Reflection.

(1) The angle of incidence is equal to the angle of reflection.

(2) The incident ray, reflected ray and the normal at the point of incidence lie in the same plane.

The first law is the one so obvious to us and the one which the ancients knew. The second law is not quite so self-evident and is rather difficult to prove experimentally. General experience has led scientists to accept it : for no matter when the law is assumed the results are always found to be strictly accurate.

Experimental Verification.—A graduated circle arranged in a vertical plane has a plane mirror fixed horizontally so that its reflecting surface includes the centre of the circle (Fig. 12). Two movable sighting tubes are so arranged that they can move round the circle with their axes parallel to the plane of the circle and directed towards the centre. Both tubes contain fine cross wires which are fixed in planes at right angles to the axes of the tubes. A is fixed at some graduation on the circle (say at 45°), and the cross wires in A illuminated by a small bright source. B is then moved until the image of the illuminated cross wires appear

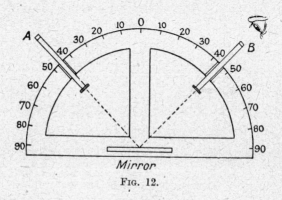

Fɪɢ. 12.

to an eye looking in B to be in line with the cross wires in B. Light from the cross wire in A is incident on the surface of the mirror in such a way that it is reflected along the tube B to the eye. This is in accordance with Law 2, for the axes of both tubes and the normal to the mirror are in the same plane. When A is fixed at 45°, B will be found to be at the other graduation 45°, and since the normal at the point of incidence passes through the zero mark on the scale, it is clear that the angle of incidence is equal to the angle of reflection, a fact which is in agreement with Law I. By repeating this experiment, using different angles, we shall always arrive at the same conclusions.

The Optical Disc.—This is a very useful modern piece of apparatus by which the laws of reflection may also be demonstrated (Fig. 13). A beam of light either from an arc lamp or a motor-car headlight bulb (12 volt, 36 watt) is made to pass through an aperture S and to fall upon a plane mirror M. The mirror is fixed to a movable graduated circle thus enabling the beam to strike the mirror at any convenient angle of incidence. The reflected beam will be seen clearly when the incident beam is passing along the plane of the circle. Thus, if the plane

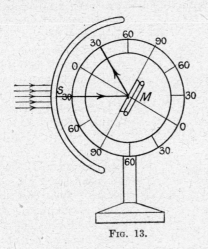

FIG. 13.

of the circle is arranged parallel to the incident light in such a way that the light travels along the surface of the circle to the mirror, the reflected beam will be observed also to move along the surface. By noting the angles of incidence and reflection the first law also may be verified.

A simple form of optical disc is a drawing-board containing holes through which a 2 B.A. bolt may pass. Attached to the bolt is a spring—a half cycle clip will do—with its end covered by a strip of rubber so as to grip the mirror firmly. A graduated circle should be drawn on the board in a convenient position for experimental work. A useful form of slit is a graining comb which should be fixed at right angles to the board and near to it. The bulb should be close to the slit and the straight filament should be parallel to it, that is at right angles to the board. The beams of light can be made very clear if a cylindrical lens (cf. page 113) is placed between the bulb and the slit and the focus adjusted. The bulb should be held in a container—a cigarette-tin which has a slot cut in it and is blackened inside is sufficient.

The above apparatus can easily be used for individual work on the bench and is much preferable to the use of pins.

Rough and Smooth Surfaces.

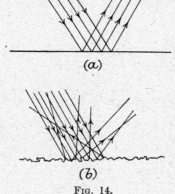

(a)

(b)

Fig. 14.

When a surface is very smooth we have seen that light obeys two definite laws, the Laws of Reflection. If, however, a beam of light is incident on a rough surface such as white paper, the light appears to be scattered. This is called **Diffused Reflection.**

We may still consider the laws of reflection obeyed if we remember that millions of rays in a small beam will strike the surface. Since the surface is rough, each ray will probably have a different angle of incidence from its neighbour and consequently all the angles of reflection will vary (Fig. 14). Thus, although the beam may be parallel at incidence, there will be no regular reflection and hence scattering ensues. The effect of this scattering is to render such things as salt or powdered substances impervious to light. In fact, we sometimes find even transparent substances when mixed giving the same effect. The familiar thunder cloud composed of water particles and air, both transparent substances, produces a barrier sufficiently opaque to turn day into night.

Image of a Luminous Point formed by a Plane Mirror.

By means of the apparatus described on the preceding page produce a converging beam of light and, hence, a point source

P on a drawing-board which is flat on the bench. Let the beams of light which diverge from the source strike a plane mirror (Fig. 15). Notice that after reflection the beams *appear* to diverge from a point I at the back of the mirror. This is the *virtual image* of P.

Place a pin upright at P. Its image will be seen at I, but in this case the path of the light which is reflected from P by the mirror is not seen.

Note that the reflection does not appear to take place at the first surface. Refraction (page 56) occurs.

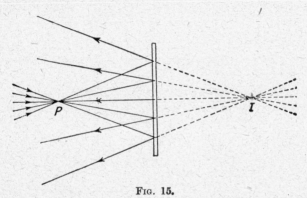

FIG. 15.

Exercise. The student should satisfy himself by the application of a little geometrical reasoning and the laws of reflection that :—

    (i) the distances of the image and object from the mirror are equal ;

    (ii) The line joining the object and image is perpendicular to the mirror.

Alternative Experiments.

(a) Remove the light beam apparatus and place a pin (Fig. 16) anywhere (P, say). Place two more pins P_1 and P_2 in such a way that P_1P_2 and I appear in the same line. Repeat this procedure two or three times, keeping the first pin P fixed, but moving the position of the eye, and thus getting

P_3 and P_4 instead of P_1 and P_2 and similarly P_5 and P_6. Remove the pins and mirror, taking care to note the exact points from which the pins have been removed (it is best to draw a small circle round each point from which a pin is taken) and also the position of the mirror. Join up as shown in the diagram (Fig. 16) and if the experiment has been carefully carried out the lines will all intersect in I, the position of the image.

On account of the finite thickness of the glass there will be a certain amount of refraction or bending of the light.

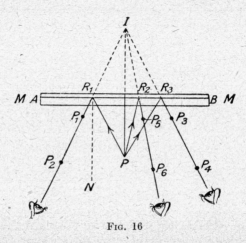

Fig. 16

This defect can be almost entirely counteracted by measuring the thickness of the glass and drawing a line AB at a distance of one-third this thickness from the back face. Treat AB as the actual reflecting surface and join R_1, R_2, R_3 to P. Draw the normals at R_1, R_2, R_3 and so measure the angles of incidence and reflection for each particular ray.

(b) There is another method commonly used which makes use of a peculiar phenomenon known as parallax. Suppose we wish to correct a watch by some large public clock such as is often seen on town hall buildings, the only manner in which this could be accurately carried out would be to stand exactly in front of the clock and make the adjustment. To an observer on the right-hand side of the clock the time at 3.28 would appear to be about 3.30 and on the left-hand side about 3.26. This is because the large hand is not in contact with the clock face. If it were, the correct time would be apparent irrespective of the position of the observer as long as the face was visible.

Again, a distant chimney and a wireless mast not attached to the chimney only appear coincident when the observer, chimney and mast are in a direct line. If an observer is walking in any direction other than along this direct line he will notice an apparent relative motion of the mast to the chimney. When, however, the mast is fixed to the chimney

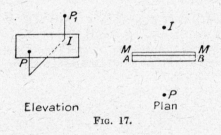

Elevation   Plan

FIG. 17.

this relative motion does not occur, and they always appear coincident. In the two cases considered above, movement of the observer always caused relative motion of the objects when the latter were not actually coincident. This relative motion is called parallax.

Parallax Method.—As before place a pin P upright in front of a plane vertical mirror (Fig. 17). At the back of the mirror place a pin P_1 about where the image of P appears to be. Move P_1 backwards or forwards until it coincides exactly with the image of P no matter from which position it is viewed. If any movement of P_1 relative to the image occurs the two are said to possess parallax. There is no parallax when the image of P and P_1 are coincident. Remove mirror and pins as before : join P and P_1 and show that their distances from the reflecting surface are equal.

Image of an Object placed in front of a Plane Mirror.—
The laws regarding point objects can be applied when the
bodies possess finite size. Every object is supposed to consist

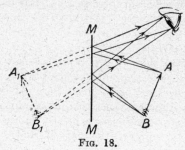

FIG. 18.

of a great number of point objects : thus (Fig. 18) A_1 is the
image of A and is seen by means of a cone of rays which
leave A, and after reflection, appear to diverge from A_1.
Similarly, the eye observes B_1, the image of B. It will be

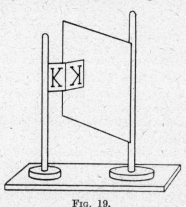

FIG. 19.

noticed that each point image is the same distance behind
the mirror as the point object is in front, and hence we have
the phenomenon known as **Lateral Inversion** (Fig. 19).
Lateral inversion produced no weird effects when we used
pins in our experiments on the laws of reflection because the

pins were symmetrical and erect. If, however, a book is held up to a mirror and is read by means of reflected light, the result is quite uncanny.

Multiple Images—Inclined Mirrors.

Two Plane Mirrors inclined at 90°.—As in previous experiments place a pin P at a point to which a number of narrow beams of light converge. Note that some of these

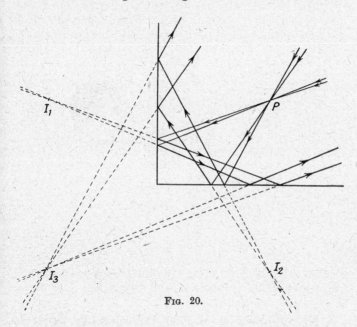

FIG. 20.

beams suffer two reflections, one at each mirror, and that as a result three images of the point P are formed, one from each mirror by one reflection and one (two coincident) formed by two reflections (Fig. 20).

Exercises.—Alter the inclination to 60°. Note the formation of 5 images. Test the formula : $n = \left(\dfrac{360}{\theta} - 1\right)$, where n is the number of images and θ is the angle of inclination.

Note how the reflected beam diminishes in intensity as the number of reflections is increased. Hence observe the diminished brightness of the nth image.

Finally, make the mirrors parallel. An infinite number of reflections is possible, but the brightness diminishes so rapidly that only a limited number of images is seen.

Applications.

1. The barber makes use of double reflection and lateral inversion in order to obtain his customer's approval. If H is a point on the back of the head (Fig. 21), the eye E is in the

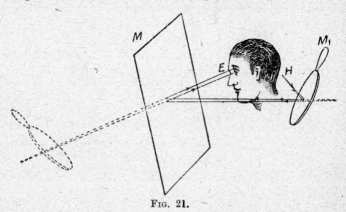

Fɪɢ. 21.

position to see H by means of the cone of rays which are first reflected by the hand mirror M_1 and then by the fixed mirror M as in the manner shown.

2. **Measurement of Angular Deflection by Reflected Light.**—Suppose a horizontal ray of light be allowed to fall on a mirror MM (Fig. 22) so that the angle of incidence is θ. Then the angle of reflection will be θ. Thus if NR is the normal to the mirror MM at N

$$\angle ANB = 2\theta$$

i.e. the reflected ray makes an angle 2θ with the incident ray. If the mirror rotates through an angle α the incident angle is increased or decreased by the amount α, and therefore its new value is $\theta \pm \alpha$. But the reflected ray makes with the incident ray an angle whose value is twice that of the angle of incidence

i.e. $2\theta \pm 2\alpha$.

Thus when a mirror rotates through any angle the reflected light is rotated through twice this angle.

Use is often made of this fact when it is desired to measure small rotations of any body. A small vertical mirror is attached to the body and the angle of reflection of the light measured. Half this quantity is the angle of rotation of the mirror. Mirror galvanometers used for measuring electric currents are made on this principle. The mirror is attached

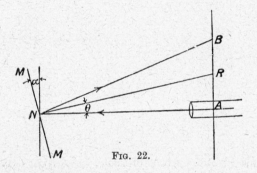

Fig. 22.

to the moving part of the instrument and the angular deflection is read by light reflected on to a scale.

The sextant employed by mariners is another instrument which employs this principle. The sextant was originally introduced by TYCHO BRAHÉ for measuring the angular distance between two objects. It was developed later by NEWTON and then by HADLEY in the form shown as a hand instrument for enabling navigators to measure the altitude of heavenly bodies.

Two plane mirrors A and B (Fig. 23) are set at right angles to the plane of the instrument, A being fixed to an arm AM, which is movable over a divided arc XY and carries a vernier scale, B being fixed to one of the rigid arms.   When

D

the arm AM is on the zero of the scale the mirrors are arranged to be parallel to each other. B is half silvered so that if an object is viewed through a telescope C attached to the instrument and looking towards B, two fields are in general observed, one direct viâ EBC and the other after two reflections along the path DABC. When the mirrors are parallel, a distant object is seen by means of rays which travel along the two paths.

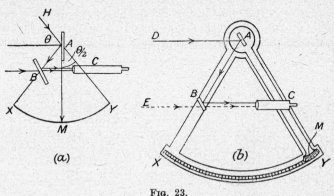

(a)   (b)

FIG. 23.

To measure the altitude of a star the sextant is held, with M at zero, so that the telescope is directed towards the horizon. The movable arm is then rotated until the star appears to rest on the horizon. When this is the case the angle ∠ MAY (Fig. 23a) through which the arm has turned is clearly equal to half the altitude of the star. The instrument is usually graduated so as to give the required angle directly.

QUESTIONS. III.

1. Explain what usually happens when light is incident on a piece of thick plane glass.

2. What is a mirror ? Compare a metal mirror with a glass mirror silvered on its back surface, indicating the advantages and disadvantages of each kind.

3. What is a normal to a curved surface ? Make a diagram showing an incident ray, reflected ray and a normal to some point on a curved surface.

4. State the laws of reflection and show how they may be verified experimentally.

5. What is diffused reflection ? Mention three examples which illustrate the effects of this type of reflection.

6. Explain what you understand by the image of a luminous body. How would you show experimentally and theoretically that the image of a body placed in front of a plane mirror is the same distance behind the mirror as the object is in front ? (The laws of reflection may be assumed.)

7. Show that if a man walks towards a stationary mirror the image moves at the same rate as the man, and if the mirror moves towards the man, the image moves at twice the rate of the mirror.

8. Explain the meaning of " parallax " and illustrate your answer by giving every-day examples of parallax. Hence describe the parallax method as applied in light for finding the positions of images.

9. What is lateral inversion and show how it occurs ?

10. Draw a diagram which illustrates how three images may be seen of an object lying in front of two plane mirrors placed at right angles to each other.

11. Why is there a limit to the number of visible images of an object lying between two parallel plane mirrors ?

12. What is the advantage of having plane mirrors on the walls of a shop ?

13. Show that when a mirror rotates the reflected ray moves through twice the angle of rotation of the mirror. To what practical uses is this put ?

14. Describe the sextant and state for what purposes it may be used.

CHAPTER IV

SPHERICAL MIRRORS

In the last chapter we dealt with the laws of reflection as applied to plane mirrors. The same laws will now be applied to the cases where the mirrors are curved.

Preliminary Definitions.

A *Spherical Mirror* is usually a portion of a sphere made so that it will reflect light regularly. If the inside portion acts as the reflecting surface the mirror is *concave*; if the outside reflects, it is a *convex* mirror (Fig. 24).

The *Pole* of the mirror (P) is the centre of the face.

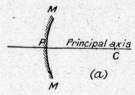 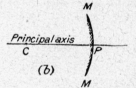

Concave.–reflecting inside.   Convex.–reflecting outside.

FIG. 24.

The *Centre of Curvature* (C) is the centre of the sphere of which the mirror forms a part.

The *Principal Axis* is the line joining the pole and centre of curvature.

The *Diameter of Mirror* is the width of the aperture MM. This is in practice made very small compared with PC, the radius of curvature.

Concave Mirrors.—Fix a concave mirror to the optical disc or its equivalent as shown in Fig. 25 in such a way that a narrow parallel beam of light, incident on the mirror, will be parallel to the principal axis. It will be noticed that all the rays incident near the pole of the mirror converge after reflection and pass through a point F on the principal axis. This

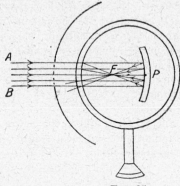

FIG. 25.

point is called the *Principal Focus* and the distance PF of the pole from the principal focus is called the *Focal Length* of the Mirror. Archimedes had to construct his "burning

mirrors" of such a radius of curvature that the parallel rays of heat and light from the sun could be brought to a focus on the ships of the enemy. Thus the focal lengths were equal to the distances of the various vessels from the mirrors.

Convex Mirrors.—A similar reflection of parallel rays causes divergence (Fig. 26), and the

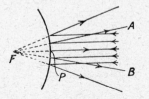

Convex
FIG. 26.

point from which the rays apparently diverge is called the Principal Focus of the Convex Mirror.

Conjugate Points.

By means of light beams (page 25) and a cylindrical [1] mirror observe what happens when a diverging beam of light is

[1] A cylindrical mirror will act as a concave or convex mirror in one plane only.

reflected by a curved mirror. As the luminous point O from which the beams diverge approaches the pole of the mirror, the image I recedes until at a particular distance of O from the mirror (the focal length) the beam is reflected as a parallel beam. If O is brought still nearer to the pole no *real* image (i.e. one through which the light actually passes) can be formed, but a virtual image can be seen behind the mirror.

When O is situated at the centre of curvature C, the image coincides with the object. This is because all the beams then strike the mirror normally.

From your experiments :

(1) Find F, the principal focus and C, the centre of curvature. Measure the radius and the focal length. Note the relation between them (page 40).

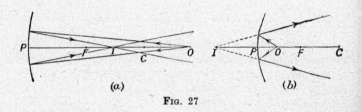

(a)   (b)

FIG. 27

(2) Note the position of I when O is beyond C. Verify (cf. page 42) that $\frac{1}{v} + \frac{1}{u}$ is a constant (when u and v are the distances of the object and image respectively from the pole). Place O where I was. Note that O and I change places.

(3) Note that when the object is between F and P a virtual image is formed (Fig. 27*b*). Trace the beams on your drawing paper, find the position of I and verify that $\frac{1}{v} + \frac{1}{u}$ is constant, if the distance v is assumed to be negative.

It will be observed that when the two points O and I are both real, they are so related that light from one point after reflection always converges to the other. They are, therefore, called *Real Conjugate Points*.

If either O or I is virtual, the two points are called *Virtual Conjugate Points.*

If the object O is placed either at the pole P or the centre of curvature C the image coincides with the object.   Such points are called *Self Conjugate Points.*

It should be clear that all conjugate points of a concave mirror are real provided that neither the image nor the object lies between the principal focus and the pole.   Otherwise they are virtual.

The conjugate points of a convex mirror are always virtual. This follows from the fact that a real object placed in front of a convex mirror always gives rise to a virtual image.

Figs. 28 (*a*) and (*b*) show a real object giving rise to a

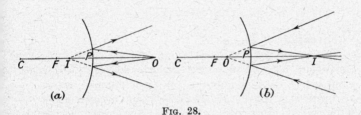

(a)   (b)

FIG. 28.

virtual image and a virtual object giving rise to a real image. In both cases the conjugate points are virtual.

Relation between the Focal Length and Radius of Curvature.—A ray AB parallel to the principal axis of a spherical mirror will either converge to the principal focus F or apparently diverge from F (Figs. 29*a* and *b*).

In each case BC is the normal at the point of incidence of the ray, since this line passes through the centre of curvature C of the mirror, and it easily follows from geometry and the law of reflection that in Fig. 29*a* $\angle$ FBC = $\angle$ BCF

or   BF = FC

But as the diameter of the mirror is assumed to be very small compared with the radius of curvature, we may consider BP

very small compared with PF and consequently BF = PF
approx. and   ∴ PF = FC approx.

i.e. F lies half-way between the pole and the centre of curvature, or the *Focal Length is half the Radius of Curvature.*

It is left as an exercise for the student to show that the
same result is obtained if a convex mirror is used as in Fig. 29*b*.

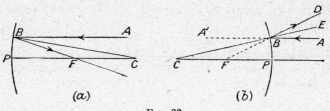

FIG. 29.

Convention of Signs.

There is a general relationship between the distances of
conjugate points from a curved mirror and its focal length.
But before we show how this can be determined, we need to
adopt a sign convention for our various measurements.

It will be remembered that a concave mirror usually produces a real image and a convex mirror a virtual image. It
seems natural, therefore, to regard a concave mirror as a positive mirror and a convex mirror as a negative mirror : in
other words, to assume that a concave mirror has a positive
focal length and a convex mirror a negative focal length. If
we carry this a step further and assume that the space in
front of a curved mirror is positive while the space behind it is
negative, we shall see that a real image is always formed in
a positive space while a virtual image is always formed in a
negative space. The same results apply if the convention is
used for convex mirrors.

Our simplest convention is, therefore, to assign *positive
spaces to real objects and real images* and *negative spaces to
virtual objects and virtual images.* Fig. 30 shows the positive
and negative spaces for both concave and convex mirrors.
With these conventions *any distances measured from the pole of a*

mirror will be positive or negative according as they are in positive or negative spaces. Thus in Fig. 27a OP, IP, FP are all positive, while in Fig. 27b FP and OP are positive while IP is negative. Again in Fig. 28a OP is positive while FP and IP are negative, and in b of the same figure IP is positive while OP is negative.

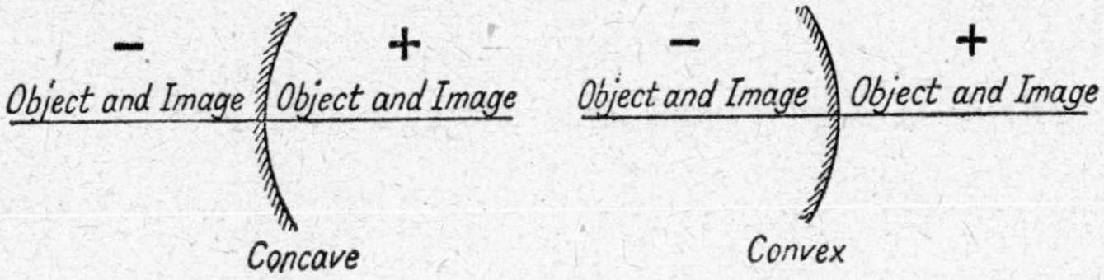

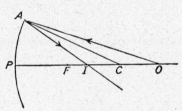

FIG. 30.

Later we shall see that the same convention can be usefully applied to lenses.

The General Formula for Spherical Mirrors.

Concave Mirror.—Consider any ray OA (Fig. 31) incident on the mirror at A. After reflection (Law 2) it will pass through I, say. As C is the centre of curvature of the mirror, AC will be the normal at A, therefore $\angle IAC = \angle OAC$ (1st law of reflection). But since

FIG. 31.

AC bisects $\angle OAI$, by a well-known proposition we have

$$\frac{IA}{OA} = \frac{IC}{CO}.$$

AP is again assumed to be very small and, therefore,

$$IA = IP, \quad OA = OP \text{ approx.}$$

or

$$\frac{IP}{OP} = \frac{IC}{CO} \quad \cdots \cdots \cdots (1)$$

But P, C and O are fixed points. Therefore I is fixed. Hence all rays from O *which are incident near* P pass through I.

Let OP, IP, CP be equal to u, v, and R respectively. Then substituting in (1), all quantities being positive, since they lie in a positive space :

$$\frac{v}{u} = \frac{R - v}{u - R}$$

$$v(u - R) = u(R - v)$$
$$uR + vR = 2uv.$$

Divide through by the product uvR and we get

$$\frac{1}{v} + \frac{1}{u} = \frac{2}{R} \quad . \quad . \quad . \quad . \quad . \quad . \quad (2)$$

But PF = FC by the last article and, therefore,

R = 2f (where f is the focal length).

Hence equation (2) becomes

$$\frac{1}{v} + \frac{1}{u} = \frac{1}{f}$$

Convex Mirror.—In this case the image is virtual because rays only apparently diverge from the point I after reflection.

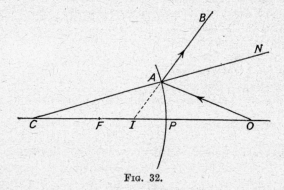

FIG. 32.

In Fig. 32 the ray OA is reflected in the direction AB, that is IA produced. The normal AN will pass, if produced, through C, the centre of curvature of the mirror.

Thus $\angle BAN = \angle OAN$

or AN is the bisector of the exterior $\angle OAB$ of the $\triangle AIO$

therefore, $\dfrac{IA}{OA} = \dfrac{IC}{CO}.$

With the same assumptions as before, IA = IP; OA = OP approx. and, therefore,

$$\dfrac{IP}{OP} = \dfrac{IC}{CO}.$$

But IP, FP, CP lie in the negative space of the convex mirror and OP in the positive.

Hence $v = -$ IP, $f = -$ FP, R $= -$ CP and $u = +$ OP, Substituting as before, we have

$$-\dfrac{v}{u} = \dfrac{-R + v}{-R + u}$$

or $vR - vu = -uR + uv$

$$uR + vR = 2uv$$

dividing by uvR, we have

$$\dfrac{1}{v} + \dfrac{1}{u} = \dfrac{2}{R} = \dfrac{1}{f}$$

which is the same formula as for a concave mirror.[1]

Power of a Mirror—the Dioptre.

You will note that the formula above contains reciprocals of distances and it is clearly quicker for purposes of calculation to use tables of reciprocals. For this reason also it is usual to specify a mirror by giving the value $\dfrac{1}{f}$ rather than that of f. The reciprocal of the focal length is called the *Power* of the mirror.

It is the practice among industrial workers in optics to express the power in terms of a unit called the *Dioptre*. This is defined as the power of a mirror whose focal length is one

[1] It is left as an exercise for the advanced student to show that for angles of incidence (θ) of any size the exact formula for spherical mirrors is

$$\dfrac{1}{v} + \dfrac{1}{u} = \dfrac{2 \cos \theta}{R}.$$

metre. It follows, therefore, that for any mirror the power in dioptres is equal to the reciprocal of its focal length measured in metres. Thus D (dioptres) $= \dfrac{1}{f \text{ (in metres)}}$.

A concave mirror of 50 cm. focal length has a power of 2 dioptres, and is called a $+ 2D$ mirror. A convex mirror of $- 20$ cm. focal length is a $- 5D$ mirror. If the image formed by a mirror of an object at an infinite distance from the mirror is also at an infinite distance, that is, if the mirror is plane, it is said to have *zero* power.

This definition of power may be extended to any reflecting instrument. Later, we shall see it applied in the case of refracting instruments also.

EXAMPLES.—In solving problems on spherical mirrors write down the standard equation and substitute in it the numerical values of the known quantities (with proper signs). Then work out the value of the unknown in magnitude and sign. The sign is an indication of the position of the image.

(1) A luminous point is situated on the principal axis of a spherical mirror and is 20 cm. from the pole. The power of the mirror is $- 5$ dioptres. Find the position and nature of the image.

The standard formula is $\dfrac{1}{v} + \dfrac{1}{u} = D$.

known values are $u = + 0 \cdot 2$ metres and $D = - 5$ dioptres.
Substituting, we have

$$\frac{1}{v} + \frac{1}{0 \cdot 2} = - 5$$

i.e. $$\frac{1}{v} = - 10$$

or $$v = - \frac{1}{10} \text{ metre} = - 10 \text{ cm.}$$

Hence the image is virtual and is situated 10 cm. behind the mirror.

(2) A beam of light which is converging towards a point 10 cm. behind a spherical mirror forms an image 5 cm. in front of the mirror. Find the power of the mirror.

The standard formula is $\dfrac{1}{v} + \dfrac{1}{u} = D$.

Known values are $u = -\ 10$ cm. $= -\ 0\cdot1$ metres
$v = +\ 5$ cm. $= +\ 0\cdot05$ m.

substituting, $D = \dfrac{1}{0\cdot05} - \dfrac{1}{0\cdot1} = 20 - 10 = 10$ dioptres.

Real Conjugate Points applied to Finite Objects.

Arrange some illuminated object A (Fig. 33) such as cross wires placed in front of an electric lamp, at such a distance from a concave mirror M that an image of the cross wires can be received on a white screen placed between the mirror and the lamp. In order to obtain this image, AM must be greater than the radius of curvature of the mirror. The image can

FIG. 33.

be found by moving S backwards or forwards until the cross wires are clearly defined.

Now interchange S and A and it will be found that the image is again in focus although different in size. From this we conclude that each point object on A will give its image on S and these will be interchangeable provided that A is not placed between the principal focus and the pole of the mirror.
Graphical Construction.

In order to find the position of the image graphically, two rays only need to be drawn :

(1) The ray parallel to the principal axis ; this passes through the principal focus after reflection.

(2) The ray drawn through the centre of curvature ; this strikes the mirror normally and, therefore, retraces its path.

The student should draw diagrams for himself so as to illus-

trate the formation of finite images by finite objects.   **Three**
examples are given :

(1) *Object between the Centre of Curvature and Infinity (Concave Mirror)* Fig 34a.

Note that the construction rays have been drawn from O

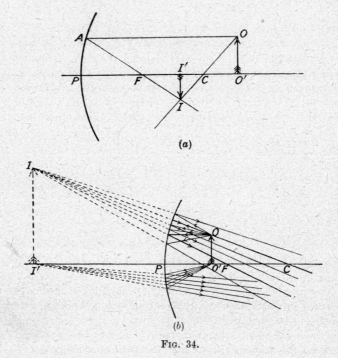

(a)

(b)

Fig. 34.

and O′.   Those from O meet after reflection in I, while those
from O′ meet at I′.   II′ is therefore the image of OO′ and is
inverted and diminished.

(2) *Object between the Principal Focus and the Pole (Concave Mirror)* Fig 34b.

The image is virtual, erect and enlarged.   Let the reader
bring a concave mirror very near to his face.   The result will

give him a better appreciation of the feelings of Gulliver when the latter found himself in the arms of a Brobdingnagian.

Shaving mirrors are often made in the shape of concave mirrors for use in the above way.

(3) *Object anywhere between Infinity and the Pole (Convex Mirror)*.

Note (Fig. 35) that the image is always diminished, erect and virtual.

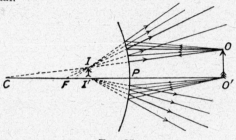

Fig. 35.

Distinction between the three Mirrors.—It is easy to distinguish between plane, concave or convex mirrors from the images that they form. A plane mirror always gives an erect image of an object (eg. observer's eye) situated the same distance behind the mirror as the object is in front. In the case of a concave mirror an inverted image is formed if the distance of the object from the mirror is greater than the focal length, while a large magnified erect image is produced when the mirror is brought near to the object. The convex mirror always gives a diminished erect image which is situated within the focal length : that is, an image always appears just behind the mirror when the curvature is great. Because of its shape, a convex mirror allows more objects around it to become visible than in the case of plane and concave mirrors ; hence its use on motor cars to enable the driver to see the approach of vehicles from the rear.

Magnification.

(a) **Transverse.**—By graphical construction draw the image IY (Fig. 36) of the object OX. Then it easily follows that the $\triangle$'s OPX and IPY are similar, since $i = r$, so that,

$$\frac{IY}{OX} = \frac{PY}{PX} \quad \cdot \quad \cdot \quad \cdot \quad \cdot \quad \cdot \quad (1)$$

Sign Convention.—It is common to regard an inverted image as having a negative magnification and an erect image as having positive magnification. In order to arrive at this it is necessary to define all lengths measured above the axis as positive and those measured below negative. Let the object be of height h and the image of height h'.

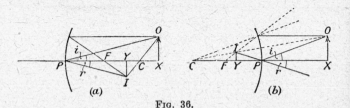

FIG. 36.

Then clearly the transverse magnification $m = \dfrac{h'}{h}$ which gives in

Fig. (a) $m = -\dfrac{IY}{OX} = -\dfrac{PY}{PX} = -\dfrac{v}{u}$

and in

Fig. (b) $m = \dfrac{IY}{OX} = \dfrac{PY}{PX} = -\dfrac{v}{u}$ (since $v = -$ PY)

In other words, we have in both cases

$$m = -\frac{v}{u}$$

Hence with this formula we see that when the image is inverted v and u are positive and, therefore, m is a negative quantity. And when the image is erect v is negative and u positive (or conversely) so that m is a positive quantity.

The student should verify the formula for all cases of reflection in spherical mirrors.

(b) Longitudinal.—If the object is lying along the axis

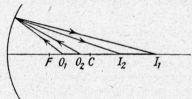

FIG. 37.

(Fig. 37) the size of the image may be found by making use of the formulæ :—

$$\frac{1}{v_1} + \frac{1}{u_1} = \frac{1}{f}$$

and

$$\frac{1}{v_2} + \frac{1}{u_2} = \frac{1}{f}$$

where v_1 and u_1 are distances respectively from the pole to I_1 and O_1 and v_2, u_2 the distances from the pole to I_2 and O_2.

Hence

$$\frac{1}{v_1} - \frac{1}{v_2} = \frac{1}{u_2} - \frac{1}{u_1}$$

or

$$\frac{v_2 - v_1}{v_1 v_2} = \frac{u_1 - u_2}{u_1 u_2}$$

∴ Longitudinal magnification $m = \dfrac{v_2 - v_1}{u_2 - u_1} = -\dfrac{v_1 v_2}{u_1 u_2}$

or

$$\mathbf{m} = -\frac{\mathbf{v}^2}{\mathbf{u}^2}$$

when the object is small.

The result follows immediately if we use the methods of the calculus, for

$$\frac{1}{v} + \frac{1}{u} = \frac{1}{f}$$

differentiating, we have :

$$\frac{dv}{v^2} + \frac{du}{u^2} = 0$$

or

$$\frac{dv}{du} = -\frac{v^2}{u^2}$$

E

The negative sign here indicates that the object and image points always move in opposite directions. This is obvious from the diagram.

Experimental Method of finding Focal Lengths and Powers.—Fig. 38a shows a thin steel rod sharpened to a point at one end and fixed by a screw into a hollow brass rod. The screw merely serves to hold the steel rod at any desirable height. The rod will be used as the object.

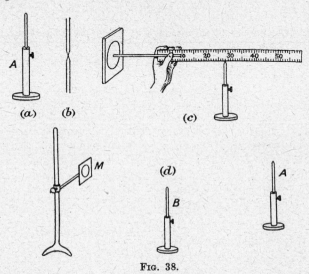

Fig. 38.

Method 1. *Concave Mirrors.*—Place A in front of the mirror and adjust the height until an inverted image is observed in the mirror. Move A until the image and A appear as in Fig. 38b, no matter from what position they are viewed; that is, find the position for no parallax (page 29) between the object and its image. This can be done with great accuracy, for it is very easy to observe the slightest movement between the two points which appear to touch. The object A is then at the centre of curvature of the mirror. Measure the distance of A from the pole by the method shown in Fig. 38c. A thin rod about 20 cm. long is flattened at the ends and placed at a definite mark on a steel scale. Holding these firmly, place the rod at the pole of the mirror and the scale near the tip of A. Read the position of A on the scale. If the measuring rod is 20 cm. long, and one end is placed at the 10-cm. mark on the scale, 10 cm. must be added to the scale reading to give the correct distance of A from the pole of the mirror. Thus, in Fig. 38c, the scale reading will be 20·8 cm. ; hence the correct distance will be 30·8 cm., and half this value will be the focal length.

The advantage of using a measuring rod is that measurement can be made from the pole itself and not near to it, as would be the case if the steel scale alone were used.

Method 2. Concave Mirrors.—Place A in such a position that an inverted image can be seen in the mirror. Bring another object B, and move it until there is no parallax between B and the image of A (Fig. 38d). Again arrange the height so that coincidence of the points may be obtained.

SUMMARY OF RESULTS

Mirror.	Position of Object.	Position of Image.	Nature of Image.	Size compared with Object.
Concave	∞	F	Real, inverted	Diminished
	Between ∞ & C	Between F & C	,, ,,	,,
	C	C	,, ,,	Same size
	Between C & F	Between C & ∞	,, ,,	Enlarged
	F	∞	,, ,,	,,
	Between F & P	Back of mirror	Virtual, erect	,,
Convex	∞	F	Virtual, erect	Diminished
	Between P & ∞	Between F & P	,, ,,	,,

Repeat and show that $\frac{1}{v} + \frac{1}{u}$ is a constant. The mean value of
$\frac{1}{v} + \frac{1}{u}$ will be the mean of $\frac{1}{f}$, which gives the mean Power.

The above methods are not good when convex mirrors are used, as no inverted images can be formed, and hence no coincidence of points can be obtained. The determination of f for convex mirrors will be considered after the student has become acquainted with the action of lenses (page 93).

Spherical Aberration.—In all our calculations we have assumed that only mirrors of diameters small compared with any of the measurements taken, have been used. Thus, we

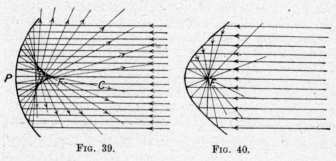

FIG. 39.   FIG. 40.

assumed that all parallel incident rays passed, or appeared to pass, after reflection, through the Principal Focus of the Mirror. If we examine reflection by means of the optical disc, we shall observe that only those rays incident near to the pole of a concave mirror converge through a point. Those incident further away from the pole do not pass through this point. This departure from our laws of reflection is called *spherical aberration*.

The effect is more strikingly shown if such homely articles as a cylindrical shaving mirror and a hair comb are used. The comb is placed across the mirror so as to split a strong beam of light into a large number of narrow beams as in Fig. 39. Each beam after reflection is seen to converge and to cut its neighbouring reflected beam at a point which lies on a curve.

This curve is called a **caustic** and is the curve of greatest luminosity. If the comb is covered by a sheet of paper and the paper is then drawn slowly across the comb the whole construction of the caustic is readily observed.

The brightest point on the curve is at F, the principal focus. In a parabolic mirror all parallel rays, after reflection, pass through a point focus (Fig. 40). Consequently, for obtaining approximately large parallel beams of light, this form of mirror is very useful.[1] It is, however, only useful for parallel light; for ordinary work it is better to use spherical mirrors and block out the eccentrical rays by means of a diaphragm of black paper with the central portion removed.

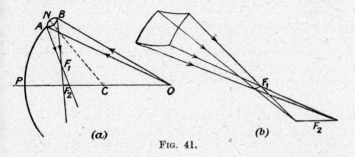

FIG. 41.

Focal Lines due to reflection at Spherical Surfaces.—When we get a cone of rays reflected as previously described, and without a point focus being obtained, the phenomenon is termed *Astigmatism*. In any astigmatic cone there are two regions where greatest intensity of the light occurs, and if we consider the cone indefinitely narrow, these two regions approximate to two straight lines at right angles to each other called *Focal Lines*. In the diagram 41(a) a narrow cone of rays is drawn incident at the surface AB, which is a small portion of the spherical mirror. Each ray in this cone is reflected and cuts the axis at different points. The two extreme rays OA and OB in

---

[1] It is interesting to note that parabolic mirrors are used commercially in the form of " local heaters." They are usually made of polished copper with a burner or electric heater placed at the principal focus of the mirror. In this way a nearly parallel beam of heat rays can be directed towards any local spot.

the plane of the paper intersect at a point F_1. By holding a concave mirror in such a way that rays from a small strong source of light strike obliquely, the complete result of the reflected pencil will be seen to be an elongated figure of 8 (Fig. 41b), where every ray after reflection passes through a line at F_1 at right angles to the plane of the paper (assuming the diagram has rotated through a small angle about OP) and cuts the axis through F_2 in the plane of the paper. From F_1 to F_2 there is a gradual twist of the pencil from a line at right angles to the plane of the paper called the *First Focal line* F_1 to a line in the plane of the paper, the *Second Focal line* F_2. At some place between F_1 and F_2 the cone passes through a circle which is at right angles to the direction of propagation. This circle is the nearest approach to a point focus and is termed the *circle of least confusion*.

It will be seen then that for oblique centrical pencils[1] a spherical mirror acts as if the focal length were less than for direct pencils, the result being that a large object produces a curved image. Moreover, for points near the edge of the object, large " circles of confusion " are produced, and these cause considerable blurring of the image.

QUESTIONS. IV.

1. Define the terms spherical mirror and centre of curvature of a mirror. Has a plane mirror a centre of curvature ? If so, where is it situated ?

2. Define the term principal focus as applied to (a) concave mirrors, (b) convex mirrors. Draw diagrams which illustrate your answers.

3. Distinguish carefully between real and virtual conjugate foci as applied to spherical mirrors.

4. Obtain a relation between the focal length and radius of curvature of a concave mirror.

5. Show that $\dfrac{1}{v} + \dfrac{1}{u} = \dfrac{1}{f}$ is the general formula for spherical mirrors where v and u represent the distances of the image and object from the pole and f is the focal length of the mirror.

6. By means of diagrams show the positions occupied by the various images formed by placing an object in front of a concave mirror—
   (a) At infinity.
   (b) Between infinity and C, the centre of curvature of the mirror.
   (c) At C.
   (d) Between C and F, the principal focus of the mirror.

---

[1] CN is a normal to the surface, AB, and therefore for this portion of the mirror CN may be taken as the axis and the cone OAB may be considered oblique but centrical.

(e) Between F and P, the pole of the mirror.

In each case draw a cone of rays from the two extremities of the object and show how the images are formed.

7. How may a concave mirror be used as a shaving glass ? Illustrate your answer.

8. Show how to distinguish between plane, concave and convex mirrors by merely looking at them.

9. Define the term " magnification." Show that the magnification produced by spherical mirrors is $-\dfrac{v}{u}$ where v and u have the usual meanings.

10. Describe carefully a good experimental method for determining the focal length of a concave mirror.

11. Write a short account of spherical aberration due to mirrors.

12. A luminous body is placed 20 cm. from a concave mirror of 15 cm. radius of curvature. Where must a screen be placed in order to receive the image in proper focus ?

13. A concave mirror of 10 cm. focal length is found to produce a real image 30 cm. from the pole on the same side as the object. What is the position of the object ? Where would the object have to be placed to produce a virtual image 30 cm. behind the mirror ?

14. If the object in question 13 were 5 cm. long, and at right angles to the principal axis, what was the size of the image in each case ?

15. An object 6 cm. long, when placed in front of a concave mirror of focal length 15 cm., forms images (a) 3 cm. long, (b) 12 cm. long. What are the positions of the object ?

16. Two concave mirrors A and B of equal focal length (25 cm.) are placed 50 cm. apart facing each other, and a luminous point object is placed on the common principal axis at a distance of 30 cm. from A. What will be the position of the image formed by a double reflection at A and B ? Illustrate your answer by a diagram.

17. An object 6 cm. long is placed at right angles to the principal axis of a convex mirror and at a distance of 20 cm. from the mirror. If the mirror has a numerical focal length of 15 cm., what is the position, size and nature of the image ?

18. An object 5 cm. long lies on the principal axis of a concave mirror of focal length 10 cm., with the centre of the object at a distance of 20 cm. from the pole of the mirror. Determine the position, size and nature of the image.

19. Two convex mirrors A, B of focal lengths numerically equal to 10 cm. and 15 cm. respectively, are placed with their convex surfaces facing each other, and at a distance of 25 cm. apart. An object 12 cm. long is placed at right angles to the common principal axis and at a distance of 15 cm. from A. Determine the position, size and nature of the image formed by rays reflected first at A and then at B.

20. What do you understand by the term spherical aberration as applied to curved mirrors ? What are the advantages and disadvantages of parabolic mirrors as compared with spherical mirrors ? How are parabolic mirrors utilised commercially ?

21. What is a caustic curve and how is it produced ?

22. Define astigmatism and focal lines. Show how a large object in front of a concave mirror may give a curved image.

CHAPTER V

REFRACTION

In our previous considerations we have assumed that the light has been travelling in the one medium, air. All our illustrations have shown that light obeys the law of rectilinear propagation and moves in straight lines. If, however, light passes from air into any transparent medium such as water, very little reflection will take place at the surface ; most of the light passes into the medium with a change of direction. This can be clearly illustrated in the following experiment.

A very strong source of light, S (Fig. 42), preferably that

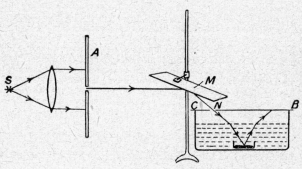

of an arc lamp or a motor-car headlight bulb, produces a very narrow beam of parallel rays which pass through a small aperture A. This beam is reflected by a plane mirror M on to the surface of some water contained in a glass trough. At the bottom of the trough is some mercury contained in a small glass tray ; this is so arranged that the beam can be reflected by the surface of this mercury. In order to make the passage of the beam visible, a drop or two of fluorescein is mixed with the water and a piece of cardboard CB, with a small rectangular hole N to allow the beam to pass, is placed over the top of the trough. The cardboard is lifted for a moment and a puff of smoke sent into the space above the water. The effect is very beautiful indeed, and clearly illustrates the bending of the rays at the surface of the two media. Moreover, if we look from the side of the trough along the direction BC, and gradually reduce the size of the hole N, we shall always observe the outside edges of the beam in the same planes ; that is, the incident ray, refracted ray, and the normal at the point of incidence lie in the same plane. This phenomenon of the bending of light at the separation of two media is called *Refraction* and the angle of refraction is the angle between the refracted ray and the normal at the point of incidence.

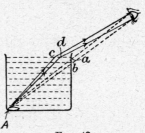

FIG. 43.

EUCLID (third century B.C.), one of the illustrious philosophers of the Alexandrian period, had noticed that a ring placed at the bottom of an empty vessel was easily seen when the vessel was filled with water, even when the view was too oblique for one to see the ring direct. He explained this correctly by assuming that light from the ring was refracted when it reached the surface of the water. Consider the point A of the ring in Fig. 43. The cone of light from A direct to the eye is intercepted by the vessel at *ab*. On filling the vessel with water, such a cone as A*cd* can reach the eye, because of its refraction at the surface. Hence the ring, which was previously invisible, is now easily seen. Another common effect of refraction is the apparent bent condition of a stick held in water. An observer sees the portion AB in the position IB. This is easily understood from our diagram (Fig. 44). A cone of light which leaves A is bent at the surface of the water so as to diverge apparently from I. Hence I is the image of A. Similarly IB is the image of AB, since all point objects along AB such as A give out light.

Ptolemy, the early astronomer mentioned in the first chapter, gave a detailed account of refraction. He described very clearly how the densities of the various transparent media affect the rays of light. In fact, he arrived at the same conclusion that we should arrive at if, in the experiment described at the beginning of the Chapter, various liquids were used to refract the light, and it was noticed which liquids were the most refracting. These conclusions are :—

(1) The angle of refraction is always different from the

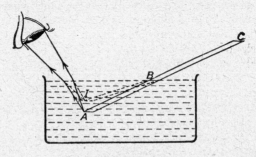

FIG. 44.

angle of incidence, unless the incidence is normal to the surface.

(2) When the light passes from a less optically dense medium to a more optically dense medium (e.g. air to water) the angle of refraction is less than the angle of incidence. When it passes from a more optically dense to a less optically dense medium (e.g. water–air) the reverse is the case ; that is, the angle of refraction is greater than the angle of incidence.

The Exact Laws of Refraction.—Although Ptolemy's conclusions came very near to giving an exact relationship between the angles of incidence and refraction, the disturbing little law was as elusive as a Will o' the Wisp, for we find Bacon, eleven centuries after Ptolemy, still struggling with the problem and with knowledge hardly more advanced than

ROGER BACON

From a print by AEGIDIUS SADELER

that of the ancients. Vitellio and Kepler had the same luck as their predecessors, although Kepler found "*that the angle of refraction is partly proportional to the angle of incidence.*"

This state of affairs lasted until 1621, when Snell [1] formulated the simple law of the constancy of the ratio of the sine of the angle of incidence to the sine of the angle of refraction.

Laws.

(1) (*Snell's*) When any ray of light is incident at the surface which separates two media, it is bent in such a way that the ratio of the sine of the angle of incidence to the sine of the angle of refraction is always a constant quantity for those two media. This constant is called the *refractive index*.

(2) The incident ray, re-fracted ray, and the normal at the point of incidence are in the same plane.

Suppose aO, $a'O$ (Fig. 45) are two rays travelling in the less optically dense medium A and incident at O, a point in the surface of separation of A, and a more optically

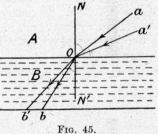

Fig. 45.

dense medium B. Then refraction will occur at O, and aO will travel along Ob and $a'O$ along Ob'. Let NON' be the normal at O.

According to Law 1 $\dfrac{\sin \angle aON}{\sin \angle bON'} = \dfrac{\sin \angle a'ON}{\sin \angle b'ON'} =$ a constant

for the media A and B. This constant is usually written $_A\mu_B$ and may be called the refractive index from A to B. If A is empty space (or air which is practically equivalent) this constant is called the absolute refractive index of B and is denoted simply by μ_B.

Experiment shows us that the directions in which light travels are reversible and therefore, if in the above diagram

[1] Cf. page 5.

we reverse the directions of the arrows, the angle of refraction, $\angle r$ becomes the angle of incidence, $\angle i$.

Thus, $\dfrac{\sin \angle b\mathrm{ON}'}{\sin \angle a\mathrm{ON}} = {}_\mathrm{B}\mu_\mathrm{A} = \dfrac{1}{{}_\mathrm{A}\mu_\mathrm{B}}.$

Hence, the refractive index for light travelling from a medium A to a medium B is the inverse of that from B to A.

If ${}_\mathrm{air}\mu_\mathrm{water} = \frac{4}{3}$, then ${}_\mathrm{water}\mu_\mathrm{air} = \frac{3}{4}$.

Exercise.—Given the relative refractive index ${}_\mathrm{A}\mu_\mathrm{B}$ and the direction of the incident light in A, find by construction the direction of the refracted light in B.

Note.—With the point of incidence P as centre, construct two circles whose radii are on any convenient scale equal to 1 and ${}_\mathrm{A}\mu_\mathrm{B}$. Produce the incident ray until it cuts the circle of radius 1 in M. Through M draw a line perpendicular to the surface cutting the circle of radius ${}_\mathrm{A}\mu_\mathrm{B}$ in N. Then PN is the direction of the refracted ray.

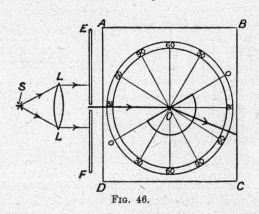

FIG. 46.

Experimental Verification of the Laws of Refraction.

A good method of demonstrating the laws is to fix a semi-circular block of glass, which has had its base frosted, to the optical disc (or its equivalent) in such a way that the centre O of the plane surface of the disc lies along the zero diameter of the circular scale (Fig. 46). A very narrow beam of parallel light is made to fall on the centre O of the glass after having travelled along the plane of the board. After refraction at O the beam will be moving along a radius of the hemisphere, that is, a normal to the curved surface, and will consequently pass out of the glass without receiving further deviation. If the incident beam is seen clearly on the board and is of uniform illumination along its line, the refracted beam is clearly visible. This is what we are led to expect from the second law.

Again, if the angles of incidence and refraction are measured we can determine μ, the index of refraction of the glass. By varying the angles of incidence, (this is accomplished in the case of the optical disc by rotating the disc, and in the alternative method by turning the glass block about O), other determinations of μ may be made and its constancy verified.

Refraction through a Rectangular Block of Glass.

This can be demonstrated quite simply by means of an optical disc or by the use of the light beams as in the experiments on plane mirrors (page 27). Let a narrow parallel beam be incident on a rectangular block of glass (frosted on the base), refracted through the glass and emerge. Turn the glass until the beam strikes the first surface at an angle to it

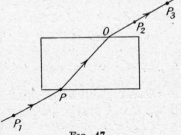

FIG. 47.

of approximately 30° (Fig. 47). Mark the position of the block on the drawing-paper and the directions of the beam on incidence and emergence. Remove the block, draw normals at the points of incidence and emergence and measure the angles of incidence, refraction and emergence. Repeat the experiment for varied angles of incidence and determine the index of refraction by the use of tables. The value should be fairly constant if the experiment has been carefully done.

If light beams are not available, place a pin upright at P

near to the block and another at P_1. Look through the block and observe the images of P and P_1. Place pins P_2 and P_3 in line with these images. Join P_2P_3 and produce to cut the surface at O. Join P_1P, P O. Find μ as before.

Replace the block of glass by a rectangular glass dish filled with water. Note that the angles of *incidence and emergence* are always equal for parallel faced layers of media. This happens no matter how many different transparent media the light traverses provided that *the first and last media are the same*.

Let us apply this result to discover a relationship between the refractive indices of substances. When we speak of the refractive index of glass we really mean vacuum and glass or air and glass (vacuum and air being almost the same where light is concerned). Some-

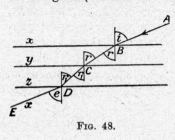

FIG. 48.

times we need to know the value of the refractive index of such a pair of media as water and glass. A ray passing from water to glass would obviously be differently refracted from what it would be if it passed from air to water or air to glass. There is, however, a relationship between the indices for these three pairs of media.

Suppose a ray of light AB passes through three media x, y, z, and finally emerges into the medium x. Let the surfaces of the media be parallel to one another.

Then (Fig. 48) $_x\mu_y = \dfrac{\sin i}{\sin r}$; $_y\mu_z = \dfrac{\sin r}{\sin r_1}$; $_z\mu_x = \dfrac{\sin r_1}{\sin e}$,

and multiplying, we have

$(_x\mu_y)(_y\mu_z)(_z\mu_x) = \dfrac{\sin i}{\sin r} \cdot \dfrac{\sin r}{\sin r_1} \cdot \dfrac{\sin r_1}{\sin e} = 1$ (since $i = e$)

therefore, $_y\mu_z = \dfrac{1}{(_x\mu_y)(_z\mu_x)} = \dfrac{_x\mu_z}{_x\mu_y} \left(\text{since } _x\mu_z = \dfrac{1}{_z\mu_x} \right).$

Thus, if x, y and z represent air, water and glass respectively, Refractive index of water to glass

$$= \frac{\text{Refractive index of air to glass}}{\text{Refractive index of air to water}}.$$

Consider a beam which travels in water (μ_1) and is incident on a glass surface (μ_2).

Then $\dfrac{\sin i}{\sin r} = {}_{\text{water}}\mu_{\text{glass}} = \dfrac{\mu_{\text{glass}}}{\mu_{\text{water}}} = \dfrac{\mu_2}{\mu_1}.$

Hence $\mu_1 \sin i = \mu_2 \sin r,$
a general relation which applies to any two media.

Deviation produced by Refraction.—When a beam of light is refracted by a more optically dense medium it is deviated and has an angle of refraction smaller than its angle of incidence. The angle of deviation d (Fig. 49) is equal to

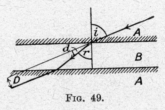

Fig. 49.

$\angle i - \angle r$, the value of which depends upon the nature of the two media A and B and the angle of incidence. It will be seen that this deviation causes a displacement D of the beam, the amount of which depends upon the angle of incidence and the thickness of the plate.

It is well known that an object which is viewed through a plate of glass appears to be brought nearer to the eye. Consider Fig. 50. Rays from O diverge and are refracted in the directions ABE to the eye. The eye sees the rays apparently diverging from a point I.

This deviation produced by refraction gives a very useful method of determining the index of refraction of liquids.

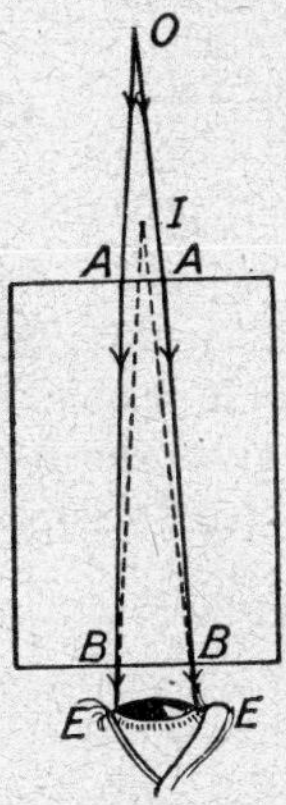

Fig 50.

Determinations of μ.—An empty beaker A (Fig. 51a) is placed under a microscope M which can only move vertically. A vertical scale provided with a

F

vernier V enables the various distances through which the microscope moves to be measured accurately. A coin or clearly visible small object, is placed in the beaker and rests flat on the bottom. The microscope is moved until the coin is brought into focus and the scale reading R_1 of the microscope is noted. The liquid for which μ is required is now put into the beaker and it will be seen that the coin is no longer in focus. Refocus and take a second reading R_2. A little lycopodium powder or dust is now

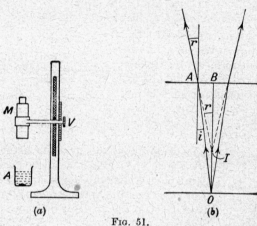

Fig. 51.

sprinkled on the surface of the liquid, and a third reading R_3 of the microscope taken when the powder is best visible.

The difference between readings R_1 and R_3 gives the real depth of the coin and between R_2 and R_3 the apparent depth or distance of the image from the surface.

Then
$$\mu = \frac{\text{real depth}}{\text{apparent depth}}.$$

Theory of Method.—It easily follows from Fig. 51b that
$$\angle AOB = i \quad \text{and} \quad \angle AIB = r.$$

But $\mu_1 \sin i = \mu_2 \sin r$ (where μ_1 is the refractive index of the liquid) and since $\mu_2 = 1$ approximately for air, we have

$$\mu_1 = \frac{\sin r}{\sin i} = \frac{\dfrac{AB}{AI}}{\dfrac{AB}{AO}} = \frac{AO}{AI} = \frac{BO}{BI} \text{ approx.}$$

since the angles are small.

Hence $\mu_1 = \dfrac{\text{Real depth}}{\text{Apparent depth}}$.

The above method can also be used for finding the refractive indices of solids if the object or coin is replaced by a distinctive mark made on a sheet of paper on which the solid substance can rest. The mark then serves as the object to be viewed.

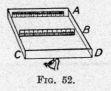

FIG. 52.

Another simple method for determining μ in the case of a rectangular glass block is to use a small wooden scale A (Fig. 52) placed in an inverted position at the back of the block and to find its image by placing a similar scale upright on the glass block. It can be so arranged that the markings of A and B appear to coincide no matter from what position they are viewed along CD; that is, when there is no parallax between B and the image of A.

Then $\mu = \dfrac{\text{distance AD}}{\text{distance BD}}$.

Multiple Images.—It will be remembered that in the experiments (page 28) on images of objects placed in front of plane glass mirrors, the reflecting surface was taken as situated at one-third the thickness of the plate from the back surface. This was to allow for refraction by the glass.

In Fig. 53a the thickness is exaggerated in order to make the diagram clearer. A ray proceeds from an object O to the mirror MM and is refracted at A. It then travels in the direction BCD, being reflected at B and refracted out at C along

CD. Thus, from the point of view of reflection only, OAB is the incident ray and B′CD the reflected ray, or we might say the place B′ is the reflecting surface and not B.

In order to find the position of this fictitious[1] surface suppose the value of μ be 1·5.

$$\mu = \frac{\text{real thickness}}{\text{apparent tihckness}} = \frac{\text{YZ}}{\text{YX}}.$$

Then $\dfrac{\text{YZ}}{\text{YX}} = \dfrac{3}{2}$ and, therefore B′ is one-third the thickness of the plate from B.

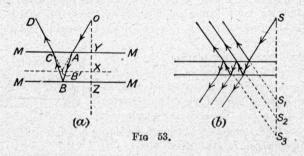

(a)   (b)

Fig 53.

It easily follows from this that the image of O will be situated at a point as far behind X as O is in front.

The student has probably found it necessary at some time to sit in the smoking compartment in the back portion of a " single decker " 'bus. If he has, he may have noticed on looking through the glass screen which separates the two compartments that it is possible to see not only the passengers but also his own image. In other words, the plate glass has both refracted and reflected the light. If in Fig. 53a the surface MM can refract light, it will also reflect, and not all the light which travels along BC will emerge and go along CD.

The effect of these two phenomena is shown in Fig. 53b. More than one image is formed, and as these are very near together, when the glass is not too thick, a considerable

[1] This will only apply when rays have small angles of incidence.

blurring is produced. Most of the rays appear to proceed from the image S_2 which is easily the brightest.

Refraction of Light through a Prism.—The cut glass through which a boy " sees colours " is important when the

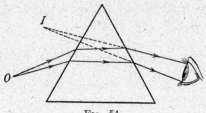

FIG. 54.

cutting of the glass or the transparent substance is done in the form of regular prisms.

When we look at an object through a prism, the image will be seen in different positions according to where the eye is placed to receive the light. In Fig. 54 a cone of rays is shown diverging from a point O and being refracted by the prism, finally proceeding to the eye as if diverging from a point I, the image. Thus the object is apparently displaced from O to I.

It will probably be noticed that the image is slightly coloured : the reason for this will be given later.

Let a narrow parallel beam of light be incident on the face AB of the

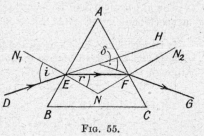

FIG. 55.

prism (Fig. 55). Note that it passes along EF and emerges along FG. The image of the incident beam will appear to be along GF produced backwards. Now turn the prism gradually in one direction and then in the other. Measure the *angle of deviation* δ between the incident and the emergent beams for different positions of the prism. Note that when the beam passes symmetrically through the prism, that is when EF is parallel to BC, the deviation is a minimum.

In this position of minimum deviation it is easily seen that
(1) the angles of incidence and emergence are equal,
(2) $\delta = 2(i - r)$,
(3) Since the quadrilateral AENF is cyclic, $\angle$ENF is the supplement of $\angle$A, and, therefore,

$$A = 2\,r$$

Hence : $$\delta = 2\,(i - r) = 2\,i - A$$

$$\text{or } i = \frac{\delta + A}{2} \text{ and } r = \frac{A}{2}$$

But $\mu = \dfrac{\sin i}{\sin r}$

$$\therefore \mu = \frac{\sin \dfrac{\delta + A}{2}}{\sin \dfrac{A}{2}}, \text{ a formula which enables us to find } \mu$$

when we know the angle of the prism and the angle of minimum deviation.

The experiment can be accurately carried out by means of a spectrometer (cf. page 176).

It is possible to deduce from the laws of refraction the experimental fact that the deviation is a minimum when the light passes through the prism symmetrically.

For, $$\sin i = \mu \sin r.$$

Differentiating, we have

$$\frac{di}{dr} = \frac{\mu.\cos r}{\cos i}$$

or $$di = \frac{\mu \cos r}{\sqrt{1 - \mu^2 \sin^2 r}}.dr$$

$$= dr \sqrt{\frac{1}{1 - \dfrac{\mu^2 - 1}{\mu^2 \cos^2 r}}}.$$

It will be seen that if r increases, $\mu^2 \cos^2 r$ diminishes : therefore, $\dfrac{\mu^2 - 1}{\mu^2 \cos^2 r}$ increases. Hence the coefficient of dr increases.

Thus, a variation of r causes a greater variation of i as r increases.

If, as in Fig. 55 above, we assume that the two angles $\angle$NEF and $\angle$NFE are each equal to $\dfrac{A}{2}$, then a small increase in r (or $\angle$NEF) must be accompanied by an equal decrease in $\angle$NFE. But from our deduction above, the increase in i or $\angle$DEN$_1$ would be greater than the decrease in $\angle$GFN$_2$ and, therefore, $\angle$DEN$_1 + \angle$GFN$_2$ would increase. In other words, the deviation would increase.

Similar reasoning would show that a decrease in r would lead to an increase in the deviation.

Hence the position of minimum deviation is that in which the beam passes symmetrically through the prism.

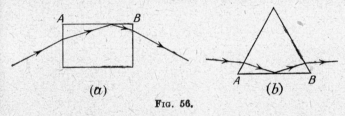

(a) (b)

Fig. 56.

Total Internal Reflection.

When experimenting with light beams it was probably observed that when the beam is travelling in the denser medium it does not always emerge from the face on which it falls. Such, for example, are those positions shown in Figs. 56a and b, where the beam strikes the face AB at a large angle of incidence.

The reason for this inability of the surface to refract the beam can be deduced from the law itself.

$$\mu_1 \sin i = \mu_2 \sin r$$

or, since $\mu_2 = 1$

$$\sin i = \frac{\sin r}{\mu_1}.$$

But, in the case of glass, $\mu_1 = 1\cdot5$, and as the maximum value of $r = 90°$, the maximum value of $\sin r = 1$

∴ the maximum value of $\sin i = \dfrac{1}{\mu_1} = \dfrac{2}{3}$

that is, i must not be greater than 41° 49′.
If $i > 41°$ 49′ the light cannot emerge from the glass, but is totally reflected internally.

The angle of incidence which corresponds to an angle of refraction of 90° is called the **Critical Angle** for the two media.

It should be obvious that total internal reflection can only take place when the light travels from *a more refracting to a less*

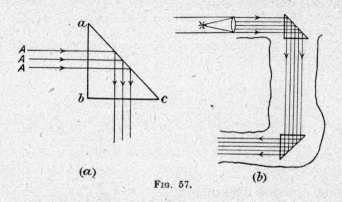

(*a*)   (*b*)

Fig. 57.

refracting medium. In the opposite direction some light is reflected, but a good deal may be refracted even when the angle of incidence is large.

The following practical applications and experiments are of interest :

(1) If a parallel beam of light AAA strikes normally on the face of a right-angled isosceles glass prism (Fig. 57*a*), the rays are not deviated in the prism but pass through until they are incident on the face *ac* at an angle of 45°. This angle is greater than the critical angle for glass to air, and consequently the beam is internally reflected in the manner shown. The adjacent diagram (Fig. 57*b*) shows the applica-

tion of this principle to the illumination of underground passages.

(2) Certain optical instruments are found to produce inverted images which are not always desirable. In order to

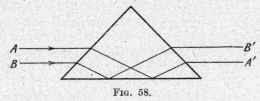

FIG. 58.

avoid this difficulty and render the instrument workable, an " erecting prism " is used. The principle of the prism is clearly illustrated by the diagram. The beams A and B are refracted and reflected so as to produce inversion without deviation.

(3) Take a fairly wide beaker containing water. Insert a test tube into the water and gradually tilt. When the inclination is such that the horizontal light cannot be refracted into the tube, total reflection occurs and the tube will be seen to have the appearance of brightly polished silver (Fig. 59). If water is gradually poured into the tube the total reflection ceases below the level of the water, the light merely suffering a slight deviation after refraction : it then passes on in a parallel direction to the original.

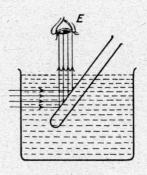

FIG. 59.

(4) Place a shilling in a tumbler of water and hold the tumbler well up to a source of light so that the shilling is brightly illuminated. Now slowly tilt the tumbler and when sufficient obliquity is obtained an image will be seen by an observer, looking up towards the surface of the water, as bright almost as the shilling itself (Fig. 60, p. 74).

(5) Probably one of the best known and least understood phenomena of nature is the " desert mirage." The heat

from the sun makes the layers of air in contact with the hot sand expand and become less dense than the layers above. In consequence, the air is less refracting near the ground, and rays from distant objects striking these layers very obliquely are totally reflected. The layers are continually in motion, and as a result the objects

FIG. 60.   produce weird and fantastic images. These, to a thirsty and probably sun-struck traveller,

appear as palms round an oasis of rippling water.

Refractive Index by the Method of Total Reflection.

If we can find the critical angle for two media, we can determine the refractive index, since $\angle c = \angle i$ when $\angle r = 90°$

$$\text{or } \frac{1}{\mu} = \sin c$$

$$\text{i.e. } \mu = \frac{1}{\sin c}.$$

(1) *Solids.*—Let the solid be glass and in the form of a prism. When a narrow beam of parallel light is available, all that is necessary is to rotate the prism XYZ (Fig. 61) until the beam just fails to emerge along the face ZY. The directions of the beam and the position of the face are then noted and the angle c obtained. (The base of the prism should be frosted in order to show the beam clearly).

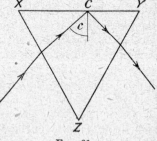

When a light beam is not available, place a pin P (Fig. 62a) upright and near to the edge XZ of the prism. If the eye is in a position such as E_1 it will see an image of the pin clearly between X and some

FIG. 61.

position C, but no further. If the face YZ is observed, the image will only be clearly visible along a portion YK.

It should be clear from the diagram that E_1 can only see refracted light from P, that is the light which is incident at less than the critical angle. E_2, on the other hand, as it looks along ZY, will see light which is totally reflected by the portion CY of the face XY, giving a clear image of P along KY, and a small amount of light which is reflected by the portion XC of the face

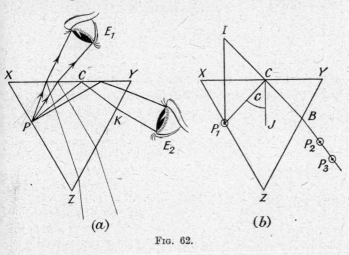

(a)   (b)

FIG. 62.

XY. The latter will be so small that a faint image only of P will be seen along ZK.

Look along YZ and place two pins P_2P_3 (Fig. 62b) in line with the image when it appears to go dim. Join P_2P_3 and produce to cut ZY in B. Then the only light refracted at B, where the image is about to go dim, is that which was not refracted by XY, but was internally reflected by it. In other words, the portion CY of the face acts as a plane mirror. Mark a point I at a distance from XY equal to the distance of P_1 in front. Join IB ; the critical angle will be P_1CJ.

(2) *Liquids.*—Two small plates of glass A separated by an air film and fixed together at the edges by sealing wax are

lowered into a glass trough containing the liquid. A is able to rotate and its angular rotation may be measured by means

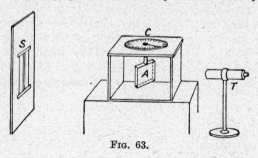

FIG. 63.

of a circular scale C. An illuminated slit S, the plates A and a telescope T are placed in line as shown in Fig. 63. An

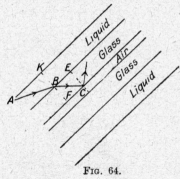

FIG. 64.

observer looking through T will in general see light which has traversed the liquid, the plates and air film in the following order:— liquid, plate, air film, plate, liquid.

Suppose A is oriented in such a manner that the light from the slit is just totally reflected from the air film, no image of S will then be seen in the teles-cope. Fig. 64 shows the rays along BC which are just totally reflected at C.

Since $\qquad \mu_1 \sin i = \mu_2 \sin r_1 = \mu_3 \sin r_2$

$$\mu_{\text{liquid}} \sin i = \mu_{\text{glass}} \sin r_1 = \mu_{\text{air}} \sin r_2$$

But $\qquad \sin r_2 = \sin 90° = 1$

$$\therefore \frac{\mu_{\text{air}}}{\mu_{\text{liquid}}} = \sin i = \sin \angle ABK$$

$$\text{or } \mu_{\text{liquid}} = \frac{1}{\sin \angle ABK}.$$

∠ABK is obtained by taking two readings of the pointer for two consecutive positions of extinction of the light. The angular rotation from one position to the other is clearly 2∠ABK and the reciprocal of the sine of ∠ABK then gives the refractive index of the liquid.

Use of a Concave Mirror for Determining μ.—For determining the refractive index of a liquid, a method frequently used when only a small amount of liquid is available, is the following : A concave mirror is placed on a table, and the centre of curvature O of the mirror is determined by the

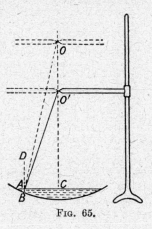

FIG. 65.

parallax method as shown in Fig. 65. A little of the liquid to be examined is then placed on the mirror, and a second position O′ is found, for which the pin and its image show no parallax. Then clearly rays from O′ after refraction at the surface of the liquid must proceed along normals to the mirror where they are reflected and made to retrace their paths. In other words, the ray O′A, when it meets the surface of the liquid, is refracted along the direction AB as if it had proceeded from O (since all rays from O are normals).

Consequently $\angle O'AD = \angle i$

and $\qquad\qquad \angle OAD =$ vertically opposite $\angle r$

Therefore $\mu = \dfrac{\sin O'AD}{\sin OAD} = \dfrac{\sin AO'C}{\sin AOC}$

$\qquad = \dfrac{AO}{AO'} = \dfrac{CO}{CO'}$ approximately.

Hence, measuring the depths O′C and OC will enable the value of μ to be found.

QUESTIONS. V.

1. What do you understand by the meaning of the term refraction of light ? Quote any examples in natural phenomena which may be explained on the principles governing refraction.

2. State the laws of refraction. A ray travelling in air is incident at the surface of separation of air and water and makes an angle of 30° with the normal at the point of incidence. If the refractive index of the water is $\frac{4}{3}$, find by construction the direction of the refracted ray. Verify your answer by calculation.

3. How would you verify experimentally the laws of refraction ?

4. Define refractive index. Show how to determine experimentally the refractive index of a rectangular block of glass.

5. Prove that the refractive index from water to glass is equal to the ratio of the refractive indices of glass and water.

6. Why does a pond appear more shallow than it really is ? Illustrate your answer by a diagram drawn to show how an object which is under water may be seen by a person looking vertically downwards on to the object. How is this fact utilised in the determination of the refractive index of a liquid ?

7. Explain why an object which is viewed through a plate of glass appears to be displaced.

8. Show that the refractive index of a liquid is the ratio of the real depth to the apparent depth.

9. Explain how the parallax method may be applied to determine the refractive index of a rectangular block of glass.

10. Why is it necessary in the case of experiments with ordinary laboratory plane mirrors to take the surface of reflection one third of the thickness of the glass from the back face of the mirror ?

11. What is a prism ?
Make a drawing to show the path traversed by a ray of light which is incident at 45° on a face of a regular prism whose refracting angle is 60°. The refractive index of the glass may be taken to be 1·5. Determine the angle of deviation.

12. How would you determine the refractive index of some transparent substance cut in the shape of a prism ?

13. Show that for a prism $\mu \sin \frac{A}{2} = \sin \frac{d + A}{2}$ where μ is the refractive index, d the angle of minimum deviation and A the refracting angle of the prism.

14. Explain what is meant by the critical angle for two media. What relation is there between the critical angle and total reflection ? When can total reflection occur ?

15. Give any practical applications of total internal reflection.

16. Find a relation between the refractive index and the critical angle. How may this be applied experimentally ?

CHAPTER VI

LENSES

Every schoolboy is familiar with the so-called burning glass or lens, and what is more, knows "how it works." We have seen also in the first chapter that the ancients knew the properties of lenses and employed them in their study of astronomy. Certainly it is impossible to give even an approximate date to the earliest use of lenses. We do, however, have the satisfaction of knowing that the methods of making them have improved immensely even in the last few years.

Strictly speaking a lens is any medium bounded by curved surfaces or by one curved and the other plane.

In order to reduce the difficulty of the theoretical consideration of lenses we shall concern ourselves mainly with very thin glass lenses whose surfaces are parts of spheres.

Refraction of Light through a Lens.—Lenses are divided into two classes :—

(1) Converging.—These are thicker in the middle than at the edges : a_1, b_1, c_1 (Fig. 66).

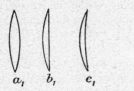

FIG. 66.

Further classification is as follows : a_1 double convex or convex ; b_1, plano-convex ; c_1, converging meniscus.

(2) Diverging.—These are thinner in the middle than at

the edges, and are further classified : a_2, double concave or concave ; b_2, plano-concave ; c_2, diverging meniscus.

The reason why convex lenses are described as converging, and concave as diverging will be readily understood if a lens is considered as built up of prisms in the manner shown (Fig. 67). In this way, and remembering how a prism refracts and deviates beams of light, the convex lens causes in general [1] the beam to converge and the concave to diverge. The " burning glass " then is obviously a convex lens.

In dealing with spherical mirrors only one curved surface had to be dealt with. In lenses two exist, and therefore we

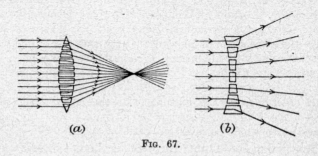

(a)   (b)

FIG. 67.

shall have two centres of curvature. If these are joined we have what is known as the *Principal Axis of a Lens*.

It will be observed that a ray of light which is made to travel along the Principal Axis must strike the lens normally to its surfaces, and therefore will suffer no deviation. There are other directions along which a ray may travel and yet experience no deviation.

In order to find another direction, suppose we have a lens as shown (Fig. 68), C_1, C_2 being the centres of curvature of the faces, and C_1C_2 the principal axis. Draw any radius C_1a to the first surface and one C_2b to the second surface parallel to C_1a. Join ab cutting C_1C_2 in O. Then O must

---

[1] Not always—a convex lens sometimes makes a diverging beam less diverging, and similarly vice versa for concave.

always be a fixed point, for no matter where the two radii are drawn, provided that they are parallel, the $\triangle$'s C_1aO and C_2bO are always similar and, therefore, $\dfrac{OC_1}{OC_2} = \dfrac{C_1a}{C_2b} = \dfrac{r_1}{r_2}$ (where r_1 and r_2 are the radii of curvature of the faces respectively). In other words, O divides C_1C_2 in a constant ratio. The point O is called the *optical centre of the lens*. When $r_1 = r_2$ we have $OC_1 = OC_2$, and consequently O is at the geometrical centre of the lens.

In the general case, when r_1 is not equal to r_2, consider any ray R_1abR_2 which passes through O. If we draw tangents ax and by to the two surfaces at a and b, they will be parallel, since aC_1 is parallel to bC_2, and a tangent is at right angles to the radius. Now it will be remembered that any ray entering a medium will emerge in

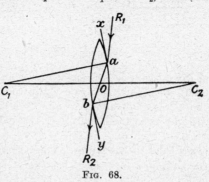

FIG. 68.

a direction parallel to that on entering, provided that the surfaces of entry and exit are parallel also (Chapter IV). It follows then that any ray passing through the optical centre is displaced but not deviated, and as we are considering the case of thin lenses only, the displacement is so small that it can be neglected.

Principal Focus, Focal Length and Power.—When a beam of light, parallel to the principal axis, falls on a convex lens, it is refracted and is made to converge to a point called the *principal focus* (Fig. 69a). It will be remembered that if a beam of sunlight is used as a source all the rays may be considered parallel to each other. The effect of interposing a convex lens is to concentrate the beam to one spot. This spot is easily found by the aid of a piece of paper which will burn when the spot is focused upon it. The distance of the paper from the lens when this takes place is the *focal length,* and the reciprocal of this in metres is the *power (D) in dioptres.*

In our second diagram (Fig. 69*b*), the beam is shown diverging after refraction as if from some point F₂ in front

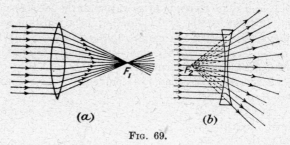

(*a*) (*b*)

Fig. 69.

of the concave lens. Again, this point is called the principal focus, but, since the rays only appear to diverge from it, the point is unreal or virtual. The focal length is again the distance from the lens to F₂. If the direction of the incident beam in each case be reversed, F₁ and F₂ would be on the other sides of the lenses. Thus, there are two positions for the principal focus of a lens.

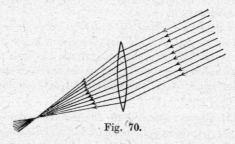

Fig. 70.

When a parallel beam of rays falls on a lens in a direction not parallel to the principal axis (Fig. 70) it is brought approximately to a focus in the *focal plane* of the lens. The focal plane is a plane at right angles to the principal axis containing the principal focus. Images of distant objects fall in this plane.

Conjugate Points.

When we examined the conjugate points of mirrors we used a cylindrical mirror and light beams. For examining these points in the case of thin lenses we use cylindrical lenses (page 113) since these are convex and concave in one plane

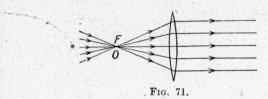

FIG. 71.

only and provide a useful means of refracting strong beams of light along the laboratory bench.

Obtain narrow converging beams of light as explained on p. 26. Let these come to a focus O and pass on. By interposing a convex or concave cylindrical lens we can examine the conjugate points quite easily.

Use the convex lens first and note the distance from O to the lens when the beams emerge parallel from the lens (Fig. 71). The distance is clearly the focal length; that is O is at F,

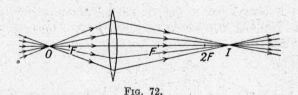

FIG. 72.

the principal focus. Move the lens away from O so that O lies between F and 2F (Fig. 72). Note that the image is real and is between 2F and infinity. Mark the points O and I; they are real conjugate points since the image and object are reversible and can be located on a screen.

Bring the lens near to O so that O lies between F and the optical centre of the lens. Note that the beam does not

converge after refraction but appears to diverge from I
(Fig. 73a). In this case O and I are virtual conjugate points.
Replace the convex lens by a concave lens. It is easy to see

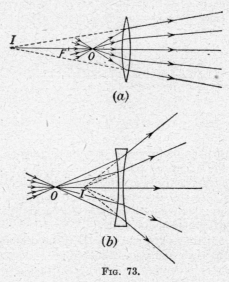

(a)

(b)

FIG. 73.

that it always makes the diverging beam more diverging
(Fig. 73b) and so produces a virtual image. Thus the conjugate points are virtual.

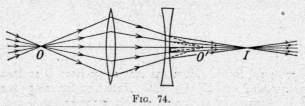

FIG. 74.

It is possible for a concave lens to form a real image if a
converging beam falls upon it. Move the lens to the position
shown in Fig. 74 and note that the converging beam is made
less converging, but a real image may be formed.

Finite Objects.

We can deal with finite objects in a manner similar to the experiments on mirrors (page 45). The mirrors are replaced by convex and concave lenses. Where real images are formed the screen will be on the side of the lens remote from the illuminated cross wires.

Compare your results with the following table :—

Lens.	Position of Object.	Position of Image.	Size of Image.	Nature of Image.
Convex	At ∞	F	Diminished	Real and Inverted
	Between 2F and ∞	Between F and 2F	Diminished	Ditto
	At 2F	At 2F	Same size	Ditto
	Between F and 2F	Between 2F and ∞	Enlarged	Ditto
	At F	∞	Enlarged	Ditto
	Between F and optical centre	On same side as object	Enlarged	Virtual and erect
Concave	Anywhere	Between F and O	Diminished	Ditto

Graphical Construction.

As in the case of mirrors we make use of our knowledge of two rays. We know from experiment that an incident ray parallel to the axis is refracted through the principal focus, while a ray through the optical centre passes undeviated, if we assume that the lens is thin.

The following diagrams illustrate the method. Fig. 75*a* shows the formation of a real image and *b* a virtual image by means of a convex lens.

The student should draw the other diagrams for himself ; the results are given in the table above. The construction for a concave lens is similar, but in this case the parallel ray after refraction will have to be produced backwards in order to cut the ray drawn through the optical centre.

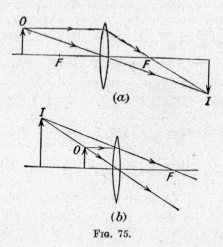

Fig. 75.

Simple Formula for Lenses.

Sign Convention.—On page 40 it is stated as a simple rule that where real objects and real images are formed the spaces will be regarded as positive, and where virtual objects and virtual images are formed the spaces will be regarded as negative. This convention which was adopted for mirrors will also be adopted for lenses.

It should follow that a convex lens which produces a real image of a distant object at the principal focus has a positive focal length and, therefore, a positive power. Hence a convex lens is called a positive lens. A concave lens, on the other hand, has a negative power and is therefore called a negative lens.

Consider Fig. 76a and b. Here the two construction rays, AN and AO have been drawn in order to obtain the image A′B′.

It is easily seen that the △'s A′B′O and ABO are similar. Also the △'s A′B′F and NOF are similar.

Therefore, $\dfrac{A'B'}{AB} = \dfrac{OB'}{OB}$ and $\dfrac{A'B'}{NO} = \dfrac{B'F}{OF}$.

But $NO = AB$ and, therefore, $\dfrac{OB'}{OB} = \dfrac{B'F}{OF}$.

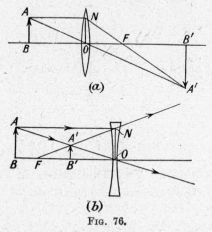

(a)

(b)

Fig. 76.

With the same notation for distances and signs as in the case of mirrors (page 41) we have :

Fig. 76a, $\dfrac{v}{u} = \dfrac{v - f}{f}$ and Fig. 76b, $\dfrac{-v}{u} = \dfrac{-f - (-v)}{-f}$

$\therefore\ fv = uv - uf$ and $fv = -uf + uv$.

Dividing through by uvf, we have in both cases

$$\dfrac{1}{v} + \dfrac{1}{u} = \dfrac{1}{f} = \mathbf{D},\ \text{the power.}$$

This is the same formula as for mirrors—a very useful feature of the sign convention adopted.

EXAMPLES.—A point source of light is placed successively on the axis of, and at two different distances from, a convex lens of power 10 dioptres. The images are both 30 cm. from the lens : (1) on the same side as the object, and (2) on the side remote from the object. Find the distances of the object from the lens in the two cases.

The two cases are illustrated in Fig. 73a and Fig. 72.

Since the power is 10 dioptres, we have $f = 10$ cm.

(1) Here f is positive and v is negative, since I is virtual.

Hence

$$-\frac{1}{30} + \frac{1}{u} = \frac{1}{10}$$

$$\frac{1}{u} = \frac{1}{30} + \frac{1}{10}$$

$$u = 7\cdot5 \text{ cm.}$$

(2) Both f and v are positive and, therefore,

$$\frac{1}{30} + \frac{1}{u} = \frac{1}{10}$$

$$\frac{1}{u} = \frac{1}{10} - \frac{1}{30}$$

$$u = 15 \text{ cm.}$$

Simple Formula for Two Thin Lenses in Contact.

In Fig. 77 the two lenses are shown separated for the sake of clearness.

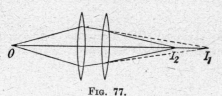

FIG. 77.

Let v_1 be the distance of the image I_1 produced by the first lens and v_2 the distance of the final image I_2.

Then $\dfrac{1}{v_1} + \dfrac{1}{u_1} = D_1$ where D_1 is the power of the first lens.

But I_1 is the virtual object of the second lens and, therefore,

$$v_1 = -u_2 \text{ or } u_2 = -v_1.$$

Hence, for the second lens we have,

$$\frac{1}{v_2} - \frac{1}{v_1} = D_2$$

where D is the power of the second lens.

Adding, we get $\dfrac{1}{v_2} + \dfrac{1}{u_1} = D_1 + D_2.$

But u_1 and v_2 are the distances of the object and final image from the combination, so that if this combination has a power D

$$\frac{1}{u_1} + \frac{1}{v_2} = D$$

Hence $\qquad D_1 + D_2 = D$

In other words, the *power of the combination is equal to the sum of the powers of the separate lenses.*

It also follows that $\dfrac{1}{F} = \dfrac{1}{f_1} + \dfrac{1}{f_2}$ where F is the focal length of the combination and f_1 and f_2 are the focal lengths of the separate lenses.

Magnification. Transverse.—As in the case of mirrors, magnification is measured by the ratio $\dfrac{h'}{h}$, where h' is the height of the image and h the height of the object.

The sign convention adopted is the same ; that is we regard heights measured above the axis as positive and those measured below as negative.

In Figs. 76a and b we have $\triangle$'s ABO and A'B'O similar.

Hence, Fig. 76a, $m = \dfrac{h'}{h} = \dfrac{-\,A'B'}{+\,AB} = \dfrac{-\,OB'}{+\,OB} = \dfrac{-\,v}{u}$

and in Fig. 76b, $m = \dfrac{h'}{h} = \dfrac{+\,A'B'}{+\,AB} = \dfrac{OB'}{OB} = \dfrac{-\,v}{u}$

that is, in all cases $\mathbf{m} = -\dfrac{\mathbf{v}}{\mathbf{u}}$

which is the same formula as for spherical mirrors.

It also follows that the magnification is positive when the lens produces an erect image of an erect object, and negative when inversion takes place.

Longitudinal.—This magnification was deduced in the case of spherical mirrors from the formula $\frac{1}{v} + \frac{1}{u} = D$. As the same formula is used for lenses, it easily follows that

$$m = -\frac{v^2}{u^2} \text{ (cf. page 49)}.$$

Experimental Determinations of Focal Lengths or Powers.

A lens is distinguished by its type and power. The following brief notes should be sufficient to enable the student to determine by various methods the value of the power of any thin lens :—

Convex.—(1) Focus the image of a distant object, such as a window, on to a sheet of white paper. The distance from the paper to the lens gives a rough value of the focal length, from which the power may be easily obtained.

(2) Adopt the beam method or failing this the pin method described on page 50. In the case of a convex lens, however, the object and real image will be on opposite sides of the lens. Apply the formula : $\frac{1}{v} + \frac{1}{u} = \frac{1}{f} = D$ or use parallel beams and note the distance from the lens to the point of intersection of the refracted beams.

The best position in the case of a finite object, such as a pin, is that where the object and image are of the same size. Hence readings should be taken when u is approximately equal to v. Add half the thickness of the lens to your distances in order to obtain closer accuracy.

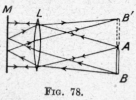

FIG. 78.

(3) Use a plane mirror M, Fig. 78 with the lens L and arrange these so that the mirror is upright behind the lens while the object AB is in front. Move the object until a real image coincides with it. The distance from the object to the lens together with half the thickness of the lens is the focal length.

(4) Keep the object and image at a constant distance l apart (this must be greater than $4f$). Obtain two positions of the lens where the image is in focus. Let d be the distance between the two positions. Then we have:

$$\frac{1}{u_1} + \frac{1}{v_1} = \frac{1}{u_2} + \frac{1}{v_2} = \frac{1}{f}$$

But $\quad\quad u_1 = v_2 \text{ and } u_2 = v_1$

also $\quad l = u_1 + v_1 \text{ and } d = u_2 - u_1 = v_1 - u_1$

Hence $\quad\quad v_1 = \dfrac{l+d}{2} \quad\quad u_1 = \dfrac{l-d}{2}.$

This gives $\quad\quad f = \dfrac{l^2 - d^2}{4l}.$

Concave.—No direct method is available when finite objects are used, since a concave lens produces a virtual image of a real object. Hence we usually use the lens in combination with a convex lens or a concave mirror.

(1) Using parallel beams, trace back the refracted beams to a point and note the distance of this from the lens.

(2) We know that $D = D_1 + D_2$ when two lenses are combined and since D must be positive in order to produce a real image of a real object the power D_2 of the negative concave lens must be less than the power D_1 of the convex lens. Hence in order to determine D_2 choose a convex lens of large power, find its value and then combine it with the unknown concave lens and find the power of the combination. The difference between D and D_1 will give the power required.

(3) A variation of the last method is to separate the lenses by a distance t and obtain a real image A_2 of a real object, Fig. 79. Let the distance of this image be v from the concave lens. Remove the concave lens and find the distance V of the image A_1 which now appears.

It is easily seen that A_1 is the virtual object of A_2 and the distance of A_1 from the concave lens is $V - t$.

Hence as regards the concave lens we have

$$u = -(V - t)$$

and, therefore, $\dfrac{1}{v} - \dfrac{1}{V - t} = D$, the power of the concave lens.

It is worth noting that by this method it is not necessary to choose a convex lens of larger power than the concave.

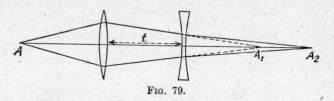

Fig. 79.

(4) Another variation is to separate the lenses by a distance t as before and to place a plane mirror upright behind the concave lens as shown in Fig. 80. The object A is then moved about until a real image coincides with it. The light is then retracing its path after refraction through the lenses and reflection by the mirror. Keep the object fixed, but remove

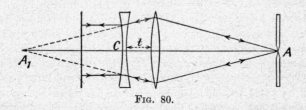

Fig. 80.

the plane mirror and the concave lens. Measure the distance v of the image A_1 from the convex lens. It should be clear from the figure that A_1C, or $v - t$ gives the value of the focal length of the concave lens.

(5) Put a concave mirror and the concave lens at a distance t apart. Move the object A until a real image coincides with it. It will be seen from Fig. 81 that when this happens the

light after refraction through the concave lens is striking the mirror normally and is therefore retracing its path. A and A_1 are conjugate points where A_1 is the centre of curvature of the mirror.

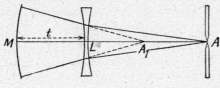

Fig. 81.

Hence $AL = u$ and $-A_1L = v$. But $A_1L = R - t$ where R is the radius of curvature of the mirror (cf. page 42), and, therefore, we have $\dfrac{1}{-R+t} + \dfrac{1}{u} = D$, the power of the lens.

(6) The last experiment suggests a method for finding the focal length of a convex mirror.

The mirror is set at a known distance from a convex lens and an object is placed in such a position that its image is coincident

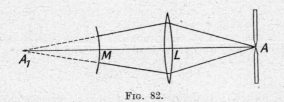

Fig. 82.

with it (Fig. 82). A_1L is easily found and since ML is known, the value of A_1M, which is the radius of the mirror, can be obtained. Half this value is the focal length.

Further Treatment of Refraction through Lenses.

The Prismatic Effect of a Thin Lens.—It is worth noting that the fundamental equation for a thin lens may be expressed in another very useful form. Let y be the height of the point of incidence M (Fig. 83) of a ray above the axis. Multiplying each term of the fundamental equation by y we have

$$\frac{y}{v} + \frac{y}{u} = \frac{y}{f} = y\mathrm{D}$$

Remembering that we are only concerned with small angles such that their tangents and circular measures are equal, we have

$$\alpha = \frac{y}{u}, \ \alpha' = \frac{y}{v}$$

where α, α' are the slopes of the object and image rays OM and MI.

Signs.—We shall assume that y is positive when M is above the axis and negative when it is below. This implies that in Fig. 83

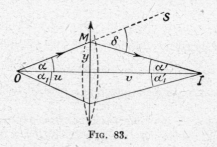

Fig. 83.

the angle of slope α of the object ray is positive, while α_1 is negative. Also α' is positive while α_1' is negative.

If δ is the deviation experienced by the ray OM in passing through the lens, we have :

$$\delta = \alpha + \alpha'$$

and, therefore, $\qquad \delta = y.\mathrm{D} \qquad \cdots \cdots \cdots (1)$

That is, for any lens the deviation of any ray depends only on its height of incidence. All rays, incident at M, whatever their slope (provided it is small) suffer the same deviation.

The Single Surface.—We have so far considered the action of the lens as a whole, and we have seen that its behaviour is completely known when its focal length or power is given. Obviously, the value of the power depends upon the radii of curvature of the surfaces and the index of refraction of the material. In order to determine how these quantities fix the power it is necessary to consider in more detail the action of the lens. Since the lens consists of material bounded by two spherical surfaces our first step must be to examine the case of refraction at a single spherical surface.

Let MPM′ (Fig. 84) be the trace of a spherical surface separating two media of indices μ_1 and μ_2. Let C be the centre of curvature. Consider a ray from an object point O incident at M and refracted along MI cutting the axis OPC in the point I.

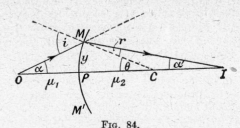

Fig. 84.

From the geometry of the figure and the second law we see that

$$i = \alpha + \theta$$
$$r = \theta - \alpha'$$

From the first law of refraction we have

$$\mu_1 \sin i = \mu_2 \sin r$$

and if we limit ourselves to small angles, we have :

$$\mu_1 i = \mu_2 r.$$

Substituting in the above expressions for i and r, we get

$$\mu_1(\alpha + \theta) = \mu_2(\theta - \alpha')$$

i.e. $$\mu_1 \alpha + \mu_2 \alpha' = (\mu_2 - \mu_1)\theta.$$

But, denoting PM by y, we have :—

$$\alpha = \frac{y}{u}, \ \alpha' = \frac{y}{v}, \ \theta = \frac{y}{r}. \quad \text{(N.B. } r \text{ is } +\text{ve ; c.f. page 98.)}$$

Hence we arrive at :

$$\mu_1 . \frac{y}{u} + \frac{\mu_2 y}{v} = \frac{(\mu_2 - \mu_1)y}{r}.$$

Dividing by y, we thus obtain :—

$$\frac{\mu_1}{u} + \frac{\mu_2}{v} = \frac{\mu_2 - \mu_1}{r} \quad \bullet \quad \bullet \quad \bullet \quad \bullet \quad \bullet \quad (2)$$

The student can verify for himself that for large angles of incidence and refraction the correct formula, assuming v and u measured along the rays, would be

$$\frac{\mu_2}{v} + \frac{\mu_1}{u} = \frac{\mu_2 \cos r - \mu_1 \cos i}{r}$$

We see from (2) that with the stated assumption that we are only dealing with rays which make a very small angle with the axis and which are incident very near to the pole P—that is, by using only *paraxial* rays—we have the result that all rays from O whatever their incidence and height (y), meet after refraction at the point I. Hence I is the image of the point O.

We obtain immediately from this equation the position of two most important points, the *first and second focal points*, F_1 and F_2. F_1 is the position of the object point for which the image point is at infinity; if we denote its distance from P by f_1, we see that by making v infinitely great we get :—

$$f_1 = \frac{\mu_1 r}{\mu_2 - \mu_1}.$$

Similarly the second focal point F_2 is the position of the image point when the object point is at an infinite distance; denoting the distance of F_2 from P by f_2 we get

$$f_2 = \frac{\mu_2 r}{\mu_2 - \mu_1}$$

We note that

$$\frac{f_1}{f_2} = \frac{\mu_1}{\mu_2}$$

and also that the equation (2) can be expressed in terms of f_1 and f_2 by the equation

$$\frac{f_1}{u} + \frac{f_2}{v} = 1 \quad . \quad . \quad . \quad . \quad . \quad . \quad (3)$$

Slope Ratio.—It is worth noting that the ratio of the slopes of the two conjugate object and image rays, OM and MI is given by

$$\frac{\alpha'}{\alpha} = \frac{u}{v}, \text{ since } \alpha = \frac{y}{u} \text{ and } \alpha' = \frac{y}{v}.$$

Transverse Magnification.—With C as centre (Fig. 85) describe two circular arcs of radii CO, CI and draw a line ACB cutting these arcs in A and B and making a small angle with the axis OPI. It is clear that A and B have exactly the same relation to the surface as O and I : that is a cone of rays emanating from A as object point will pass through B as image point. Now, since OA and IB are short arcs, they may be taken as coincident with the short perpendiculars OA, IB and we see that any small object OA has IB as its image.

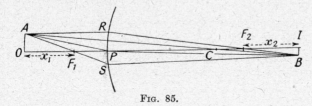

FIG. 85.

Then from the figure we have at once

$$\frac{IB}{OA} = \frac{CI}{CO}$$

and, hence, if we denote the heights of the object and image by h_1 and h_2, taking as before positive and negative values as they are above or below the axis, we have for the transverse magnification, m

$$m = \frac{h_2}{h_1} = \frac{-IB}{+OA} = -\frac{CI}{CO}$$

ı.e.

$$m = -\frac{v-r}{u+r}.$$

Using the fundamental equation (2) we can at once get from this the expression,

$$m = \frac{h_2}{h_1} = -\frac{\mu_1 . v}{\mu_2 . u}. \quad . \quad . \quad . \quad . \quad (4)$$

which of course we could also obtain by considering the rays AP and PB.

Helmholtz's Equation.—Combining the last equation with the result for the slope ratio, we obtain

$$\mu_1 h_1 \alpha = -\mu_2 h_2 \alpha'. \quad . \quad . \quad (5)$$

This is an important relation which is known as the Helmholtz Law.

The Newtonian Equation.—It is sometimes convenient to express these results in terms of the distances of O and I measured

H

from F_1 and F_2 respectively. Call these distances x_1 and x_2. Then we have (Fig. 85)

$$m = \frac{h_2}{h_1} = -\frac{IB}{OA} = -\frac{IB}{PR} = -\frac{F_2 I}{F_2 P} = -\frac{x_2}{f_2}$$

$$= -\frac{PS}{OA} = -\frac{F_1 P}{F_1 O} = -\frac{f_1}{x_1}$$

Equating these two expressions for m, we get

$$\mathbf{x_1 x_2 = f_1 f_2} \quad . \quad . \quad . \quad . \quad . \quad . \quad (6)$$

The Power and Sign of a Surface.—We have seen that the fundamental formula for a single refracting surface is given by :—

$$\frac{\mu_1}{u} + \frac{u_2}{v} = \frac{\mu_2 - \mu_1}{r}$$

The quantity $\dfrac{\mu_2 - \mu_1}{r}$ is called the Power D of the Surface.

The sign of the surface depends upon the sign of the numerator $(\mu_2 - \mu_1)$ and the denominator, r. The sign of the numerator obviously depends on whether $\mu_2 >$ or $< \mu_1$. In order to find the sign of r it should be noted that the radius of any surface does not concern us until the light reaches the surface and, therefore, we may regard r as connected with the image space and not the object space. Following our previous convention, therefore, we consider r is positive if it lies in a real image space and negative if it lies in a virtual image space. Hence, for a convex lens in air, the front surface has a positive radius and the back surface a negative, while for a concave lens the front surface has a negative radius and the back positive.

It follows from our formula that the power of each surface of a convex lens is positive and of a concave lens negative.

If we denote the power of the surface by D, we have for the case in which the first medium is air,

$$\frac{1}{u} + \frac{\mu}{v} = \frac{\mu - 1}{r} = D.$$

Equation for a Thin Lens.

Since a thin lens merely consists of two surfaces separating a medium of refractive index μ_2 from two media of refractive indices μ_1 and μ_3 respectively, our equation for a single surface may be applied at each surface.

Then at the first surface (Fig. 86), we have

$$\frac{\mu_1}{u_1} + \frac{\mu_2}{v_1} = D_1,$$

where u_1 is the distance of the object, v_1 is the distance of the image I_1 produced by this surface and D_1 is the power.

The image I_1 becomes the virtual object O_2 of the second surface, and, therefore, $u_2 = -v_1$, if we assume that the lens is of negligible thickness.

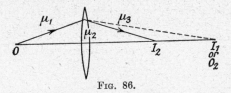

FIG. 86.

Hence, at the second surface we have

$$\frac{\mu_2}{-v_1} + \frac{\mu_3}{v_2} = D_2,$$

where v_2 is the distance of the final image and D_2 is the power of the second surface. Adding the two equations together, we have

$$\frac{\mu_1}{u_1} + \frac{\mu_3}{v_2} = D_1 + D_2.$$

This shows that the refraction produced by the two surfaces is the same as that produced by a single surface of power $D_1 + D_2$.

Call the power of the lens D, its refractive index μ, and let $\mu_1 = \mu_3 = 1$ as for a lens in air.

Then
$$D = D_1 + D_2$$
$$= \frac{\mu - 1}{r_1} + \frac{1 - \mu}{r_2}$$
$$= (\mu - 1)\left(\frac{1}{r_1} - \frac{1}{r_2}\right)$$

But $D = \frac{1}{f}$, since $\frac{1}{u_1} + \frac{1}{v_2} = D_1 + D_2$, and therefore,

$$D = \frac{1}{f} = (\mu - 1)\left(\frac{1}{r_1} - \frac{1}{r_2}\right) \quad \ldots \quad (7)$$

If the above equation refers to a convex lens in air it is important to remember that r_2 is a negative quantity, since it lies in a negative image space.

Experimental Determinations of the Optical Constants of Thin Lenses.

A simple method of determining experimentally the optical constants of thin convex lenses is a variation of Expt. 3, page 91, for finding the power of a thin concave lens. The lens L_2 whose constants are required is arranged as shown in Fig. 87, so that *two* images are formed.

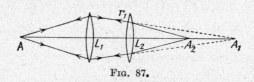

FIG. 87.

(1) at A_2 after refraction through an auxiliary convex lens L_1 and the lens L_2, and

(2) coincident with the source A after refraction through L_1 and reflection at the surface r_1.

It easily follows that if an image is to be formed coincident with the source, the reflection at r_1 must be normal. Hence the distance $L_2A_1 = r_1$.

But turning the lens L_2 round and repeating the experiment we can find the radius r_2.

The power D is determined in exactly the same way as on page 90 and the value of μ, the refractive index of the lens, may be calculated from the formula : $D = (\mu - 1)\left(\dfrac{1}{r_1} - \dfrac{1}{r_2}\right).$

If our unknown lens is a concave lens, the procedure outlined above can still be applied.[1] In this case, however, as Fig. 88 shows, reflection will take place from the second surface r_2.

Hence $r_2 = L_2A_2.$

[1] In this case it is simpler to determine r_1 and r_2 directly without the aid of the convex lens; i .e. to treat each surface as a concave mirror.

It is important to use care in setting the lenses in position so that the reflection actually does take place at the surfaces r_1 and r_2 and not from either surface of the auxiliary lens.

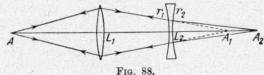

Fig. 88.

Systems of Lenses and Principal Planes.—Very often in the construction of optical instruments we are concerned with a series of spherical refracting surfaces arranged with their centres on a common axis. To calculate the position of the image formed by such a lens system, the straightforward way is to proceed step by step; that is, find the position of the image formed by refraction at the first surface and then regard this image as the object for the next refraction, and so on. In essence there is nothing more difficult in this than is involved in the calculation for a single surface, but if there are many surfaces the calculations would soon become tedious and we should have to carry them through separately for each position of the image point.

Now, it has been shown—mainly by the great German mathematician Gauss—that the behaviour of such systems can be surveyed more easily once the position of certain important points on the axis have been found. First, there are two focal points, F_1 and F_2, defined in exactly the same way as we have already done for a single surface. Next, there are always two conjugate planes perpendicular to the axis such that a small object on the axis in one of them has an erect image of equal size formed in the other; that is, a pair of planes for which the *magnification*, $m = +1$. These planes are called *Unit Planes* or the *Principal Planes*. Let the points where such planes cut the axis be denoted by H_1 and H_2, the first and second *principal points* respectively (Fig. 89). It should be noted that these points F_1, F_2, H_1 and H_2 may occur anywhere along the axis; their positions, of course, will depend upon the particular set of lenses.

Construction for the Image.—As we know the position of the four points we can at once find the image of a given object by a simple geometrical construction similar to that used for a single surface. Thus, let OA be the object. From A draw a ray which passes through F_1 and cuts the first principal plane in the point R_1. We know that the direction of the conjugate image ray 1′ must (a) be parallel to the axis, because 1 passes through F_1 and also (b) it must pass through a point R_2 in the second principal plane, such that $H_2R_2 = H_1R_1$. This is because R_1 and R_2 are conjugate points; in other words, all rays passing through R_1 must give image rays which pass (actually or virtually) through R_2. Similarly, the ray 2 through A parallel to the axis must give an image ray 2′ in the direction M_2F_2. The intersection B of the rays 1′ and 2′ must then be the image of A. Clearly also the object ray 3 has its corresponding image ray 3′ in the direction H_2B. It will be seen that if H_1 and H_2 coincided, this figure would be exactly the same as that for a single surface.

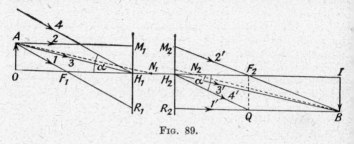

FIG. 89.

Focal Lengths.—The two distances H_1F_1, H_2F_2 are called the first and second focal lengths of the system. Denote these by f_1, f_2. The reason for calling these distances focal lengths will soon be clear from what follows.

Newton's Equations.—Let x_1, x_2 as before denote the distances of O and I measured from F_1 and F_2 respectively. Using the same sign convention as before, we have in our figure

$$x_1 = + F_1O, \quad x_2 = + F_2I, \quad f_1 = + H_1F_1, \quad f_2 = + H_2F_2.$$

Then from the figure, we see that the magnification m is given by

$$m = \frac{h_2}{h_1} = -\frac{IB}{OA} = -\frac{H_1R_1}{OA} = -\frac{F_1H_1}{F_1O} = -\frac{f_1}{x_1}$$

or

$$= -\frac{IB}{H_2M_2} = -\frac{F_2I}{H_2F_2} = -\frac{x_2}{f_2}.$$

From these two expressions for m, we get

$$x_1x_2 = f_1f_2.$$

These results for the magnification and the equation which followed (Newton's) will be recognised as having exactly the same form as those for a single surface; that is, the lengths F_1H_1, F_2H_2 can justifiably be looked upon as focal lengths because they enter into the equations in the same way as the focal lengths do in the case of a single surface.

Ratio of the Focal Lengths.—In Fig. 89 an object ray 4 parallel to AR_1, and incident in a direction passing through H_1 will give rise to an image ray 4' in a direction H_2Q where Q is the intersection of the ray 1' with the second focal plane. Q is the image point corresponding to an infinitely distant object point in the direction α. Denoting the angle F_2H_2Q by α' and applying the Helmholtz equation at the conjugate points H_1 and H_2 we have, since for a small object and image in these planes $h_1 = h_2$,

$$\therefore\ \mu_1\alpha = -\ \mu_2\alpha'.$$

It can be shown that no matter how many surfaces are concerned this relation between the product $\mu h \alpha$ for the first object space and the corresponding quantity $\mu'h'\alpha'$ for the final image space always holds.

Now from the diagram we have, remembering sign convention page 94,

$$\alpha = -\ \frac{H_1R_1}{f_1} \text{ and } \alpha' = +\ \frac{F_2Q}{f_2} = +\ \frac{H_1R_1}{f_2}$$

and, consequently

$$\frac{f_1}{f_2} = \frac{\mu_1}{\mu_2}$$

which is again the same result as for a single surface. If the initial and final media are the same the first and second focal lengths are equal.

Equations referred to Principal Planes.—Another very important property of the principal or unit planes is very easily proved. Let u, v be the distances of O and I from the two principal points H_1 and H_2. That is, in our figure

$$u = +\ H_1O \qquad\qquad x_1 = u - f_1$$
$$v = +\ H_2I \qquad\qquad x_2 = v - f_2.$$

Substituting these values for x_1 and x_2 in the Newtonian equation we get

$$\frac{f_1}{u} + \frac{f_2}{v} = 1$$

which is again identically the same as for a single surface.

Thus we have shown that *provided we measure the distance of the object and image from the first and second principal points,* the same relation holds as for a single surface. No such simple relation holds if the distances are measured from the first and last surfaces.

Equivalent Focal Length.—It is clear from the figure that a single thin lens of focal length f_2 placed in the plane through H_2 would produce the same image—in size and position—of an infinitely distant object as the actual lens system does. For this reason f_2 is often called the *equivalent focal length of the system.* It should be pointed out, however, that such a single thin lens is only equivalent to the lens system in this very restricted sense. There is no thin lens which will produce images of the same size *and position* as those produced by the system for all positions of the object.

Nodal Points.—Another important pair of conjugate points is the pair N_1, N_2 which have the property that any object ray incident in a direction through N_1 has a corresponding image ray whose direction passes through N_2 and is parallel to that of the object ray (dotted lines in Fig. 89). Such a pair of points are called the first and second nodal points.

Their positions may easily be found by applying the Helmholtz equation. For, at these points we have $\alpha = -\alpha'$ and hence we must have $\mu_1 h_1 = \mu_2 h_2$. That is, the magnification $\dfrac{h_2}{h_1}$ for object and image in the first and second nodal planes is given by

$$\frac{h_2}{h_1} = \frac{\mu_1}{\mu_2}.$$

Hence if x_{n_1} and x_{n_2} denote the distances of N_1 and N_2 from F_1 and F_2 respectively, we must have

$$m = -\frac{f_1}{x_{n_1}} = -\frac{x_{n_2}}{f_2} = \frac{\mu_1}{\mu_2}$$

i.e.

$$x_{n_1} = -\frac{\mu_2}{\mu_1}.f_1 = -f_2$$

$$x_{n_2} = -\frac{\mu_1}{\mu_2}.f_2 = -f_1.$$

If the two focal lengths are the same, which is the case when the initial and final media are the same, we see that $m = 1$ and so N_1 and N_2 are coincident with H_1 and H_2 respectively; that is, the principal points are then also nodal points.

These three pairs of points F_1, F_2, H_1, H_2 and N_1, N_2 are sometimes called the **Cardinal Points** of the lens system. We see that once we know their positions it is easy to understand the action of the system.

Equivalent Focal Length of a System of Two Thin Lenses. —As an example of the foregoing, suppose we have two thin lenses of powers D_1 and D_2 placed at a distance d apart. In Fig. 90 consider a ray LS_1 incident parallel to the axis at a height $P_1S_1 = y_1$ above the axis. This will be deviated an angle δ_1 by the first lens, proceeding in a direction $S_1S_2F_{2a}$ where F_{2a} is the principal focus of the first lens. At S_2 it is further deviated by the second lens through an angle δ_2: it then crosses the axis at F_2, the second principal focus of the system. Let LS_1 produced cut F_2S_2 produced in a point M_2. Then a plane through

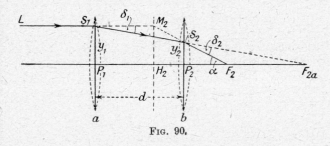

Fig. 90.

M_2 is clearly the second principal plane of the system and the distance H_2F_2 is the required equivalent focal length. We have :—

$$\delta_1 = y_1D_1 \text{ (p. 94)}$$
$$y_2 = y_1 - d.\delta_1 = y_1 - y_1dD_1 = y_1(1 - dD_1)$$
$$\delta_2 = y_2D_2 \qquad = y_1D_2(1 - dD_1)$$
$$\alpha = \delta_1 + \delta_2 \qquad = y_1(D_1 + D_2 - dD_1D_2)$$

and, hence

$$H_2F_2 = f_2 = \frac{y_1}{\alpha} = \frac{1}{D_1 + D_2 - dD_1D_2}.$$

That is, the equivalent focal power of the system is given by

$$D = D_1 + D_2 - dD_1D_2.$$

A single thin lens of this power placed at H_2 would produce the same image for a very distant object as the system.

In the same way, by considering a ray parallel to the axis incident from the right-hand side we could find the position of F_1 and thence, since here we have $f_1 = f_2$, the position of H_1.

Thick Lens in Air.—In this case let AM_1 (Fig. 91) be a ray parallel to the axis, incident at a point M_1 at a height y_1 above the axis. At M_1 it is refracted along the line M_1M_2 toward the point F_{2a}, the second focal point of the *first* surface. At

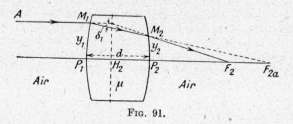

FIG. 91.

M_2 it is refracted through F_2, the second focal point of the lens. At the first refraction we have

$$\frac{\mu}{P_1F_{2a}} = D_1$$

(since in the fundamental equation for a single surface $u = \infty$ and $v = P_1F_{2a}$)

Multiplying this by y_1 and calling the deviation δ_1 we have

$$\mu\delta_1 = y_1D_1 \quad (\text{since } \frac{y_1}{P_1F_{2a}} = \delta_1).$$

The height of incidence at the second surface is given by $y_2 = y_1 - \delta_1 d = y_1(1 - \dfrac{d}{\mu}D_1)$, where d is the thickness.

For the second refraction we have (since u for this is $- P_2F_{2a}$)

$$-\frac{\mu}{P_2F_{2a}} + \frac{1}{P_2F_2} = D_2.$$

Multiplying this by y_2 and transposing, we have

$$\frac{y_2}{P_2F_2} = y_2D_2 + \frac{\mu.y_2}{P_2F_{2a}} = y_2D_2 + y_1D_1$$

i.e. $$\frac{y_1}{H_2F_2} = \frac{y_2}{P_2F_2} = y_1\left[D_1 + D_2 - \frac{d}{\mu}.D_1D_2\right].$$

Hence, the equivalent power or the reciprocal of the second focal length H_2F_2, is given by

$$\frac{1}{H_2F_2} = D = D_1 + D_2 - \frac{d}{\mu}.D_1D_2.$$

It is interesting to note that this is the same as for the two thin lenses of powers D_1 and D_2 separated by a distance d except that in place of d we have $\frac{d}{\mu}$.

Experimental Methods for Thick Lenses.

We can determine the focal length or the power of a thick lens experimentally without the need for finding the positions of the Principal Planes.

(1) *Concave or Convex Lenses.*—Treat the lens as a thin lens, but measure distances of object and image from the principal foci, and apply Newton's equation $x_1x_2 = f^2$.

(2) *Convex Lens.*

(a) Magnification $m = -\frac{v}{u} = -\left(\frac{v}{f} - 1\right)$

we have $\qquad \frac{\delta m}{\delta v} = -\frac{1}{f}$ or $f = -\frac{\delta v}{\delta m}.$

Therefore by measuring the ratio of the change in v to the change in m we can determine f.

It is sufficient to measure v from the surface of the lens, since this distance is related to the distance from the Principal Plane by a constant quantity.

(b) Another magnification method is to measure distances between the object and its image and the magnifications.

For real images we have $l = v + u$ approximately, provided that v and u are large enough for the distance between the principal planes to be negligible

$$m = -\frac{v}{u} \text{ or } -\left(\frac{v}{f} - 1\right).$$

Hence $\qquad ml = -\frac{v}{u}(u + v) = v(m - 1)$

and $\qquad v = -f(m - 1)$

therefore, $\qquad ml = -f(m - 1)^2$

or $\qquad f = -\frac{ml}{(m - 1)^2}.$

Lens Aberrations.—All the preceding results for lenses have been based on the assumption that the angles of incidence and the slopes of all the rays were very small ; that is to say, all the rays forming the image were supposed to be contained within a narrow cylindrical region around the axis of the lens. The results were accordingly only strictly correct for images, formed by very small angled pencils of light, of small objects on the axis. In practice, however, we must always make use of rays outside these limits. For example, in a compound microscope or a high-power telescope the function of the objective is to form a magnified image of objects lying within a narrow field of view. It is also necessary for the lens to collect wide pencils of light from each object point, because not only must the image be bright but also (as is explained in the Chapter on Diffraction), even if the lens were perfect we shall only get a sharp image when the beam forming it has a wide cross section. On the other hand, in a magnifying glass or the eye-piece of a telescope or microscope we require a wide angle of view ; that is, we wish to form images of points widely off the axis, yet we need only narrow pencils of light from each object point. In the case of a camera lens the demands are still greater, for we not only need as much light as possible and so a wide aperture, but it is also necessary for clear images to be formed when objects cover a wide field of view.

For practical purposes, therefore, it is necessary to consider how a lens behaves when we no longer restrict ourselves to paraxial rays. When we look into this we find that there are many ways in which its behaviour deviates from that given by elementary theory. These deviations are called *aberrations of lenses*.

Spherical Aberration. (Central or Longitudinal.)—Consider a wide parallel beam falling on a convergent lens (Fig. 92) parallel to its axis. The rays near the axis are brought to a focus at a point F_a while rays some distance from the axis are refracted so as to cross it at points nearer the lens, those passing through the edges of the lens—the so-called marginal rays—cutting the axis at F_m. Thus the lens does not give a point image of a distant point source. Instead we have another example of a caustic surface (page 52) like that we noted in the reflection of a wide beam at a spherical mirror. A lens showing this behaviour is said to have longitudinal (or central) spherical aberration. The distance $F_m F_a$ may be taken as a measure of it. It is found that by properly choosing the curvatures of the surfaces it is possible almost to eliminate the trouble. It can be shown that the separation F_mF_a is reduced to a minimum when the deviations of the rays produced at the first and second surfaces are equal. The fact that the more nearly equal these deviations are the less is this difference in position of the axial and marginal foci can easily be shown by a simple experiment.

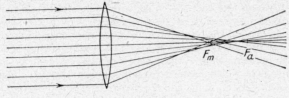

FIG. 92.

Take a plano convex lens (Fig. 93) and measure the distance between F_m and F_a (this is done by blocking out first the axial rays and then the marginal ones), first when the plane surface is towards the incident light and then with the lens reversed. We find that the difference F_mF_a is much less in the second case and it is clear that in this case the deviation is shared between the two surfaces, whereas in the first it is all performed

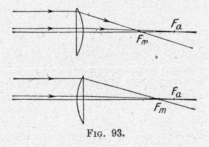

FIG. 93.

at the second. With glass of refractive index 1·5 it can be shown that this aberration can be almost eliminated if the lens is bi-convex with the radii of the surfaces in the ratio 6 : 1, the more curved surface facing the incident light. Such a lens is called a *crossed lens*. It must be noted, however, that even if the lens is so formed that it accurately focuses in a point all rays incident parallel to the axis, it will not do so for rays diverging from some point at a finite distance from the lens. The lens can be corrected for one, but only one, pair of conjugate object and image points.

Coma.—Suppose we have a lens which produces no central spherical aberration for a particular object point on the axis ; that is, brings all rays of even wide angled pencils to a definite point focus on the axis. Even so, it does not follow that it will also give a sharp point image of an object point a little off the axis. In general the image of a small flat object would be sharp at the middle and be surrounded by a blurred region. Abbé, the German optician, showed that this arises because in the ordinary way the rays which proceed from the object through different zones of the lens form images of different sizes which overlap and, hence, give a blur. He showed that if this is to be avoided it is necessary that for all rays from the axial point of the object

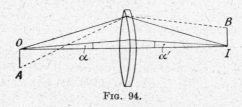

FIG. 94.

the ratio of the sines of the angles of the slopes of the object and image rays must be a constant ; that is sin α/sin α' must be the same for all pairs of rays (Fig. 94). If this—the well-known sine condition—is fulfilled, then the lens will bring all the rays from such a point as A to a sharp focus in a point B, and hence the lens will give a sharply defined image of a small flat area around O. A lens corrected for this and also for central aberration is called an *aplanatic lens* (cf. page 114).

This formation of images of different size is also the cause of an effect called *coma*. Take an ordinary positive lens and make it form an image on a white screen of a point source of light (a small motor-car bulb will do), placed not on the axis but to one side. The image will be found to be distorted into a kind of pear-shaped—or comet-like—blur. This blur, or *comatic flare*, as it is called, tapers off either towards the outside or inwards. Try the experiment with a plano-convex lens, first with the plane side and then the curved towards the light. A telescope objective which was not so shaped as to avoid this defect would give sharp images of stars only in the centre of the field, those off the axis being represented by comet-like particles of light, the size of which would increase as we moved further out in the field of view.

Radial Astigmatism.—There is another defect of the image shown by every lens that is not specially designed to avoid it,

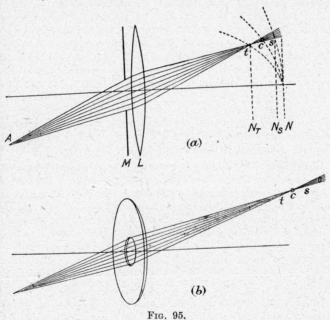

FIG. 95.

even though the lens may exhibit no central aberration or coma. It arises from those pencils of light which pass obliquely through the lens, and though it usually occurs with the coma it is quite a separate defect and arises from a different cause. A simple experiment will show it clearly. Let A (Fig. 95a) be a point source of light some distance off the axis of an ordinary positive lens L. In front of this is placed a screen M with a hole so that only a narrow pencil of light is allowed through the lens. This stop cuts down the comatic flare and allows the effect with which we are concerned to be clearly seen. We find that in no position of the focusing screen N is the pencil of refracted rays brought to a sharp point ; but for one position N_T the rays are focused in a short line perpendicular to the plane of the paper, while if the screen is drawn back a short distance to N_S, the image on the screen is a short vertical line in the plane of the paper. This arises because the emergent pencil of rays is not a conical one with all its rays passing through a single point, but an astigmatic pencil having two focal lines (cf. page 53). The character of the pencil is shown in Fig. 95*b*. The nearest approach to a sharp image of the point is obtained somewhere between the two focal lines, where a circular patch of light—the *circle of least confusion*—is obtained on the screen. The distance between the two focal lines is called the astigmatic difference. It increases with the obliquity of the pencil. The image of a plane object perpendicular to the axis is thus formed of two curved surfaces ; in one T the image of each point object is a short line tangential to circles centred on the axis, and in the other S each object point is imaged as a little radial line.

Curvature.—By making use of two or more lenses separated from each other so that one compensates the other, it is possible to get rid of the astigmatic difference. But even when this is done in all probability the image of a plane object would still be a curved surface. Hence, if we wish to have a sharp image on a screen the simplest plan is to make the screen curved, as was done in the camera obscura. This is, of course, inconvenient if the image is to be received on a photographic plate ; in this case it is necessary to design the lens system so that the image will be flat.

Distortion.—When we have a compound lens system which is free from all the above defects, we find that it is possible for the image to be sharp and flat but not geometrically similar to the object. This may be shown by experiment. Take as object a plate ruled in squares. It will be found that the real image of this will have the general character shown in Fig. 96*a* ; that is, we get barrel-shaped distortion with a positive lens. The virtual image of such an object formed by the same lens would exhibit pincushion distortion (*b*). The character of the distortion of the real image can be altered very much by a suitably placed screen with a small aperture. If this is placed on the object side of the lens the image shows barrel distortion, but if it is placed some distance behind the lens, the distortion will be of the pin-cushion type. This suggests a means often adopted to overcome distortion ; that is, to place a stop with an aperture between the two parts of the lens system, so that the barrel distortion produced

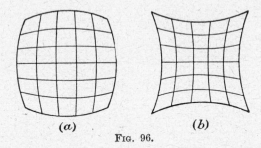

(a)   *(b)*

Fig. 96.

by the back part will be neutralised by the pin-cushion produced by the front.

General Observations.—This brief indication of the nature of the five aberrations gives some idea of the immense difficulty of designing a compound lens system that will give a sharp flat image free from all distortion ; it enables one to appreciate the skill and ingenuity shown by lens designers in the production of modern optical instruments.

Before closing the subject a description will be given of two useful lenses, the cylindrical lens and the aplanatic lens.

The Cylindrical Lens.—This provides an interesting example of astigmatism. The lens is a medium bounded by two cylindrical surfaces. It is common in practice to make one surface plane as in Fig. 97. We shall assume that the lens is thin.

Let OF_1F_2 be the axis of the lens and XOX', YOY' be two lines lying in planes at right angles to the axis and at right angles to each other.

Refraction of light takes place in the plane XOX' as if this part of the lens is an ordinary spherical lens. In the plane YOY', that is, the plane containing the axis of the cylinder, refraction takes place as if this part of the lens were a parallel-sided plate. Thus the light emerges parallel to its incident direction and undeviated (since the lens is thin) and a circular cone of light which falls on the lens in such a way that its axis coincides with the axis of the lens will be refracted through the lens as an astigmatic bundle of rays.

The light in the plane XOX' will come to a focus at F_1 while that in the plane YOY' will pass on without deviation to F_2.

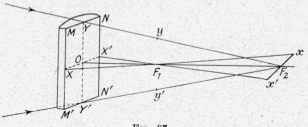

FIG. 97.

All other planes parallel to XOX' will bring the light to foci at points above and below F_1, that is, along yF_1y'. Those planes parallel to YOY' will pass the light undeviated to xF_2x', that is, a line at right angles to the axis of the lens.

These two lines are obviously focal lines. The production of a line image from a point source accounts for the use of the lens in the experiments on mirrors and lenses.

Aplanatic Lens.—This lens has the quality of bringing all rays which fall upon it from a point source on the axis to a point focus in the axis. Fig. 98 represents a hemispherical surface

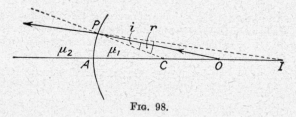

FIG. 98.

with axis AI, and centre of curvature C. The surface separates two media of refractive indices μ_1 and μ_2 ($\mu_1 > \mu_2$).

Consider an object placed at O at a distance from C equal to $\dfrac{\mu_2 AC}{\mu_1}$, where AC is the radius of curvature.

A virtual image is formed at I and it easily follows that

$$\frac{CP}{CO} = \frac{\sin \angle POC}{\sin i}.$$

But $$CO = \frac{\mu_2}{\mu_1}.CP \text{ (since AC} = CP)$$

or $$\frac{CP}{CO} = \frac{\mu_1}{\mu_2}.$$

Hence, $$\angle POC = r.$$

But $$\angle POC = \angle PIO + r - i.$$

$$\therefore \angle PIO = i.$$

Hence in $\triangle CPI$, we have

$$\frac{\mu_1}{\mu_2} = \frac{\sin r}{\sin i} = \frac{\sin \angle CPI}{\sin \angle PIO} = \frac{CI}{CP}$$

consequently, $CI = \frac{\mu_1}{\mu_2}.AC$ and is, therefore, *a constant*, no matter at what angles the light is incident to the surface. In other words, O and I are such points that any light diverging from O will, after refraction, appear to diverge from I.

It will be noted that this lens satisfies for these two points the sine condition referred to earlier (cf. page 110).

QUESTIONS. VI.

1. What is a lens and what action has it on a beam of parallel light ?
2. How are lenses classified and why are they so treated ?
3. Define principal axis and optical centre of a lens. Show where the latter is situated.
4. What is the principal focus of a convex lens and how is it easily obtained ?
5. Distinguish between real and virtual conjugate foci as applied to lenses.
6. An object 6 cm. long stands upright with its base on the principal axis of a convex lens. If the object is situated 12 cm. from the optical centre of the lens and the focal length of the latter is numerically 15 cm., determine graphically the size and position of the image.

7. Prove the formula $\frac{1}{v} + \frac{1}{u} = \frac{1}{f}$ as applied to lenses where v and u are the distances respectively of the image and object from the optical centres and f is the focal length. Why are conventional signs necessary ?

8. What is the focal length of a lens ? An object 8 cm. long is placed upright on the axis of a convex lens and 15 cm. from the latter. If the image is formed 60 cm. from the lens on the side remote from the object determine the power of the lens and size of the image.

9. Illuminated cross wires and a white screen are placed 200 cm. apart. Where must a convex lens of 15 cm. numerical focal length be placed in order that an image of the cross wires may be clearly in focus on the screen ?

10. The focal length of a convex lens has a numerical value of 15 cm. Where must an object be placed if a real image is to be formed 6 times as large as the object ?

11. Describe any accurate method of determining the power of (a) a convex lens, (b) a concave lens.

12. An object 6 cm. long is situated 50 cm. from a convex lens of numerical focal length 10 cm. Light from this object, after passing through the lens, is made to fall on a concave lens of focal length 3 cm. situated at a distance of 12 cm. from the first lens. Determine the position, size and nature of the final image.

13. Describe an accurate method of finding the focal length of a convex mirror.

14. Given the radii of curvature of the surfaces of a lens and the refractive index, deduce a formula for the focal length.

15. What is an achromatic lens ? Deduce an expression for the focal length of an achromatic lens in terms of the focal lengths of its separate lenses.

16. What do you understand by equivalent focal length ? Deduce an expression for the equivalent focal length of two thin lenses.

17. What are the cardinal points of a system of lenses ?

18. What do you understand by the term spherical aberration of a lens ? What are the causes and how may it be minimised ?

19. What do you understand by the statement that a lens is aplanatic ? What are aplanatic foci and how are they obtained ?

20. What is astigmatism ? In what way may a cylindrical lens be regarded as providing a good example of astigmatism ?

CHAPTER VII

THE COMPOSITE CHARACTER OF SUNLIGHT

Sir Isaac Newton (1642–1727) became a lecturer in Optics after his election to the Chair of Mathematics at Trinity College, Cambridge, in 1667. One of his first tasks in research was to deal with the problem of blurring of the images seen through a telescope. He used his knowledge of mathematics in the construction of new and more up-to-date lenses, but to little purpose. Finally he came to the conclusion that

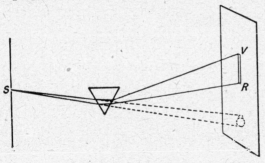

FIG. 99.

the light was at fault, or perhaps the law of refraction. In order to satisfy himself, he bought a prism and tested this conclusion by allowing a beam of sunlight to enter through a small round hole [1] in a darkened room and fall on the prism in the manner shown (Fig. 99). To his surprise, instead of the round image of the sun's disc appearing upon the screen, he noticed that the image was considerably elongated in a direction at right angles to the edge of the prism, and brilliantly coloured at the extremities. By moving the screen

[1] A narrow slit was subsequently used.

to various distances and measuring the patch of light, he
easily satisfied himself that light still travelled in straight
lines so that the prism had not affected this law. What then
had happened to the light ? If the spreading of the light
was merely a function of the prism a second prism should
produce still more colouring. By selecting one of the constituents after passing through the first prism, and allowing
this to be deviated by another prism (Fig. 100), Newton found
that no further colouring was produced.

The results of his experiments showed that the " single "
constituent was different from sunlight in that it did not

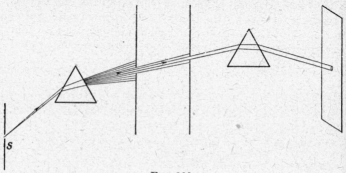

Fig. 100.

contain more than the one colour. One was simple and the
other complex.

Again, by inverting the second prism, it was discovered
that when the whole " band " was allowed to fall upon it,
the sunlight was brought to its original state. This was not
so, however, if the band were robbed of a constituent before
falling on this second prism.

By many such experiments Newton proved conclusively
that white light consisted of an infinite number of constituents
all refracted by the prism at different angles, but grouped
together in seven different colours—Red, Orange, Yellow,
Green, Blue, Indigo, Violet. It was a wonderful discovery,
and caused not a little sensation. All the old theories of colour
collapsed. As one writer put it, " the light does not get

Sir Isaac Newton

From a painting by Sir Peter Lely

dyed red as it passes through a red glass plate, nor is a body red because a something called a red colour lives inside the body." In the first case all the constituents of the white light are absorbed except the red, and only this is able to reach the eye, and in the second case only the red light emerges from the body.

A Pure Spectrum.—The "rainbow" image produced by Newton's experiment is called a *Solar Spectrum*.

It will be remembered that only the extremities were brilliantly coloured. The other colours were all mixed up on account of overlapping. If we want to get the constituents " pure " we must prevent this overlap.

Let us consider the original experiment again in more

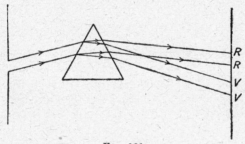

FIG. 101.

detail. The parallel beam may be considered as composed of a large number of thin parallel beams, each one of which is separately split up by the prism into its various constituents.

The red rays have the smallest deviation, and the violet the largest. This means that the glass has a different refractive index for each colour, μ being largest in the case of the violet rays and smallest for the red. It is easy to see that overlapping of the colours will occur (Fig. 101) and a glance at Fig. 102 will show that when the source of light is near and a cone of rays falls on the prism the overlapping is quite pronounced. What we need in order to obtain a pure spectrum is to have all the differently coloured rays brought to separate foci on the screen.

If a convex lens is placed in such a position as to give a clear image of a slit on a screen and a prism is interposed in the path of the rays, either immediately before or after the lens, then the light is dispersed by the prism and the lens brings each coloured component to an image. These images

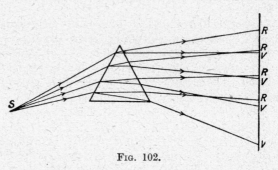

Fig. 102.

will be more clearly defined if formed by rays all having about the same deviation. This can be accomplished by ensuring that all the yellow rays pass through the prism at minimum deviation. The others will then be nearly at minimum deviation.

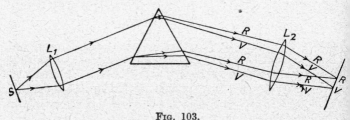

Fig. 103.

The best spectrum is formed in the manner shown (Fig. 103). A strong source of light, such as that from an arc or a high-power electric bulb having a very small filament, illuminates a narrow slit S in a screen. This slit is placed at the principal focus of a lens L_1 in such a way that a parallel beam of rays falls on the prism. The prism is so placed that the yellow rays pass through it at minimum deviation. A second lens, L_2, then brings the rays to their different foci on a screen.

From what has been said it then follows that a pure spectrum of any source of light may be obtained if the following conditions are complied with :—

(1) a narrow aperture to give good definition.
(2) the rays passing through the prism in parallel groups at approximately minimum deviation.
(3) the different colours all being brought to different foci in the same plane.

Dispersion through a Lens.—It will be clear now that the blurring produced by Newton's lenses was not the fault of the lens, but was due to the splitting up of the light which passed through. Had Newton illuminated his objects with monochromatic light, that is light of one single colour such

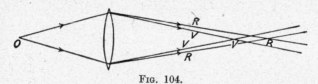

FIG. 104.

as red or yellow, this defect would not have been observed.

A lens acts in the same manner as a prism, consequently the rays will come to different foci (Fig. 104). The spectrum will not be pure along the axis, that is, we shall not have clearly defined images each of a pure colour for the reasons given above, but we shall most certainly get a changing of the colour of the image as a screen is moved from V to R.

Usually what one observes if the object is an ordinary gas burner is a distinct blue near the violet end and a distinct red at the opposite end. The colours, of course, will vary according to the quality of the illumination used.

This defect produced by lenses is called *Chromatic Aberration*, that is aberration due to colour, and is commonly observed in cheap projectors. It is interesting to note that early astronomers overcame the trouble to some extent by using telescope lenses of very long focus.

Achromatic Combinations.—Newton, as a result of his experiments, came to the conclusion that it was impossible to combine two prisms or two lenses so as to produce deviation without dispersion. Suppose a parallel beam of white light falls on the face AB of a prism ABC (Fig. 105). The light which emerges from the face AC consists of a fan of beams ; each constituent of the original beam gives a parallel emergent beam which is deviated downwards through an angle dependent upon the colour, the red the least and the violet most. If these differently coloured beams are again to be made parallel to one another we must clearly introduce into their paths a prism which will deviate the violet upwards more than the red. Let DEF be such a second prism placed with its

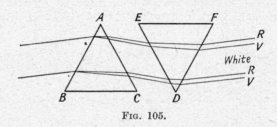

FIG. 105.

refracting edge parallel to that of the first, but with the base above, so that it deflects the beams upward, the violet, of course, more than the red. If we choose the angle of the second prism correctly, we can arrange that the greater downward deviation of the violet (as compared with the red) produced by the first prism is just counteracted by the greater upward deviation produced by the second.

The question now arises : In what direction will the beam travel after passing through both prisms ? If the prisms are made of the same material and the angle of the second prism is the same as the angle of the first, the emergent beams will be parallel to the incident beam. Thus the fan of coloured beams will be closed up, except for a little overlapping at the edges due to sideways displacement, and the resultant beam will be undeviated.

Newton thought this would always be the result no matter of what materials the prisms were made. He had found that with prisms of water and several different types of glass the angle between the emergent red and violet rays always bore the same ratio to the mean angle of deviation, so that if this were the case it was not possible to arrange the second prism to compensate for the dispersion due to the first without also compensating for the deviation as a whole. But later experiments showed that Newton had been too hasty in coming to this conclusion ; the ratio of spreading or *dispersion* to the average bending or deviation is *not* the same for all materials. Thus, for a flint glass this ratio is considerably greater than for a crown glass. Hence if our first prism is of crown glass we should find that the spreading it produced could be compensated by a second flint prism of much less refracting angle, producing a much less deviation in the opposite direction ; so that in the resultant emergent beam the red and the violet rays would be parallel to each other but would still be deviated downwards.

This difference in the behaviour of flint and crown glass can also be used to construct a compound lens which will not separate the blue and red and yet will still converge them to a focus. The first telescope lens of this type was presented to the Royal Society in 1758 by Dolland. The principle of its construction is illustrated in Fig. 106. The convex lens of crown glass brings the blue and red rays to a focus at two points B and R, the average deviation produced in the particular ray indicated being D_1 and the difference in deviation between R and B being δD_1. In b a divergent lens of flint glass produces the same spreading but in an opposite direction for a ray at the same height above the axis ; that is, $\delta D_2 = \delta D_1$. But, since with flint glass the same spreading is produced for a less mean deviation (i.e. $D_2 < D_1$), when the two lenses are in contact as in c we shall have the red and blue rays proceeding together, but they will still be deviated. Such a combination of lenses is called *achromatic*.

It is, of course, necessary in order that a combination of lenses may be achromatic to obtain a relation between the focal lengths which will satisfy the above conditions. This has been left for consideration by the advanced students (page 136).

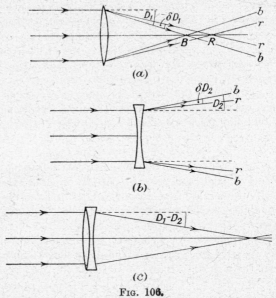

(a)

(b)

(c)

Fig. 106.

Colour.

Absorption plays a very important part in determining the colour of natural bodies. If white light passes through a body some of the light ingredients are absorbed and the light which emerges is, therefore, coloured. The eye perceives the resultant effect of these colours and it is this which determines the "Shade."

Again, if a coloured body is seen by means of reflected light, it owes its colour to the scattered light received by the eye. Irregularity in the arrangement of the molecules of the body not only causes this scattering, but allows of a certain amount of penetration by the incident light. As absorption takes place in the body, the light which emerges has lost some of its original constituents and has, therefore, a shade dependent on what colours the body retains. This may be clearly demonstrated by examining the images of an object seen by reflection from a thin piece of coloured glass. The image from the front surface shows the natural colour of the object no matter what the colour of the glass may be. The image from the back surface, on the other hand, has a colour which is dependent partly on the natural colour of the object and partly on the colour of the glass.

Many substances in powder form are found to be white. This is because almost all of the light is reflected from millions of tiny portions of the surface and very little penetration takes place. Crushed ice is a good example of this. In the crystal state it is almost transparent on account of the small amount of light reflected. When powdered into dust it becomes exceedingly opaque because of the numerous surfaces it can offer to the incident light. The froth of beer is a further interesting example. In the liquid state, as distinct from its froth, beer possesses a definite colour due to absorption. A film of froth, however, reflects almost the whole of the light and so appears to be quite white. Differently coloured specimens of glass all tend to possess the same white appearance when finely powdered.

Colour Mixing.

The formation of colour, mentioned above, is of a *subtractive* nature. In other words, the incident light is reduced in intensity and robbed of constituents by absorption within the body ; the light which emerges is, therefore, coloured. But it is possible to *add* together light beams of different colours and by means of suitable mixtures of red, green and blue to obtain any coloured light required. These three, *red*, *green* and *blue*, are called *Primary Colours*, for when added together in suitable quantities they produce white light.

An arrangement suggested by E. G. Savage [1] for demonstrating colour mixing is shown in Fig. 107. A shoe-box contains three windows of red, green and blue filters which are illuminated by pocket electric torches. An opaque object **A**

[1] See *Colour*, by E. G. Savage.

is placed between the windows and a screen.   If one light, the
blue, is first shown, the general appearance of the screen will

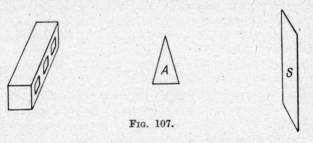

Fɪɢ. 107.

be blue, while a black shadow of the object will appear.   By
adding red illumination the screen generally will have a
mixture of red and blue light (Fig. 108a) and will, therefore,

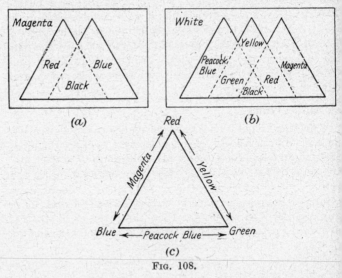

Fɪɢ. 108.

appear magenta, while two shadows will be seen, one red and
the other blue.   When the green light is made to appear, the
screen is seen to become white generally and six shadows

appear (Fig. 108*b*). The triangle illustration in Fig. 108*c* shows how the colours are related. The black shadow has no illumination ; the shadow illuminated by red and blue has a magenta colour ; that from the red and green is yellow while the blue and green produce a peacock blue.

The production of a " compound " yellow by the addition of red and green illumination is interesting since yellow is also one of the spectral colours. If either form is mixed with blue light, a white sensation may be produced.

Two colours which when added together produce white light are called *Complementary* colours. Thus, the following are complementary : Red and Peacock Blue, Green and Magenta, Blue and Yellow. Each may be either a mixture of colours or contain a " range of wave-lengths " of its own colour. Helmholtz discovered that it was possible also to mix colours of definite wave lengths and produce white light. Such for example are particular wave-lengths of Yellow and Blue, Orange and Blue, Red and Greenish Blue. These " monochromatic " colours give the same colour sensations as compound mixtures and, therefore, have the same effect. A possible explanation is given on page 131.

Pigments.

If three primary filters of high-grade quality are arranged to overlap as in Fig. 109*a* and white light from a source passes through the filters on to a screen, the light through 1, 2, 3 and 4 will be almost wholly absorbed and the screen images will be nearly black. If instead of the primary colours we use filters of magenta, peacock-blue and yellow (Fig. 109*b*) only 1 will give a black image ; 3 will show the residual colour common to magenta and peacock-blue, that is blue ; 2 will have the common colour green, while 4 will be red.

The absorption of colour by filters illustrates the action of pigments. It is mixture of light by subtraction and is the reverse of what takes place when colours are added together. When white light falls on to a pigment some of the constituents are absorbed ; the colour or colours which emerge give the natural colour of the pigment.

K

No pigment is spectrally pure, otherwise a mixture would always produce black. When white light was passed through the two filters, peacock-blue and yellow, the only common colour was green. Similarly a mixture of peacock-blue and yellow pigments produces a green pigment since the blue and red constituents of white light are absorbed, the red by the blue pigment and the blue by the yellow. If the blue pigment were completely free from green (i.e. spectrally pure) the mixture would appear black. An artist takes care to use a blue pigment which will give him the right green for his requirements.

In one system of colour measurement the standards of reference are a series of permanent red, blue and yellow glass

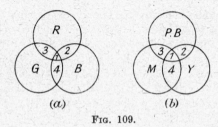

Fig. 109.

slides. The slides of each colour are made to differ gradually from a faint colour perception to a deep one. Each is numbered in such a way that there is a definite relationship between the three standard slides. When the numerical values are the same a certain proportion of white light is absorbed; in the faint colours a light grey is produced and in the dark a black. Thus a grey is black illuminated by white light. If red and yellow slides of equal " value " are introduced an orange tint is produced, while a blue and yellow give green.

It should be clear from the above that the absorption of light by coloured glass, filters and pigments depends a good deal upon the nature and depth of the colouring of the substance used. If the red and yellow slides are deeply coloured the only light which can pass through both with ease is red since this is the only common colour. Hence the orange becomes more and more red (vermilion) as the colour depth of the slides increases.   Again if the blue and yellow slides are deep, a faint green appears and this is because the blue slide is rarely free from some green colour.   Red and blue slides produce a purple since the light which emerges is a mixture of red and blue.   Only the green in the blue is completely absorbed.   The triangle shown in Fig. 110 shows how the pigment colours are related.   Compare them with Fig. 108c.

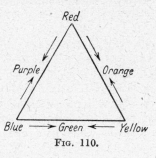

FIG. 110.

Experiments.

Using a motor-car headlight bulb, a cylindrical tumbler of water, a hollow prism filled with Xylol or Nitrobenzene, produce a clear spectrum.   The sides of the beam after emerging from a tumbler should be blocked out by two rectangular blocks of wood.   Reflection by the surface of the water may be reduced by a piece of paper.

(1) Use different filters to show the colours absorbed.   Note that a yellow lets red and green through.

(2) Show the effect of a peacock-blue and a yellow when both are placed in front of the beam.   Compare this with a mixture of blue and yellow pigments.

(3) Notice the colours of different materials when placed across the spectrum.

Theory of Colour Vision.

There is no theory of colour vision which can be regarded as completely satisfactory.   The best known is that due to Young and Helmholtz and is named after them.   According to this theory, there are three sets of nerves in the eye which are perceptible to colour ; each set is supposed to be highly responsive to certain colours and less so to others.   **For** example, one set is strongly affected by red, another by green

and the third by blue. White light affects each set equally.
Thus, according to this theory the colour of a body is dependent upon the amount of excitation which each set of nerves
receives.

It will be remembered that white light can be produced not
only by a mixture of the primary colours but also by a suitable
combination of colours of certain wave lengths. In fact there
are numerous combinations which produce white light and
these may be used to form colour equations and so enable us
to obtain information about each set of nerves. ABNEY
experimented with the primary colours and obtained colour
equations which gave him the curves shown in Fig. 111.

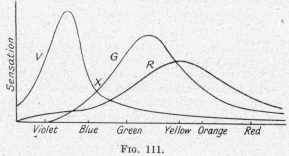

Fig. 111.

They are interesting curves for according to the theory they
show that each part of the spectrum excites all the nerves
to a varying extent. They show that yellow mainly excites
the red and green nerves and hence they explain why a spectral
yellow has a similar appearance to a suitable mixture of red
and green.

They also show why it is impossible to reproduce certain
spectral colours by combinations of others. For if we take
a colour which gives a maximum excitation of say green to
red it will be observed that a combination of other colours
cannot produce the same ratio.

Curious phenomena are observed when the retina is fatigued
by light of a particular colour. For example, if the eye has
been subjected to a blue light for a time a white screen will

appear yellow (the complementary colour). According to the theory, the blue nerves cease to act with their customary efficiency and the predominant action is that of the red and green nerves so that the screen appears to be yellow. It is possible that a similar explanation may account for the complementary colours exhibited by shadows when their background is illuminated. The theory is substantiated to some extent by the defect known as *colour blindness* (or Daltonism as it is sometimes called, since Dalton discovered that he suffered from the defect himself). A colour-blind person is assumed to be lacking in one set of nerves—usually the red —so that if Abney's curves are drawn for the colour-blind person the blue and green curves should approximate closely to those of a normal-eyed person. Experiment shows this to be the case. Thus a colour X appears to be white since it excites the two nerves equally. It will be noticed that the visual spectrum is reduced in size for a colour-blind person.

The chief objection to the theory is that there is no anatomical evidence of the existence of these different sets of nerves.

The Infra-red and Ultra-violet.—It is as well at this stage to remind the student that, according to the Wave Theory, light is energy which is transferred by wave motion through the ether. Later on we shall show methods by which the lengths of the various waves may be determined experimentally. Here we shall assume that the lengths of light waves all lie approximately between 0·000076 cm. and 0·000039 cm. The red are the longest and the violet the shortest, the wavelengths gradually decreasing as we proceed from red to violet through the visible spectrum.

It is found by experiment that heat radiation can be reflected and refracted in a similar way to light. Moreover we can heat some bodies until they become red hot and eventually white hot, from which it would appear that heat energy is being converted into light energy. These experiments lead us to suppose that there may be some intimate connection between the two types of energy. If heat is transferred by waves, the question we naturally ask ourselves is : Is it possible to have an invisible spectrum of heat ?

The answer to this is in the affirmative. The heat waves appear outside the longer limit (i.e. the red) given above, and the region of their spectrum is called the *Infra-red*. The first person to observe this was the celebrated astronomer HERSCHEL in 1800. He noticed the effect produced by placing a thermometer with a blackened bulb in this region. The rise in temperature indicated the absorption of heat. Screens for fire-places are often made of glass on account of the latter's opacity to heat waves. The glass is perfectly transparent to short waves but absorbs the longer infra-red waves freely. Prisms of glass are therefore of little value in experimental work on refraction in the infra-red. Rock-salt and quartz prisms are generally used.

Because of the ease with which infra-red waves penetrate the atmosphere (the shorter waves are scattered), it is common nowadays to use them for the photographing of landscapes and objects situated a great distance away.

In the violet region we find a similar extension beyond the visible limit. Waves exist which are too short to excite the nerves of the eye but which are capable of decomposing such chemicals as the salts of silver. They are termed *actinic waves* and are usually examined by means of a camera. The region in which they make their presence felt is called the *ultra-violet*.

Ultra-violet waves have a very penetrating influence and are used a great deal in medicine. The smallest waves known are the X-rays, their lengths being as short as $0 \cdot 00000029$ cm. and these, as you well know, are able to pass through flesh quite easily : hence their use in the examination of bone fractures.

Fluorescence.—When light waves fall on a body they usually tend to make it hot. That is, light waves are transformed into the longer heat waves, or we might say energy of the visible part of the spectrum is transformed into energy of the invisible part. In the case of certain substances we find that the transformation occurs wholly in the visible spectrum. For example, violet waves may be absorbed by a substance and green waves emitted. Substances which produce this effect are termed *Fluorescent*. Ordinary paraffin oil, when exposed to sunlight, will give a bluish appearance.

Fluorescein will produce a beautiful and brilliant yellowish-green. Both these substances are only affected in the layers which absorb the light, that is, near to the surface of incidence.

Phosphorescence.—Certain substances have the power of retaining the fluorescent state even after the light is removed. This phenomenon is known as *Phosphorescence*. It is exhibited by diamond, calcium sulphide and Balmain's luminous paint, all of which, if exposed to sunlight, will continue to be luminous even in a dark place.

Fraunhofer Lines.—Wollaston found in 1802 that the solar spectrum is crossed by thin dark lines. A few years later Fraunhofer, a German optician, counted 600 of them and measured the position of 324, to some of which he assigned letters, e.g., D for sodium, C and F for hydrogen, etc. The meaning of these lines remained a mystery until the work of Bunsen and Kirchhoff on spectra appeared in 1859. It was then realised that the lines were due to absorption by the cooler gases and vapours surrounding the visible sun.

It is a general rule that a vapour will absorb at a lower temperature the particular light it emits at a higher temperature. Consequently, the relatively cooler gases and vapours in the *chromosphere* absorb the light of certain wavelengths from the continuous spectrum of the *photosphere* (the inner part of the sun) and, hence, at positions in the spectrum corresponding to these wavelengths there is a loss of light. This interpretation has led us to a knowledge of the existence of many of the terrestrial elements in the sun.

Dispersive Power. When the angle of a prism is very small the refractive index is given approximately by

$$\mu = \frac{d + A}{A} \text{ or } d = (\mu - 1)A.$$

If μ_r, μ_v are the refractive indices for the red and violet rays respectively

$$d_r = (\mu_r - 1)A$$
$$d_v = (\mu_v - 1)A.$$

Thus the limiting ratio of dispersion to deviation or $\dfrac{d_v - d_r}{d}$ where d is the mean deviation of the two extreme rays, is equal to $\dfrac{\mu_v - \mu_r}{(\mu - 1)}$ where μ is the mean refractive index. This fraction is called the *Dispersive Power*, and may be written in terms of the Calculus $\dfrac{d\mu}{\mu - 1}$ where $d\mu$ is the small increase in the refractive index in passing from the red to the violet rays.

Condition of Achromatic Combinations.

Consider the equation for a combination of thin lenses in contact, viz. :

$$\frac{1}{F} = \frac{1}{f_1} + \frac{1}{f_2}$$

or $\qquad\qquad D = D_1 + D_2$ with the usual notation.

In order that chromatic aberration may be avoided the power D must remain constant and the differential of D in this equation, as μ varies for the different colours, must vanish.

Hence $\qquad\qquad d(D_1) + d(D_2) = 0$ . . . . (1)

But $D_1 = (\mu_1 - 1)\left(\dfrac{1}{r_1} - \dfrac{1}{s_1}\right)$, where r_1 and s_1 are the radii of curvature of the two faces of the first lens, and

$$D_2 = (\mu_2 - 1)\left(\frac{1}{r_2} - \frac{1}{s_2}\right),$$

where r_2 and s_2 are the radii of the second lens.

Hence

$$d(D_1) = d\mu_1\left(\frac{1}{r_1} - \frac{1}{s_1}\right) = \frac{d\mu_1}{\mu_1 - 1}.D_1,$$

by substitution, and

$$d(D_2) = d\mu_2\left(\frac{1}{r_2} - \frac{1}{s_2}\right) = \frac{d\mu_2}{\mu_2 - 1}.D_2.$$

Equation (1) therefore becomes

$$\frac{d\mu_1}{\mu_1 - 1}.D_1 + \frac{d\mu_2}{\mu_2 - 1}.D_2 = 0.$$

If we call the dispersive powers of the two lenses ω_1 and ω_2 respectively, it follows that the condition for achromatism is

$$\frac{\omega_1}{\omega_2} = -\frac{D_2}{D_1} = -\frac{f_1}{f_2}.$$

In other words, the ratio of the focal lengths must be in the ratio of the dispersive powers and one lens must be positive and the other negative.

Achromatic Combination of Lenses separated by an appreciable Distance.

Although it is impossible to combine two lenses of the same material *together* and obtain an achromatic lens, it is interesting to note that in one form of eye-piece invented by Huygens, a contemporary of Newton, it is possible to have a combination of two lenses of the same material and still avoid chromatic aberration *provided the lenses are separated by a definite distance.*

It will be remembered that the power of an " equivalent lens " is given by :

$$D = D_1 + D_2 - D_1 D_2 t. \,^1$$

But an equivalent lens is one which will produce an image the same size as that produced by the combination, and since the sizes of the coloured images must not vary if the lens is to be achromatic, we must have :—

$$d(D_1) + d(D_2) - d(D_1 D_2 t) = 0$$

or, $$d(D_1) + d(D_2) - t\{D_1 d(D_2) + D_2 d(D_1)\} = 0$$

i.e. $$(1 - t D_2) d(D_1) + (1 - t D_1) d(D_2) = 0 \qquad . \quad (1)$$

We found on page 136 that $d(D_1) = \dfrac{d\mu_1}{\mu_1 - 1}.D_1$

and $$d(D_2) = \frac{d\mu_2}{\mu_2 - 1}.D_2$$

substituting in (1) we have,

$$(1 - t D_2)\frac{d\mu_1}{\mu_1 - 1}.D_1 + (1 - t D_1)\frac{d\mu_2}{\mu_2 - 1}.D_2 = 0 \quad . \quad (2)$$

As the lenses are made of the same material their dispersive powers must be equal, or

$$\frac{d\mu_1}{\mu_1 - 1} = \frac{d\mu_2}{\mu_2 - 1}.$$

Hence from (2) we have $D_1 + D_2 - 2 D_1 D_2 t = 0$

or $$t = \frac{D_1 + D_2}{2 D_1 D_2} = \tfrac{1}{2}\left(\frac{1}{D_1} + \frac{1}{D_2}\right)$$

$$= \frac{f_1 + f_2}{2}.$$

Thus we get an achromatic combination if the two lenses are separated by a distance equal to half the sum of their focal lengths.

---

[1] t replaces d in the formula (p. 105) so as to avoid confusion.

The Rainbow.

This is probably the most interesting example of dispersion. It is caused by the sun's rays falling on raindrops which disperse the light by refraction and deviate the different colours by refraction and reflection to the eye of the observer. Let us consider the action of a spherical raindrop on a beam of sunlight. Some of the light is allowed to pass through while some of it suffers first refraction, then internal reflection and finally is refracted out again. It is this second portion which provides us with the *Bows*. A good deal of it only receives

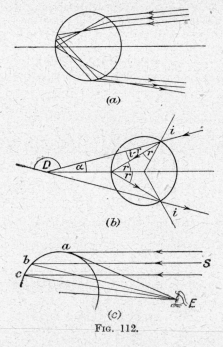

(a)

(b)

(c)

Fig. 112.

reflection once (Fig. 112*a*); this gives us the *primary bow*. If two reflections take place before the light finally emerges a *secondary bow* is produced; this will be fainter owing to absorption at each reflection.

From Fig. 112b it will be noticed that the light, which of course is parallel, is deviated most when it strikes the drop normally, for then its deviation is 180°. In other positions the deviations will vary between 180° and a minimum value which is approximately 138°. At the position of minimum deviation there is little variation in the direction of the light on either side of this position, so that the quantity of light which emerges in this direction will be greater than in any other. In fact it is this light which has the chief effect on the eye.

If there are many such drops of water assembled together, they will all behave in the same way towards the light. Those at a, b, c, etc. (Fig. 112c) which are situated on a cone with the eye as apex and which make angles with the sun's rays and the eye equal to the angle of minimum deviation will refract bright beams of light towards the eye. The centre of this circle of light will be immediately opposite to the sun so that it will be below the horizon. Only an arc of the circle is, therefore, seen, and its angular radius is equal in value to the minimum deviation.

More than one circle will be produced owing to the dispersion of the light into its constituent colours. The red colour has the smallest deviation and, therefore, will form the outside bow. The inside bow will be violet and between that and the red there will be concentric bows of the various spectral colours.

We can determine the angles of minimum deviation for the various colours of the primary bow by examining Fig. 112b and applying the laws of refraction.

Except when the deviation is 180° we have

$$D = 180 - 2\alpha$$
$$= 180 - 2\{r - (i - r)\}$$
$$= 180 + 2i - 4r.$$

To find the minimum, differentiate :—

$$\frac{dD}{dr} = \frac{2di}{dr} - 4.$$

Hence D is a minimum when $\frac{di}{dr} = 2$.

But
$$\sin i = \mu \sin r.$$
$$\therefore \cos i \, di = \mu \cos r \, dr.$$

Substituting for $\dfrac{di}{dr}$ we have :—

$$2 \cos i = \mu \cos r$$

or
$$4 \cos^2 i = \mu^2 \cos^2 r$$

or
$$4 - 4 \sin^2 i = \mu^2 - \mu^2 \sin^2 r$$
$$= \mu^2 - \sin^2 i$$

$$\therefore \sin i = \sqrt{\frac{4 - \mu^2}{3}}.$$

For red and violet light the values of μ are 1·33 and 1·34 approximately. This gives

$i = 59 \cdot 6°$ and $D = 137°$ for Red approximately

and $i = 58 \cdot 8°$ and $D = 139°$ for Violet approximately.

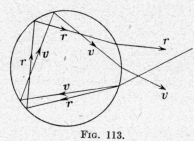

Since the deviation at each reflection is increased by $(\pi - 2r)$ it is easy to show that the deviation for n reflections is given by :—

$$D = n(\pi - 2r) + 2(i - r).$$

When $n = 2$, as in the case for the formation of a secondary bow (Fig.

FIG. 113.

113), we can show that the angle of incidence is given by

$$\sin i = \sqrt{\frac{9 - \mu^2}{8}}$$

and this gives the angle of minimum deviation as approximately 230° and 233° for the red and violet respectively. Since these angles are between two and three right angles the emergent rays of violet light make a greater acute angle with the sun (having crossed the incident rays) than the emergent red rays. Thus, as the figure illustrates (Fig. 113) the violet bow will be the outer one.

It is rare to observe more than the two bows.   Those formed by three and four reflections lie towards the sun and are, therefore, not visible.   The fifth which is away from the sun is seldom visible on account of the loss of light produced by so many reflections.

We sometimes see the primary bow accompanied by others inside it.   These are called *supernumerary bows*.   They are due to phase differences in the beams on emergence from the raindrops.   In our simple theory above we have assumed that the total effect was limited to the beams.   Later (Chapter XII) we shall see that waves of light can differ in phase as well as length and when this takes place we get a series of positions of maximum and minimum brightness.

QUESTIONS.   VII.

1. How would you demonstrate that white light is of a composite character ?

2. What is a pure spectrum and how is it obtained ?

3. Why does a lens produce dispersion ?   Hence explain chromatic aberration and give examples of its occurrence in everyday life.

4. Newton concluded that it was impossible to obtain deviation without dispersion.   Criticise this.

5. What are the primary colours ?   Illustrate what happens when primary colours are mixed in varied proportions.

6. Contrast the mixing of colours with the mixing of pigments. Hence explain why a mixture of blue and yellow pigments produces a green pigment.

7. What are complementary colours.   Name a few.

8. How may colour vision be explained ?   What is colour blindness ?

9. What reasons are there for believing that light, heat and electricity are closely related ?

10. Distinguish between fluorescence, calorescence and phosphorescence.

11. What do you understand by the term dispersive power ?   Deduce the condition that a combination of two lenses may be achromatic.

12. Show that two thin lenses separated by a distance d may form an achromatic combination when d is equal to half the sum of their focal lengths.

13. How is a rainbow formed ?   Why may there be more than one bow ?

14. An optical bench is used to obtain two coloured images, one red and the other blue, of an illuminated cross wire.   If the lens which refracts the light is convex with surfaces having radii of curvature 25 cm. and 15 cm. respectively and the refractive indices for the red and blue light are 1·513 and 1·525 respectively, what will be the distance apart of the two images when the object is placed 30 cm. from the lens ?

CHAPTER VIII

THE EYE AND VISION

The eye is nature's optical instrument. In shape it is nearly spherical and, within limits, it has power to turn in its socket. Encasing it is a hard white substance called the *sclerotic coat* (Sc) (Fig. 114). Part of it, the well-known " white of the eye," is visible when the lids are opened. Light enters the eye first through a hard transparent substance called the *cornea* (C) which is really the eye's natural

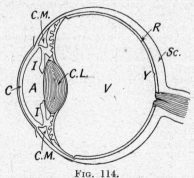

Fig. 114.

window and is shaped like a convex lens ; it then enters the anterior chamber which is filled with a transparent fluid A called *aqueous humour* and arrives at the *crystalline lens*. The function of the lens is the same as that of a glass convex lens in that it serves to throw a real image on to the sensitive nerve plate at the back of the eye. Fortunately, the crystalline lens is much more accommodating than a glass lens, for by means of what are known as *ciliary muscles* (CM) it can alter its curvature within limits at will and hence it is of variable power. The amount of light which passes through the crystalline lens is regulated by the *iris* (I) which is a diaphragm pierced with a circular aperture called the *pupil*. The iris thus acts as a shutter : moreover it is the coloured portion, " blue eyes or brown eyes," that fortune-tellers use as a means of giving advice to the credulous. Its chief function is to guard the nerves and prevent an excess of light, which might be dangerous, from falling upon them. On a bright day the pupil is nearly closed by it, whereas at night time or in poor light quite a large amount of pupil is visible.

After passing through the lens, the light, in the form of converging cones, traverses a transparent jelly-like substance V called the *vitreous humour* until it arrives at the *retina* (R). This latter is the sensitive nerve plate mentioned above. It is an extremely delicate, almost transparent membrane and is attached to the inside of the *choroid coat*, which serves as the lining of the sclerotic coat. On the retina the optic nerve spreads itself, with the result that the image impressions received on the retina are carried to the brain. The writer knows of a case where a soldier, during the Great War, was shell shocked. As a result the retina of the left eye had become loosened and blindness had ensued. No sign of this blindness is apparent to an onlooker.

The retina possesses the property of continuing to act for a short time under the impression of light which has been received by it. This property, which is termed *Persistence of Vision*,[1] is shown by a colour disc (Maxwell's top) on which are painted the seven colours of the spectrum. On whirling the disc rapidly, each colour in turn is impressed on the retina, the last one, in fact, being seen before the first impression has faded. Thus the colours blend and form white light, or rather a dirty grey colour on account of the impurity of the colours. The more intense we make the light, the longer does the impression on the retina last. In the retina and lying almost on the principal axis of the crystalline lens is Y the *Yellow Spot*.[2] This is the most sensitive portion and the place where vision is most acute. The eye involuntarily looks at an object in such a way as to cause the image to be focused on the yellow spot except when the light is very weak ; then it is less sensitive than the other parts and objects should be viewed obliquely. The pupil appears black because the whole mem-

---

[1] The best example of this is the cinematograph.
[2] The most sensitive portion of the Yellow Spot is called *Fovea Centralis*.

brane enclosing the vitreous humour is filled with a black pigment. This prevents numerous images of an object from being seen by internal reflection of the rays. Where the optic nerve enters the eye is situated the *Blind Spot*. An image falling there is not observed. This can easily be demonstrated by making a black circle of an inch diameter on a sheet of white paper, holding this about a foot from the eye and, by closing the left eye, allowing the right eye to move horizontally inwards from the circle to the left. When the eye arrives at a spot about three inches from the circle no image is seen and the circle disappears from view.

Vision.—When an object AB (Fig. 115) is placed in front of the eye, provided the distance is large enough, a real

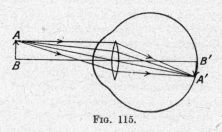

FIG. 115.

inverted image A'B' is cast upon the retina. Almost the only difference between the action of the natural lens of the eye and a convex lens is the fact that the natural lens can adjust its focal length but not its distance from the image, and the glass lens maintains the same focal length, but the image moves along its axis from the lens to infinity. In order to see an object, a real inverted image must be formed on the retina. When we look at an upright chair an inverted image of that chair is thrown on the retina. By means of the optic nerve the brain is immediately informed that a certain sensation has been received and this sensation corresponds with what our mother, father, uncle, cousin, etc., have always told us is an upright chair. Invert the chair and the brain receives an inverted impression and so associates it with an inverted effect. The whole explanation lies in the fact that the brain merely

receives " telegraphic " impressions and does not possess a
" brain-eye " to compare the position of the chair and its
image on the retina.

Defects of Vision.—When the ciliary muscles are relaxed,
the lens is set for parallel light.   In other words the muscles

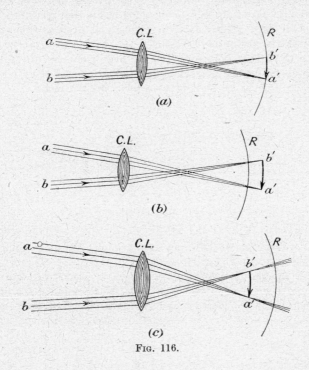

(a)

(b)

(c)

FIG. 116.

are relaxed when we view an object at infinity.   When the
eye is normal the rays come to a focus on the retina as in
Fig. 116a.   In certain abnormal eyes this does not happen
(Figs. 116b and 116c).

In Fig. 116b the defect illustrated is called *Long-sight* or
Hypermetropia.   The focal length of the lens of the eye is
too great and an object at infinity would produce a blurred

image. Actually this does not occur, for the ciliary muscles come into play and shorten the focal length. These muscles, however, only possess a certain range of *accommodation* and consequently the limit is reached for near vision sooner than it would be in a normal eye. The position of the limit is called the *near point*. In order to correct this defect we must cause the rays to be more converging before they pass through the eye lens. This can be brought about by converting the parallel beams into converging beams by means of a convex lens (Fig. 117). Moreover, at the near point any diverging beams will be made less diverging before striking the eye and so are able to be brought to a focus on the retina.

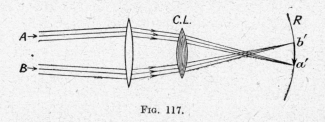

Fig. 117.

For a normal eye without any straining, the near point is situated about 25 cm. from it.

In calculating problems on defective vision the student should bear in mind two facts : (1) the distance of the final image is always constant and unknown. (2) Two lenses are being used—one, the eye lens and the other, the auxiliary lens, and these may be connected [1] by the relationship $\dfrac{1}{F} = \dfrac{1}{f_1} + \dfrac{1}{f_2}$ where F is the focal length of the combination.

EXAMPLE.—What spectacles are required by a person whose near point is 2 metres, to enable him to read a newspaper at a distance of 36 cm. ?

---

[1] This is only true if the spectacles and eye are in contact : otherwise $\dfrac{1}{F} = \dfrac{1}{f_2} + \dfrac{1}{f_2} - \dfrac{d}{f.f_2}$ or $D = D_1 + D_2 - dD_1D_2$ (cf. p. 105).

Since the minimum distance of distinct vision is 2 metres, without the spectacles, we have for the eye lens alone

$$\frac{1}{v} + \frac{1}{200} = \frac{1}{f_1} \quad \cdots \cdots \cdots (1)$$

where v is the distance from the crystalline lens of the eye to the image on the retina, and f_1 is the limiting focal length of the eye.

When the spectacles are used u must be 36 cm. and F is the focal length of the combination of eye and spectacles.

Thus
$$\frac{1}{v} + \frac{1}{36} = \frac{1}{F}.$$

Now
$$\frac{1}{F} = \frac{1}{f_1} + \frac{1}{f_2} \quad \text{and, consequently,}$$

$$\frac{1}{v} + \frac{1}{36} = \frac{1}{f} + \frac{1}{f_2} \quad \cdots \cdots (2)$$

Subtracting equations (1) and (2) we get rid of the unknown v and f_1 and

$$\frac{1}{36} - \frac{1}{200} = \frac{1}{f_2} = D \quad \text{where D is the power of the lens.}$$

Hence $D = 2 \cdot 2$ dioptres, that is: the lens is positive or convex.

Fig. 116c illustrates the defect known as *Short-sight* or *Myopia*.

A blurred image is again formed, but this time it is due to the focal length of the eye being too short. Moreover the ciliary muscles cannot correct this, for as soon as they come into play the focal length is shortened still more. Consequently, a person with short sight needs spectacles for viewing long distances. The limiting distance for the eye alone is called the far point.

It should be clear from the diagram (Fig. 118) that a concave lens will be necessary to correct this defect. Parallel rays which, without the spectacles, would come to a focus in front of the retina, must be made diverging in order to throw the image on to the retina. An example will show that the same method of solution as for long-sight may be used, so long as the student remembers that the correction is required for long distances this time.

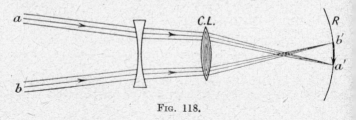

Fig. 118.

EXAMPLE.—A person finds that his furthest distance of distinct vision is 100 cm. What spectacles will he require in order to see a star distinctly?

For the eye alone,

$$\frac{1}{v} + \frac{1}{100} = \frac{1}{f_1}.$$

For the combination,

$$\frac{1}{v} + \frac{1}{\infty} = \frac{1}{f_1} + \frac{1}{f_2}.$$

Subtracting and remembering $\dfrac{1}{\infty} = 0$

$$-\frac{1}{100} = +\frac{1}{f_2} = D$$

or $D = -1$ dioptre.

Thus concave spectacles are required.

Another defect that comes with age is *Loss of Accommodative Power*, or *Presbyopia*. The lens of the eye loses its elasticity and consequently the ciliary muscles are unable to function as fully as they ought. It is interesting to note that the ciliary muscles are rings of muscular tissue and consequently, when brought into action, tend to make the lens more convex or of less focal length. When therefore full tension of the muscles occurs, an object placed at the near point casts an image on the retina. If with increasing age or for any other reason it becomes impossible to exert the necessary contraction or if the eye lens fails to respond, then the maximum curvature that can be produced becomes less, and the near point moves further away. The student has probably observed the amusing attempts made by old men to read their newspapers without glasses. They stretch their arms at full length and their eyelids wrinkle in an effort to force the crystalline lens to become more curved.

It should be clear that the result of this defect is to make long sight more pronounced. Thus a child suffering from long sight tends to become more so as it gets older, whereas shortsightedness tends to be replaced by normal eyesight.

Astigmatism.—The student will remember that when a cone of rays falls obliquely on a lens, an astigmatic bundle of rays is produced after refraction. That is, no true point focus is formed and the result is a blurred image. If the arrangement of the eye is not symmetrical about an axis the same defect occurs : two focal lines are formed at different distances behind the lens and indistinct vision ensues. To remedy this defect cylindrical spectacles are used which we have seen are able to produce an astigmatic cone in the incident rays so as to counteract the astigmatism of the eye.

Spherical Aberration.—The crystalline lens is not homogeneous, but increases in density from the outer surface to the middle. HELMHOLTZ calculated the refractive indices of the various portions of the lens and then determined the refractive index of a homogeneous lens which would be equivalent to it. He found the value to be 1·4371.

It will be remembered that the effect of spherical aberration in a homogeneous lens was to make eccentrical rays come more quickly to a focus. In the crystalline lens of the eye the eccentrical rays all pass through material of less refractive index than those near the centre, and consequently their refraction is less and their focus further off. Thus the defect of a homogeneous lens tends to be compensated in the eye lens.

It is interesting to note that over correction occurs when the eye is accommodated for near vision.

Chromatic Aberration.—This colouring defect is present but is not generally noticed on account of the increased luminosity in the rays of intermediate refrangibility as compared with the extreme rays. To realise its presence the following experiment due to Helmholtz should be tried :—

Examine a distant source of light through a piece of plane

glass which has been coloured by cobalt oxide. Only the red and blue rays will be transmitted, the middle of the spectrum being absorbed. The result is that an image is observed of a red source of light surrounded by a bluish-violet halo. This is what we should expect, since the blue rays are refracted more than the red.

The Luminosity Curve.—We have mentioned that light is a special form of radiation of exactly the same character as other kinds, such as wireless waves, X-rays, etc., and differing from them only in wave length and in being able to stimulate the eye.

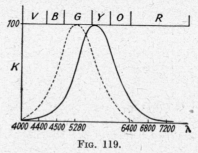

Fig. 119.

The range of wave lengths to which the eye is sensitive is very short compared with the vast range (70 octaves) which exists from the very short γ waves emitted by radioactive atoms to the long waves used in radio. For the average eye it extends approximately from 7700 Å (Angström units)[1] at the extreme red to 3800 Å at the violet, that is approximately one octave. Not only is the eye insensitive to radiations of wave lengths outside this range, but its sensitivity varies greatly with wave length within the range. It is found to be most sensitive for radiations of wave length approximately 5540 Å, that is very nearly in the middle of the visible spectrum, and to fall rapidly towards the violet and red ends.

The variation is shown in Fig. 119, which represents the

[1] One Angström unit = 10^{-8} cm.

average results of a large number of tests. The curve shows the relative sensitivity of the eye, K (ordinates) plotted against the wave length λ (abscissæ). From the curve we note, for instance, that for $\lambda = 4700$ Å the value of the sensitivity is only one half of the value for the maximum. This means that a beam of light of this wave length would have to be twice as intense as one of wave length 5540 Å in order to produce on the eye a sensation of equal brightness. The quantity K may evidently be regarded as a measure of the relative brightness—called the luminosity—of the radiations of different wave length. The curve is usually called the average luminosity curve.

Purkinje Effect.—It is interesting to note that the full curve of Fig. 119 does not apply if the intensity of the light used is very small. In this case we get a curve similar in shape but displaced towards the blue (the dotted curve). This means that for dim lights the eye becomes relatively more sensitive to blue and less to red. This alteration in the colour sensitivity of the eye is called the Purkinje Effect ; it probably accounts for the bluish tinge of objects seen by moonlight.

QUESTIONS. VIII.

1. Give a description of the eye and carefully explain the function of its important parts.

2. Compare the lens of the eye with an ordinary glass convex lens. Why do objects not appear inverted ?

3. An optician supplies a person who is suffering with long sight with a pair of convex lenses, each of 20 cm. numerical focal length. If the person's near point, without the glasses, is 5 feet, how near may he bring a book so that the print may be visible ?

4. Define short sight.
If a man finds that he cannot see objects clearly when they are distant more than 200 feet what kind of spectacles must he obtain in order to see a star distinctly ? What also must be the focal length of the spectacles ?

5. What is Loss of Accommodative Power and how is it remedied ?

6. What is astigmatism ? Illustrate by drawing cones of rays showing how the image of a distant object will appear to a person suffering from both short-sightedness and astigmatism.

7. Show how the eye is corrected for spherical aberration. Does nature make any allowance for chromatic aberration ?

CHAPTER IX

OPTICAL INSTRUMENTS

The Projection Lantern.—The essential parts of a lantern-slide projector are an illuminating system behind the slide and a projection lens which can form an image of the slide on the screen. The chief difficulty is to obtain sufficient illumination. The general optical arrangements are shown in Fig. 120. C is the so-called condensing lens or condenser; its function is to collect as large a cone of light as possible from the source and converge this light, as shown by the dotted lines, so that it all passes through the slide B and the projecting lens L. The condenser should be so placed that it forms an image of the

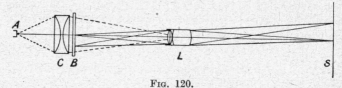

Fig. 120.

source at the aperture of the lens. To minimise the effects of spherical aberration (cf. page 108) it is usual to make the condenser of two plano-convex lenses arranged as shown. The projecting lens may be any good photographic objective of wide aperture. All the light passing through any point of the slide and collected by the lens L is focused on the corresponding image point on the screen. Since the illumination on the screen is proportional to the brightness of the source it is preferable to use an arc for the latter.

In a cinematograph projector the condenser forms an image of the source very close to the film.

An *epidiascope* is a modern development of the projection lantern which may be used not only with transparent slides, but also to project a picture of an opaque object. For the latter (episcopic projection) the illumination of the object must be very intense since a good deal of the light is absorbed by the object and a great deal of the reflected light is scattered in such directions that it does not pass through the projecting lens. In order that the latter may collect as much light as possible it must have a very wide aperture. The great difficulty in the design of an epidiascope is to obtain the required

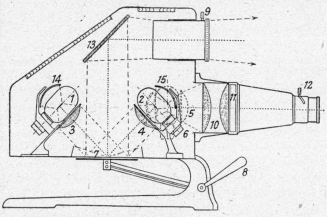

FIG. 121.

intense illumination without undue heating. Some of the earlier types were very efficient toasting arrangements!

Fig. 121 gives a sectional view of a modern form of epidiascope [1]. The sources of illumination are 500 watt lamps (1, 2). The lenses (3, 4 and 5) are specially constructed so as to withstand heat. The object stage is movable by means of the lever 8. The mirrors 14 and 15 are highly reflecting spherical mirrors. The plane mirror 13 is used for reflecting the light through a helical focusing device (9). The condenser, lantern-slide holder and focusing slot are shown by 10, 11 and 12.

The Photographic Camera.—Although there is much evidence to show that the principle of the camera was known

---

[1] The Edwards epidiascope.

to the ancients the first actual account of its construction was given by GIOVANNI BATTISTA DELLA PORTA in 1558. No mention was made by him of the use of a lens until thirty-one years later, and in the meantime (156§) BARBARO, a Venetian noble, explained the formation of images in a camera when a convex lens is used. Kepler (1600), who made use of the camera for solar observations, gave to it the name of "*camera obscura.*" It was Kepler in fact who discovered the principle of the telephoto lens (page 157). The earliest mention of the camera in England appears in Bacon's *De Augmentis Scientarum.* After that we find such men as Newton, PRIESTLEY, 1772, and WEDGWOOD, 1794, devoting time to its improvement. The latter, together with SIR HUMPHREY DAVY, succeeded in " fixing " the images—that is, they converted the camera obscura into a photographic camera.

The modern photographic camera consists essentially of a light-tight box, at the back of which is a sensitive plate and in the front of which is fitted a lens for the purpose of forming an image on the plate. In many cameras the sides are formed by leather bellows so that the distance between the lens and the plate may be varied to allow sharp focusing of the image for different object distances.

Speed, Aperture, Ratio.—The lens is usually fitted with a stop of variable size by means of which the light passing through may be varied. It is clear that the exposure necessary will depend on the illumination of the image, and from considerations on page 219 we know that for objects at a great distance away this is directly proportional to the area of the aperture and inversely proportional to the square of the focal length ; i.e. proportional to $\left(\dfrac{d}{f}\right)^2$, where d is the diameter of the aperture.

This quantity $\dfrac{d}{f}$ is called the *aperture ratio* and it is usual to specify it by giving it as a fraction, $\dfrac{f}{n}$ indicating an aperture whose diameter is $\dfrac{1}{n}$-th of the focal length. The number n is called the *f number* and since the exposure needed under given conditions may be assumed to be proportional to the square of this number, it is customary to mark apertures in a series such that the exposure needed is doubled in passing from one to the next; thus we have the series

$$\frac{f}{1}, \frac{f}{1\cdot4}, \frac{f}{2}, \frac{f}{2\cdot8}, \frac{f}{4}, \frac{f}{5\cdot6}, \frac{f}{8}, \frac{f}{11\cdot3}, \frac{f}{16}, \frac{f}{22\cdot6}$$

Depth of Focus.—The aperture of the lens has a great effect on the so-called " depth of focus " obtainable. This point can easily be appreciated from a consideration of Fig. 122. Let a plate P be placed in the focal plane of the lens L so that, assuming that the lens is perfect, it will give a sharp image of all objects sufficiently far away. On the other hand, an object O will have a sharp image O′ behind the plate and, hence, a cone of rays from O will intersect the plate in a small blurred circle *bb*. It is clear that for a given position of O, the diameter of this circle will be

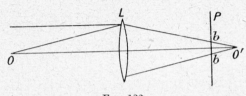

Fig. 122.

smaller the less the aperture of the lens. If the limiting size of this circle is say $\frac{1}{100}$ inch, then O must recede as the size of the aperture increases. This explains why, in a simple box camera in which the plate is fixed in the focal plane of the lens, an object can be brought quite close to the camera if the aperture is very small, and still produce a reasonably clear picture.

Types of Lenses.—The design of fine camera lenses calls for the highest skill and ingenuity, for not only must they have a wide aperture so that pictures of rapidly moving objects in poor light may be taken, but they must be able to produce sharp *flat* images when use is made of both paraxial rays and rays entering at great obliquity. The brief account of the various aberrations given on page 108 will be sufficient to indicate how difficult it is to combine these requirements. In fact, perfection is not possible and the designer aims at the best compromise for the particular purpose in view. Hence we have many types of lenses.

Three well-known lenses are illustrated in Fig. 123. The first (*a*) is the simplest and is used in 80 per cent. of cameras. It is a meniscus lens, corrected for chromatic aberration (page 123) and is arranged with a front stop P. Such a lens has considerable astigmatism, but if the stop is properly placed the rays can be made to pass through the lens in such a way that the two focal line image surfaces (page 111) are curved in the opposite directions. As the circles of least confusion lie approximately midway between

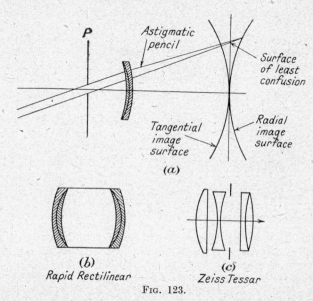

(a)

(b)
Rapid Rectilinear

(c)
Zeiss Tessar

FIG. 123.

these two surfaces, the result is that they lie on a *flat* surface. This flat field is obtained at the expense of sharpness of the image. For ordinary purposes, however, the image is sharp enough, if the aperture is not greater than about $\frac{f}{11}$. There will also be some distortion in the outer parts of the picture. This can be largely overcome in the type of lens shown in (*b*), the so-called RR or rapid rectilinear. In this form two lenses, each an achromat, are used and a stop is placed between them. The back lens by itself would give barrel distortion and the front lens pin-cushion. It can be thus arranged for the two to compensate each other. Such lenses can be used up to about $\frac{f}{8}$ and so only transmit about twice as much light as the simple meniscus type (*a*).

Fig. *c* shows an example—the well-known Zeiss Tessar—of a modern *anastigmat* lens. The chief quality of these lenses is that they give a flat field, not in the artificial manner of the simple lens in Fig. *a*, but by actually removing the defect of astigmatism (hence their name) and curvature of the field at the same time. Moreover, they combine this with large aperture. The development of this lens was due to Abbé and the great German glass firm, Schott, about 1890. Since then progress has been rapid and to-day still more remarkable types of glass and lenses are being produced.

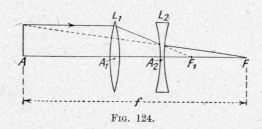

FIG. 124.

Telephoto Lens.—When a camera is used to photograph a distant object the size of the image obtained is proportional to the angle the object subtends at the camera and to the focal length of the lens. Hence, if a large image of some distant detail is required, it is necessary to have a lens with a long focal length. If we used a single lens this would mean a long distance between the lens and plate and an inconveniently long camera would be needed. This is avoided by the use of a telephoto lens, which consists of a pair of lenses as shown in the Fig. 124. Both are usually achromatic; the negative component L_2 occupies the normal lens position in the camera, while the positive lens L_1 is some distance in front. The action should be clear from the diagram. Rays from a very distant point on the axis are brought to a focus at F, where

A_2F is quite short, while the equivalent focal length (page 104) is equal to AF. That is, the lens system behaves as a single lens of focal length $f = AF$, placed at A (the second principal point of the lens system, cf. page 101).

The Stereoscope.—Whilst we are still on the subject of photography it might be of interest to the student to learn the common method adopted to get rid of the " lack of depth " of a photograph. The primary object of landscape

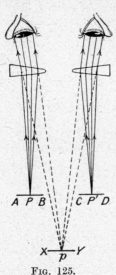

photography (not necessarily portrait) is to be able to bring some usually inaccessible scene of beauty before one's eyes. Since the photographic view is always depicted on a plane, very little idea of distances in the scene can be conveyed except by imagination, and consequently much of the beauty is destroyed. A one-eyed man sees every object in a two dimensional form and, therefore, thickness or depth is never apparent. This will be readily appreciated by the student if he closes one eye and tries to touch a chair quickly. Nature has therefore provided us with two eyes and as each eye gets a slightly different view of a scene two slightly different images are conveyed to the brain by the two optic nerves. The action of the brain fuses the images into

FIG. 125.

one conveying a three dimensional view, and, therefore, gives a sensation of " depth."

WHEATSTONE (1802–75) and later SIR DAVID BREWSTER (1781–1868) used this principle of binocular vision in the construction of a stereoscope for enabling photographs to be taken which would convey this sense of depth. BREWSTER'S form is as follows :—

Two photographs, AB and CD, are taken of the view as seen first by one eye and then by the other. They are then mounted side by side and viewed through two prisms of small angle fixed as shown in the diagram (Fig. 125). With the prisms so arranged it is possible for a point P on one photograph, and a point P′ on the other, to be seen as if in the position of a point p. By a suitable adjustment of the distances of the photographs from the prisms, therefore, the images of the two photographs, when viewed by the two eyes, may be made to appear coincident in XY. The two images thus superposed will be found to convey a sense of depth.

Magnifying Instruments. Apparent Size, Visual Angle, Acuity.—All magnifying instruments are based upon certain principles. First, the apparent size of any object is determined by the size of the image formed by the eye lens on the retina. This in its turn depends upon the angle the object subtends at the eye. Thus, in Fig. 126 it is clear that the size

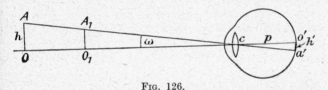

FIG. 126.

of the retinal image h' of the object h is given by $h' = p\omega$, where p is the distance of the eye lens from the retina and ω is the angle ACO. The quantity p is practically constant, the eye focusing objects at different distances by altering the power of its lens. Hence the image h' depends simply on ω. An object O_1A_1 subtending the same angle ω would appear equal in size to OA. The angle ω is called the *visual angle* of the object (sometimes the apparent magnitude).

Two points of an object cannot be distinguished as separate points if their retinal images are too close together. This is because the eye cells are of finite size and if two images fall upon one cell they produce the same sensation. It is found that when the image of an object is formed on the most sensitive part of the eye (the yellow spot) it is not possible for two object points to be separated if they subtend at the eye a visual angle ω less than one minute. This limiting angle is called the *visual acuity* of the eye ; it varies within small limits according to the particular eye and conditions.

The visual angle will, of course, increase as the object is brought nearer to the eye, until the normal near point (approximately 25 cm.) is reached. At this distance the object is clearest for the average unaided eye. Any details of the object which subtend an angle smaller than one minute will not be seen. Similarly, in the case of distant objects such as a star whose distance from the eye we cannot control, if the visual angle subtended by two points (e.g. two stars) falls below the visual acuity, the eye will not be able to distinguish them as separate.

The purpose of magnifying instruments is to extend the range of the eye by a suitable use of lens systems—microscopes for examining small near objects, telescopes for the distant objects. The principle is the same in each case. The lenses form a virtual image of the object which subtends a much greater angle at the eye, and the eye observes this image instead of the object directly. The effectiveness of the instrument or the magnifying power depends on the extent to which it increases the size of the image formed on the retina.

The *magnifying power* of a *microscope* is defined as

$$M = \frac{\text{Angle subtended at the eye by the image}}{\text{Angle subtended at the eye by the object placed at the near point}}$$

The denominator obviously gives a measure of the best the unaided eye can accomplish and so is a suitable basis of comparison.

The *magnifying power* of a *telescope* is simply the ratio of the angle subtended at the eye by the image to that subtended by the object.

Simple Magnifying Glass.—This is the popular name applied to a convex lens—reading glass is another. Let OA be the object. A pencil of rays from any point A after passing through the lens will proceed as if it came from the corresponding image point B, and the eye will be able to focus it sharply on the retina provided that B lies between the near and far limits of accommodation.   Consider first the case where the object is at such a distance from the lens that the image is at the near point of the eye (d).   If the eye is very close to the

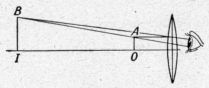

FIG. 127.

lens, the image must be at a distance d from the lens.   That is, $v = -d$, and we must have

$$\frac{1}{u} + \frac{1}{-d} = \frac{1}{f} \text{ where } u \text{ and } f \text{ have the usual meanings.}$$

That is, $u = \dfrac{df}{d + f}$

the angle ω' subtended at the eye by the image will be

$$\omega' = \frac{h'}{d}.$$

But if the object itself were placed at the near point it would subtend at the unaided eye a smaller angle ω given by

$$\omega = \frac{h}{d}$$

and hence the magnifying power M is given by

$$M = \frac{\omega'}{\omega} = \frac{h'}{h} = -\frac{v}{u} = \frac{d+f}{f} = 1 + \frac{d}{f}.$$

With the image formed in this position the eye must exert its maximum accommodation.   The eye strain which this involves can be avoided by arranging that the image is formed at the far point of the eye, so that with the accommodation fully relaxed a sharp image is formed on the retina.   For a normal eye with the far point at infinity this means that the object must be placed in the focal plane of the lens (Fig. 128). In this case the pencil of rays from A after passing through the lens forms a parallel pencil appearing to come from a point B at infinity in the direction ω' given by

$$\omega' = \frac{h}{f}.$$

Hence, in this case the magnifying power is given by

$$M = \frac{\omega'}{\omega} = \frac{d}{f}$$

that is, less than the previous value by unity.

It is clear that a sharp image may be obtained for any position of the object between the focus and the point for which the image is at the nearest distance of distinct vision.

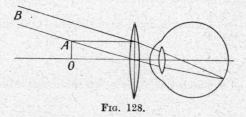

Fɪɢ. 128.

The Telescope.—The telescope was first invented by Galileo in 1609 as the result of an idea received from a Dutch optician. This first telescope had a magnifying power of 3, but after much research on the lenses themselves Galileo was successful in making a telescope with a magnifying power of 30.

The original idea of the Dutchman forms the principle of the *Astronomical telescope*. A convex lens is used to form a real image of a distant object and this is magnified by a second convex lens.

To understand how the final image is formed, a diagram has been drawn showing the two lenses in position (Fig. 129).

The first lens O is the object glass or objective, since it is the lens nearer to the object. A beam of parallel rays A from the top extremity of a distant object is brought to a focus A' and, if A' is situated within the focal length of the second lens E the rays on striking E are refracted so as to appear

to diverge from A″. E is called the eye lens. In a similar
way the beam B causes the formation of a virtual image at B″.
Thus B″A″ is the final inverted virtual image. The angle
subtended by the object at the object glass is $\angle AOB$ and since
the object is a distant one we may consider $\angle AOB$ to be the
angle the object subtends at the eye. The angle subtended

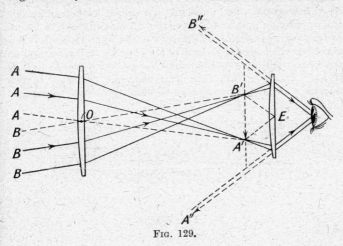

Fig. 129.

by the final image is $\angle B″EA″$ and therefore the magnifying
power

$$M = \frac{\angle B″EA″}{\angle AOB} = \frac{\angle B′EA′}{\angle B′OA′}.$$

The student is reminded that E merely acts as a magnifying
glass and therefore enables B′A′ to be formed much nearer
to the eye than would be possible if E were not present.

Again the most restful condition for the eye is when focused
on the far point and as this is at infinity as a rule, B″A″ will be
formed at infinity, and therefore B′A′ will be at the principal
focus of the eye lens E. It is also easy to see that B′A′ lies
at the principal focus of O.

Consequently $M = \dfrac{\angle B′EA′}{\angle B′OA′} = \dfrac{f_1}{f_2}$

where f_1 and f_2 are the focal lengths of object glass and eye-piece respectively.

This result shows that in order to obtain high magnifying power the telescope must have a *long focus object glass* and *a short focus eye-piece*.

Experimental Methods of Finding the Magnifying Power of a Telescope.—The following is a simple method of finding the magnifying power of a telescope. A vertical scale is placed as far away as possible, say attached to the wall of a room. The telescope which should be near to the opposite wall is focused on the scale. The observer then reads the scale with one eye looking through a telescope and the other observing directly. In this manner a magnified image may be seen apparently superposed

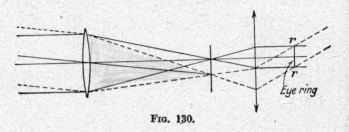

Fig. 130.

on the scale itself. The number of divisions which lie between one magnified image of a division is clearly the magnifying power.

If we examine Fig. 130 we shall note that the light which falls on the object glass will, after passing through the instrument, pass through a small area rr which is the image of the object glass formed by the eye-piece. This circle is called the exit pupil, or eye ring or Ramsden circle.

Let D be the diameter of the objective and d that of the Ramsden circle. Then from the figure it follows that

$$\frac{D}{d} = \frac{f_1}{f_2}$$

that is, the magnifying power is equal to the ratio D/d. This provides another simple method of finding the magnifying power. The instrument is focused for infinity and the exit pupil is located and its diameter compared with that of the objective. The location of the exit pupil is found by directing the telescope towards some bright surface—such as the sky—and moving a piece of ground glass backward and forward behind the eye-piece until the position is found where a sharply defined circular patch of light is formed on the screen.

Galileo's Telescope.—In this form a concave lens is used as an eye-piece. It is the principle on which an opera glass is constructed and it was an improvement, Galileo thought, on the original idea because it gave an erect image. Unfortunately, it cannot be made to give as much magnification as an astronomical telescope, but for a given magnification it requires a smaller length of tube than that for an astronomical

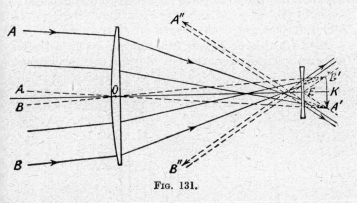

FIG. 131.

telescope and is consequently much more useful as an opera glass than as a telescope.

As before, parallel beams of light from the extremities of the object are shown entering the object glass so that the object subtends at the telescope an angle AOB (Fig. 131). If the eye lens were not present these rays would form the image B'A'. A concave lens, however, prevents this and the rays AA which would come to a focus at A' are made to diverge as if from a point A". Similarly BB' form a virtual image B" and consequently an erect virtual image of the object appears at A"B". If the eye is normal and accommodated as before for vision at the far point, A"B" will be at infinity and those rays proceeding to the points A′ and B′ will be refracted by the eye lens E as parallel beams. In this case it should be clear that A′B′ is at a distance of the focal length of the lens E from the optical centre of E ; that is $KE = f_2$. Again $OK = f_1$ since parallel light is incident on the object glass O.

Hence the magnification is $\dfrac{\angle A''EB''}{\angle AOB} = \dfrac{\angle B'EA'}{\angle B'OA'} = \dfrac{f_1}{f_2}$

or $$m = \frac{focal\ length\ of\ objective}{focal\ length\ of\ eye\text{-}piece}.$$

Plano-convex lenses are used in the objective in order to diminish the effects of spherical aberration. More will be said of this later on in the chapter.

Field Glasses or Prism Binoculars.—In Field Glasses we want a high-power telescope which is not cumbersome,

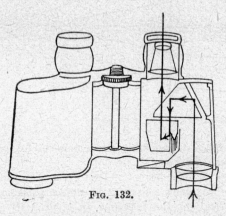

Fig. 132.

an erect image and stereoscopic vision. The opera glass has not sufficient power in the ordinary way and, consequently, with the aid of prisms the optical length is increased without increasing the actual length of the tube. This means that the object glass can be of much greater focal length with the result that the magnifying power is considerably augmented. Fig. 132 illustrates a modern form of the instrument.

GALILEO GALILEI

[From engraving of portrait by PASSIGNANI

Reflecting Telescope.—When Newton discovered that the blurring of his images (Chapter VII) was the " fault " of the light and not of his lenses he gave up trying to improve on Galileo's invention and turned his mind to a different form of telescope, one that would obviate any use of refraction of light. The result was a reflecting telescope 1 inch in diameter and 6 inches long, capable of magnifying forty times. It lies at present in the library of the Royal Society and, compared with some of the modern " giants," bears a relation to them similar to that exhibited by Nelson's ship the *Victory* when compared with a modern battleship. The object glass is a concave mirror C (Fig. 133) which reflects the rays on to a plane mirror MM′, or alternatively a totally reflecting prism. This produces an image at *b′a′* instead of at *ba*. The image *b′a′* is viewed in the eyepiece in the usual manner. When the telescope is used for astronomical purposes and a parabolic concave mirror forms the object glass, the telescope is free from both spherical (central) and chromatic aberration.

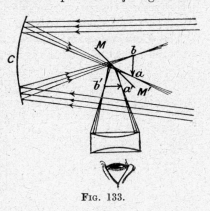

FIG. 133.

Many improvements have been made on the reflecting telescope, first by HADLEY and then by such men as HERSCHEL, GREGORY and CASSEGRAIN. The principle of using a concave mirror as the objective remained the same, but the methods of viewing the images varied.

Although the refracting telescope will no doubt continue to be employed for astronomical purposes, the telescope of the future will probably be the " reflector," particularly for the observation of objects having low luminosity. Large lenses of pure optical glass are difficult to produce ; the largest object glass, that of the great Yerkes telescope, is only 40 inches in diameter. In a mirror, the light of the star is merely reflected and the internal faults that would be fatal in an object glass pass unnoticed. Hitherto, telescope mirrors have been made of glass and have proved sufficiently satisfactory for use although the difficulties of making very large glass mirrors are enormous. The 200-inch mirror which was recently constructed for the Mount Wilson Observatory is the largest in existence. At Greenwich a reflector telescope of 30 inches aperture is used for photographing the stars. This is not as large as some of the earlier forms, but is more accurate on account of its mounting. Nowadays, the movements of large telescopes are electrically controlled; this has made observation easier and more accurate.

The Compound Microscope.—The Compound Microscope, so named in order to distinguish it from a magnifying

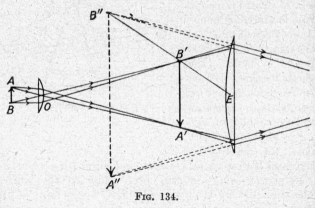

Fig. 134.

glass or simple microscope, was invented by Galileo soon after the invention of his celebrated telescope. In its simplest form it is constructed in a similar way to that of an astronomical telescope. The essential difference between a telescope and a microscope is the position in which the object is placed. In the former we view objects which are distant, in the latter we aim to bring the object as near to the instrument as possible.

In Fig. 134, AB is the object and a real magnified inverted image of this object is formed at B'A'. For this to occur AB must lie between F (focus) and a point 2F from the object glass, and as it is essential in order to produce high magnification that AB should be as near as possible to the lens, O must be of very short focal length. (N.B.—In a telescope O is of long focal length). The eye-piece E acts as before, viz. as a magnifying glass, and it may produce a virtual inverted image at B"A" anywhere between the near and far points. A'B' must consequently fall within the focal length of the eye-piece E.

Magnifying Power of a Microscope.—The overall magnifying power will clearly be given by the product of the magnification due to the objective and the magnifying power of the eye-piece.

$$\text{i.e. } M = m_o \times M_e$$

The object is situated just outside the focal length f_o of the objective. Hence the magnification of the objective, m_o, is given approximately by

$$m_o = -\frac{v}{f_o}$$

where v is the distance of the first image from the objective.

This image falls just within the focal length f_e of the eye-piece, so that if the final image is formed at the distance of distinct vision d, we have, approximately,

$$M_e = \frac{d}{f_e}$$

Hence, $$M = -\frac{v\,d}{f_o f_e}$$

It follows from this equation that the smaller we make f_o and f_e the larger will be the magnifying power. In practice objectives are usually specified by their focal lengths, e.g. 1-in., $\frac{1}{2}$-in. objectives, while eye-pieces are specified by their magnifying power.

A better way of expressing the magnifying power of a microscope is as follows :—

Using Newton's equation $m = -\dfrac{x_2}{f}$, (page 98)

we have $m_o = -\dfrac{g}{f_o}$

where g is the distance between the second focal point of the objective and the first focal point of the eye-piece.

Also $M_e = \dfrac{d}{f_e}$ as above.

Hence $M = -\dfrac{gd}{f_o f_e}$

g is called the *optical length of the microscope* and is usually made about 15 cm.

It is perhaps helpful to note that if the image formed on the screen by a cinematograph projector were observed from the back by a magnifying glass, the combination of projector and magnifier would be essentially the same as a compound microscope.

The Objective and Eye-piece.—As telescopes and microscopes are merely arrangements of lenses, it follows that the defects of lenses, spherical and chromatic aberration, will make themselves apparent if only single lenses are used for objective and eye-piece. The eye-piece, you will remember, acts in the same manner for telescopes as for microscopes ; the objective does not, and therefore will need different consideration.

The Objective.—For a telescope, a combination of a convex lens of crown glass and a concave of flint glass is generally used. The lenses are cemented together by Canada balsam, and are made achromatic for paraxial pencils. The spherical aberration is reduced by making the free surface of the convex lens of less curvature than that of the concave, or, as described at the end of Chapter VI, by the use of a plano-convex lens.

In the case of the microscope objective, much more care has been devoted to its perfection, and a really good objective is an expensive piece of apparatus. The essential conditions to be obtained as nearly as possible are : (1) to ensure that a great deal of light shall enter the microscope ; (2) to have the objective free from chromatic and spherical aberration.

In ABBÉ's immersion objective (Fig. 135), an aplanatic surface
s used (page 114). The lowest lens L_1 is a plano-hemispherical
onvex lens, and between this and the object to be examined is
a space filled with cedar wood oil, which has the same refractive
ndex as the glass. Thus no refraction of the rays will occur
until they leave the lens L_1. If
O and O_1 are aplanatic points
with respect to the point A, no
matter how oblique the rays from
O may be, they will, after refrac-
ion, appear to diverge from O_1.
A second lens L_2 is placed above
L_1 and its face B is of such a
curvature that O_1 is its centre.
Thus the rays leaving L_1 are only
refracted by the spherical face C
of the lens L_2. Moreover L_2 is
situated so that the points O_1
and O_2 are aplanatic with respect
o it. We thus have a beam of
ays of very large angle when
hey leave O being converted
nto a beam of such an angle
hat they can make an easy entry
nto the microscope. In order

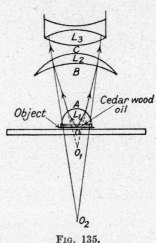

FIG. 135.

o correct for chromatic aberration compound lenses (L_3 etc.)
of flint and crown glass are placed above the lens L_2.

The Eye-Piece

Huygens' Eye-piece.—Huygens was the first to invent an
eye-piece which was free from both spherical and chromatic
aberration. His real intention was to diminish, as much as
possible, the effects of spherical aberration, and therefore he
constructed his eye-piece in such a way that two plano-convex
lenses separated by a certain distance produced equal deviation
on a ray parallel and close to the axis (see page 109). By a
stroke of good luck the system was discovered by BOSCOVICH
to be free from chromatic aberration.

Let f_1 and f_2 be the focal lengths of the two lenses E (called
the eye lens) and F (the field lens) respectively (Fig. 136). Then
a ray PA is deviated equally at A and B and consequently
$\angle BCG = 2 \angle BDG.$

These angles are supposed to be very small and so we may
say $GC = \frac{1}{2}GD$.

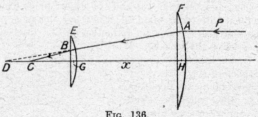

Fig. 136.

Remembering that D is the virtual object of the real image
C and applying the formula $\dfrac{1}{v} + \dfrac{1}{u} = \dfrac{1}{f_1}$

we have

$$\frac{2}{GD} - \frac{1}{GD} = \frac{1}{f_1}$$

which gives

$$GD = f_1.$$

But since PA is a ray parallel to the axis we have $HD = f_2$
therefore $x = f_2 - f_1$.

We see then that *the condition for equal deviation is that the
distance apart of the lenses should be the difference between their
focal lengths.*

Huygens chose the focal lengths so that they should be in
the ratio of 1 to 3, and for these particular values $x = \dfrac{f_2 + f_1}{2}$,
which is (page 137) the condition for achromatism.

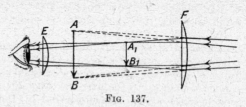

Fig. 137.

As we look through a telescope with the eye in its most restful
position, the rays leaving the eye lens must enter the eye in
parallel beams. A_1B_1, the image formed by F, is consequently
situated at the principal focus of E (Fig. 137).

From the relation $\dfrac{f_1}{f_2} = \dfrac{1}{3}$ in this particular case, it follows that A_1B_1 lies midway between the two lenses. Thus the distance A_1B_1 from F is equal to f_1.

Now $\dfrac{1}{v} + \dfrac{1}{u} = \dfrac{1}{f}$, applied to the lens F, gives

$$\frac{1}{f_1} + \frac{1}{u} = \frac{1}{f_2} = \frac{1}{3f_1}.$$

Therefore, $u = -\dfrac{3f_1}{2}$. The negative sign indicates that the object is virtual, that is, it is on the same side of the lens as A_1B_1. On account of this rather interesting result Huygens' invention is called a negative eye-piece.

Ramsden's Eye-piece.—It is sometimes found very convenient to fit up telescopes and microscopes with cross wires in order to take

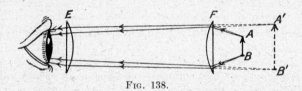

FIG. 138.

measurements. In such cases a positive eye-piece is better, because then the eye-piece can be used to view this real object through both lenses. If a negative eye-piece were used, the cross wires would only be seen through one lens. Ramsden's eye-piece has been designed to meet these requirements. Two plano-convex lenses are used which are of equal focal lengths and which are separated by a distance equal to two-thirds the focal length of either (Fig. 138). This system is not entirely achromatic, as the necessary conditions are not fulfilled : the defect, however, is very slight. Moreover, the deviation is very small, and consequently the amount of spherical aberration is small. The lenses are placed with their convex surfaces facing each other, and this tends still further to reduce spherical aberration.

The rays leaving E must be parallel, and consequently before striking E must have proceeded from the focal plane $A'B'$. $A'B'$ then is the image of the object AB produced by the lens F.

Again $EF = \frac{2}{3} \cdot f$, and therefore from F to A′B′ $= \frac{f}{3}$ numerically

i.e. $$v = -\frac{f}{3}.$$

$$\frac{1}{v} + \frac{1}{u} = \frac{1}{f},$$

therefore $$-\frac{3}{f} + \frac{1}{u} = \frac{1}{f},$$

therefore $$u = \frac{f}{4}.$$

This is a positive quantity, and is therefore in front of th eye-piece.

The Spectrometer.—This instrument was designed t give a close examination of spectra.

It consists essentially of a prism which can be fixed to table capable of being rotated, and this lies in the centre of divided circle B to which is fixed a collimator and round whic a telescope may revolve (Figs. 139A and B). The movemen of prism and telescope can be measured accurately by mean of vernier scales. The collimator contains a slit of adjustabl width placed at the principal focus of an achromatic lens The source of light S illuminates the slit and consequentl a parallel beam is made to fall on the prism at any desire angle. After deviation the rays enter an astronomical tele scope provided with a Ramsden eye-piece, and the imag can then be focused on cross wires fitted into the telescope In the more elaborate forms the table and circle may b clamped and the movement of the telescope made by a slow motion screw. The table carrying the prism is also of adjust able height.

Adjustments of the Spectrometer.—Before the instru ment is ready for use certain adjustments are necessary :—

(1) The eye-piece must be adjusted until the cross wire are in focus.

(2) The telescope must be focused to receive parallel light.

(3) The collimator must be focused to emit parallel light

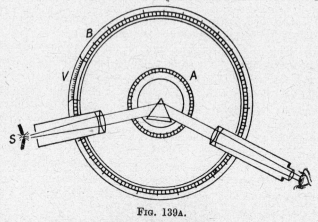

FIG. 139A.

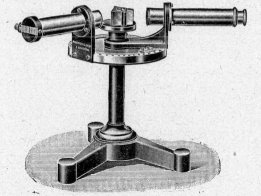

FIG. 139B.

(4) The refracting edge of the prism must be parallel to the axis of rotation of the table.

(5) The optical axes of the telescope and collimator must be at right angles to the axis of rotation of the instrument.

The Eye-piece.—(1) is carried out by turning the telescope away from the instrument and adjusting the eye-piece until the cross wires are clearly seen without any eye strain.

N

Telescope and Collimator.—(2) and (3). Two methods are available for focusing these for parallel light :—

(*a*) Remove the telescope, take it to an open window, select a distant object such as a church spire, and focus this in the telescope. When there is no parallax between the image of the spire and the cross wires it is evident that the image lies in the focal plane of the cross wires. Next replace the telescope on the instrument and turn it into line with the collimator so that the slit may be examined in the telescope. A sodium flame is used in order to provide monochromatic light. Adjust the slit to a convenient size and focus the collimator until an image of this slit is seen without parallax in the focal plane containing the cross wires. The instrument is then set for parallel light.

(*b*) The adjustment of (*a*) takes some time and is very inconvenient when the telescope cannot be moved from the instrument. In addition, distant objects are not always available and so the following method due to SCHUSTER is now the one generally adopted.

Place the prism on the table and adjust the height until it is in line with the collimator and telescope. Rotate the telescope until a blurred image of the slit is seen by refraction. If the table is now slowly turned the image will move. Follow this in the telescope and, provided the table is moving in the right direction, the image of the slit will finally stop and then move back in an opposite direction. When this change takes place the image is at minimum deviation, as the student will remember if he recalls the experiment for finding the angle of minimum deviation of a prism (page 70). It follows therefore that there are two positions of the prism on either side of minimum deviation where the deviation is slightly greater than the minimum. On the one side the image will be rather broad and on the other very narrow. A (full lines) and B (dotted) (Fig. 140) represent the positions of the prism in each case.

Put the prism in the B position so that the beam falls more obliquely on the prism than for minimum deviation.

Focus the telescope until the image is seen sharply defined

and without parallax on the cross wires. Rotate the prism to the A position. The image will be found to be blurred. Focus the collimator this time. Rotate to B and again focus the telescope, repeating these operations, first

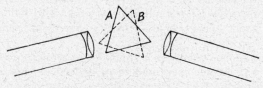

Fig. 140.

telescope then collimator, until the image is sharp in both positions. Three or four adjustments should bring about the desired effect and both telescope and collimator are then fixed for parallel light.

The principle on which this depends should easily be followed from a consideration of the diagram (Fig. 141). A converging beam of light ABC is supposed to strike the prism in such a way that the narrow pencil B passes through at minimum deviation to form an image at b, and A is incident less obliquely and C more obliquely than minimum deviation,

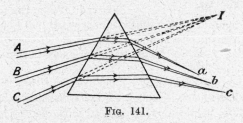

Fig. 141.

forming images after refraction at a and c respectively. The less oblique pencil A with a smaller value of $\angle i$ becomes more convergent after refraction, and the more oblique pencil C less convergent after refraction. Now consider Fig. 140 again. If the prism is in the B position the rays are falling as in C (Fig. 141), that is, more obliquely : therefore

they will enter the telescope in a more parallel direction than
in the A position. A re-focusing of the telescope will consequently improve it for parallel light. Now return to
position A. The pencil of light now entering the telescope
is too converged and if we correct this with the collimator
we improve the latter's adjustment for parallel light.

The same theory holds true for divergent pencils of
light.

If the order—telescope, collimator—is wrongly used, the
image will become more and more blurred as each change
takes place and the student will soon realise the necessity
for reversing his order.

Adjustment (4).—Sometimes this is carried out at the instrument makers. Usually adjustment screws A, B, C are given

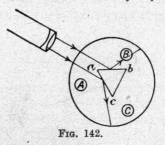

FIG. 142.

to put it right. When this is
the case the prism is placed
in the position shown (Fig.
142) with the edge *ab* at right
angles to the direction of two
screws BC. The collimator is
placed so that it illuminates
both *ab* and *ac*: then two
images by reflection will be
observed. When the telescope
faces the light from *ab* adjust the screws B and C until the
image is seen in the middle of the field of the telescope.
When facing *ac* adjust A only until the image is again in the
middle of the field.

After this somewhat lengthy but necessary description of
what the instrument is, and what must be done before it is
ready for use, we will now proceed to show one or two of its
uses.

To Find the Angle of a Prism. *Method* I.—Arrange
to receive the incident light on two faces at the same time.
Focus the image I_1 (Fig. 143) on the cross wire of the telescope and take the reading of the circular scale. Move T_1
to T_2 and focus I_2. Take this second reading. Then the
difference between the two readings will be seen from the

diagram to be equal to twice the value of the angle of the prism.

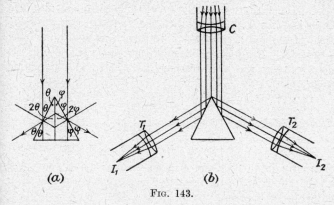

(a) (b)

FIG. 143.

Method II.—As before allow the light to be incident on one face AB (Fig. 144). Find the image and take a reading of the table scale. Keeping the telescope fixed, rotate the table containing the prism until the edge AC has come into the same position as the edge AB was in previously, that is, AC has moved from AC through the ∠DAC to the line BD. Take a second reading. The difference is the ∠DAC which is the supplement of the angle of the prism.

This method is adopted for prisms with large angles.

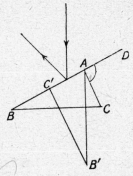

FIG. 144.

To Find the Angle of Minimum Deviation.—Place the telescope with the prism about in line with the collimator and get an image of the slit on the cross wires. Take the reading of the circular scale. Replace the prism in the position shown in Fig. 139a, that is, in such a position that an image is seen in the telescope by refracted rays. By slowly revolving the table containing the prism and keeping the image of the slit in the field of view, find the position of the telescope such that the revolution of the table in one direction causes the image to move up to the vertical cross wire (say to the right) and then causes it to turn back again (i.e. back to the left). Read this position of the telescope. The difference between the two readings is clearly the minimum deviation.

Refractive Index.—From $\mu = \dfrac{\sin \dfrac{d + A}{2}}{\sin \dfrac{A}{2}}$

we can, by obtaining d and A in the manner shown above, get an accurate value for the refractive index of a substance cut in the shape of a prism.

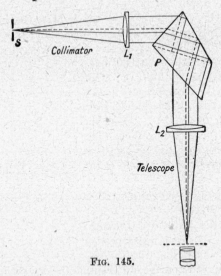

Fig. 145.

Constant Deviation Prism.—At this stage it will interest the advanced students to refer to Fig. 145. This represents a constant deviation prism P specially constructed for examination of spectral lines at minimum deviation. The collimator SL_1 and telescope L_2 are rigidly fixed and in order to make observations through the spectrum the prism is rotated by means of a drum attached to the table carrying the prism. The drum is calibrated so that the wave-length of the line under observation may be read off directly on the scale.

Spectrum Analysis—Astronomy.—A chapter will be devoted to spectra later on. It is sufficient here to realise that the spectrometer has been a master key to all the hidden knowledge of this branch of science. In astronomy the lessons of the spectrometer appeal most vividly. Not only have we learned what substances exist in the further regions of space, but we have further determined the constitution of certain stars, comets, and nebulæ. Stars, in fact, are now grouped under four classes according to their spectra ; each class may be taken to indicate a certain stage of decay or growth in the stars that belong to that class.

Direct Vision Spectroscope.—It is sometimes desirable to examine merely the colours and positions of spectra without

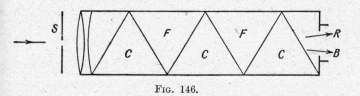

Fig. 146.

taking actual measurements of angles. Instruments designed for this purpose are called *Spectroscopes*,[1] and they may be made in a less bulky and more compact form than the spectrometers.

The direct vision spectroscope consists of alternate crown and flint prisms so arranged that the flint prisms produce equal and opposite deviations to those produced by the crown prisms. As, however, the dispersive power of the flint

[1] Thus a spectrometer is a spectroscope which will enable measurements to be made.

glass will be greater than that of the crown glass it follows that dispersion will occur without deviation.

The diagram (Fig. 146) shows a narrow beam of light passing through a slit S and a lens. It then traverses a combination of three crown and two flint prisms. The light is dispersed and by means of an eye-piece situated behind the prisms a distant virtual image of the slit may be observed corresponding to light of any given quality.

QUESTIONS. IX.

1. What do you know of the photographic camera ? Explain the action of a stop.

2. What is a telephoto lens and how is it used commercially ?

3. How is it possible to photograph an object so as to produce a picture which will show depth ?

4. Describe the stereoscope and explain the principle of its construction.

5. What is a simple magnifying glass ? Describe how it works.

6. What do you understand by the magnifying power of a lens ?

7. Describe an astronomical telescope and draw a careful diagram illustrating the path of a beam of rays through the telescope. Indicate the magnification to be expected.

8. Compare the opera glass with the astronomical telescope. Give a description of the former and show how to find its magnifying power.

9. What are prism binoculars ? Why are they so useful at race meetings ?

10. Show how you would convert an astronomical telescope into one which would be of service terrestrially.

11. Write a short essay on the reflector telescope and compare its action with that of the refractor type.

12. Show how to determine experimentally the magnifying power of a telescope.

13. Draw a careful diagram which will illustrate the action of a compound microscope. How is its magnifying power determined ?

14. Write an essay on the defects in telescopes and microscopes.

15. Describe Huygens' eye-piece and show why it is free from both spherical and chromatic aberration. Why is it usually called a negative eye-piece ?

16. Describe Ramsden's form of positive eye-piece. What are its advantages and disadvantages as compared with Huygens' eye-piece ?

17. Write an essay on the spectrometer and its uses.

18. Describe some form of direct vision spectroscope.

CHAPTER X

VELOCITY OF LIGHT

History.—Until the 17th century the transmission of light was thought to be instantaneous. The finite velocity of sound has been an established fact from time immemorial, but because the methods adopted for its measurement failed when applied to light, it was concluded that light possessed an infinite velocity. Even Galileo could think of no better method of testing this conclusion, for his writings show that he sent two men with lanterns to two distant neighbouring mountains and arranged that each should watch alternate displays of the lantern by the other. When we consider that if the mountains were four miles distant the actual interval between display and observation would only be $\frac{1}{37200}$ sec., there is little wonder that the velocity was thought to be infinite. It is easily understood why astronomers were keen to know the truth about light, for the observations on two stars might be entirely false if the transmission of light was not instantaneous. We might, for example, be observing the state of one star as it was two years ago and the other as it was last month. ROEMER, a Dane (1644–1710), who eventually became professor in the University of Copenhagen, discovered in 1674 that the discrepancy between the calculated and observed times of the disappearance of Jupiter's Satellite into the shadow caused by Jupiter could be explained on the assumption that light possessed a finite velocity of about 200,000 miles per second. This was not accepted on account of the complications involved in trying to work out a theory of the movement of Jupiter's Satellites, and it was thought that either the observations were not sufficiently accurate or gravitation was responsible for the discrepancy. Roemer's discovery was therefore shelved until the investiga-

tions of Bradley became known fifty-five years later. JAMES
BRADLEY (1692–1762) as a professor at Oxford University
had been making observations on some of the fixed stars in
order to try to discover whether or not any parallax existed
that is, whether any shift occurred between the various
stars when measured at different intervals, since, he argued
the position owing to the velocity of the earth will appear
to differ at each measurement. It is common experience to
notice the effects of relative motion. In a train, for example,
the telegraph poles appear to move very quickly : further
away the movement is not so great, and at very large distances
it is not observable by the naked eye. Unless the stars were
all at the same distance or an infinite distance away
the velocity of the earth (19 miles a second)
must produce an apparent movement between
them. Bradley failed in his quest, but by acci-
dent discovered something even more important.
That was that a star (γ Draconis) apparently
moved in a small orbit of its own. It was impossible to believe that a star would regulate its
movement to that of the earth's and consequently
he concluded that the phenomenon must have been
an apparent motion. Four years later, whilst boating on the
Thames, he noticed the apparent change in the wind every
time the boat started and then the explanation of the movement of the star occurred to him. He had been observing
an apparent direction instead of the true one. The velocity
of the earth causes the telescope to move through a certain
distance OB (Fig. 147) in the time taken by light from a star
to pass through the telescope. Consequently, if AO is the
direction in which the telescope is pointing (and represents
the distance light travels whilst the earth moves OB) A'O
will be the true direction of the light. From his measurements he calculated the velocity to be 193,000 miles a second.

FIG. 147.

One hundred and twenty years elapsed before astronomical
experiments gave place to terrestrial determinations. In
1849 FIZEAU (1819–96), a French physicist, hit upon the idea
of using a toothed wheel which, by being rotated at high

speeds, could allow light to pass through its spaces, and then, after reflection from a mirror some distance away, be received on a tooth. The time taken for the light to travel this double distance was equal to the time required for the wheel to travel through this small angle. By his measurements he obtained a velocity of 315,000,000 metres a second, or 195,000 miles a second.

Between 1874 and 1878 CORNU (1841–1902) of Orleans, a professor at the *Ecole Polytechnique*, repeated Fizeau's experiments using greatly improved apparatus. For example, one of the troubles Fizeau encountered was the accurate timing of the wheel's revolutions. Cornu adopted an electrical device which enabled him to find the speed at any instant. In addition, much greater distances were used for the light to travel. His determinations which gave him a mean value of 300,400,000 metres a second, or 186,000 miles a second approximately, appealed so much to his contemporary scientists that he was awarded in 1878 the " prix Lacaze," the membership of the Academy of Sciences in France, and the Rumford medal of the Royal Society in England.

In 1880 JAMES YOUNG and GEORGE FORBES, two British scientists, modified Fizeau's arrangement by introducing two distant reflectors in the same line but at unequal distances. Instead of receiving the light on a tooth of the wheel and so obtaining extinction with either reflection, observations were made when the light was of equal intensity from both reflectors. The value obtained was 301,382,000 metres a second.

In 1838 ARAGO proposed the use of a rotating mirror in place of the toothed wheel, the purpose being to deflect the light on its return journey and so cause a deflection of the image. The amount of deflection would enable anyone to calculate the angle of deflection of the light, and this would give half the angle turned through by the mirror. From this hint Fizeau and FOUCAULT (1819–68) together designed an arrangement to carry out the investigation. The experiments were conducted separately and as a result Foucault discovered that light was transmitted more slowly in water than in air. His determination for the velocity in air gave a value of 298,000,000 metres a second.

MICHELSON (1879–1931), whilst a young officer on duty at the United States Naval Academy, Annapolis, improved considerably the method of the rotating mirror. The chief improvement was a modification of the arrangement of his apparatus whereby the distance between the rotating and fixed mirror was increased to 600 metres. This increased the deflection of the image from 0·7 mm. to 133 mm. He gave the velocity of light a value lying between 299,913,000 metres per second and 299,853,000 metres per second. Further experiments by NEWCOMBE, a collaborator of Michelson, were so successful that the velocity of light was determined with a possible error of not more than 20,000 metres per sec. The value obtained was 299,853,000 ± 10,000 metres per second in vacuo.

METHODS OF DETERMINATION OF THE VELOCITY OF LIGHT.

Roemer's Method.—The observations were made on Jupiter's first satellite because the plane in which it revolves round Jupiter is nearly the same as Jupiter's orbit round the

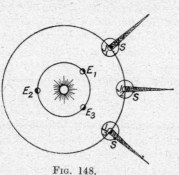

sun. The satellite S is shown in the diagram (Fig. 148) just entering the shadow cast by Jupiter. The large and small circles represent the different orbits—the smallest is the satellite's orbit round Jupiter—the intermediate one is the earth's round the sun and the large circle Jupiter's round the sun.

FIG. 148.

The period of revolution of Jupiter is 11 years 10 months so that if the Earth and Jupiter are in conjunction at $E_1 J_1$, we shall have them in opposition at $E_2 J_2$, approximately 6 months later. After a further equal period they will again be in con-

unction at $E_3 J_3$. Now as the satellite rotates uniformly
.bout Jupiter as does Jupiter about the sun, successive eclipses
hould occur at equal intervals of time. This, however, does
ot happen. Observations on the mean intervals between
uccessive appearances of S when the earth moves from E_1 to
E_2 show longer times than the mean intervals between dis-
ippearances when the earth moves from E_2 to E_3. This can
nly be accounted for by supposing that light takes a finite
ime to reach the earth and this time will vary according to the
listance from Jupiter to Earth. The average period from
me year of observations was calculated and the value used
o predict eclipses during a second year. It was found that
or the first half year the eclipses occurred late by an amount
that gradually increases up to a maximum of 16 mins. 26 secs.
They then begin to catch up and at the end of another half
year agree. In other words light has taken 16 mins. 26 secs.
to travel across the diameter of the earth's orbit. Knowing
this distance it is easy to calculate the velocity.

Bradley's Method.—Suppose we view a star S (Fig. 149)
through a telescope fixed at E.
If the earth were stationary
SE would be the direction
along which the light would
enter the telescope. Suppose
that during the time that
the light takes to travel along
the telescope LE, the telescope moves into the position L'E', then this light
would not be observed. If,
however, the telescope is

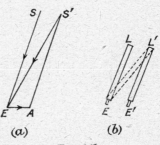

FIG. 149.

turned in the direction L'E the light travelling in the
direction L'E' entering at L' would be received by E at E'.
What we really see then when we look at a fixed star S is
its image S' in the direction S'E. S' will vary according
to the movement of the earth and as this is orbital so the
variation of S' will be orbital and Bradley's observations

become clear and easily understood. If S is the mean position of the fixed star, SE represents the velocity of light and EA the earth's velocity. Also since SE is large compared with EA, generally we may say

$$\tan \angle SES' = \frac{SS'}{SE} = \frac{EA}{SE} = \frac{v}{V}$$

(where SES' is the angle of displacement, v and V are the velocities of the earth and light respectively) and consequently V can be found.

It is interesting to note that the maximum value of $\angle SES'$ is only about $\frac{1}{3}$ minute or $\frac{1}{180}$ degree.

Fizeau's Method.—The complete arrangement is shown

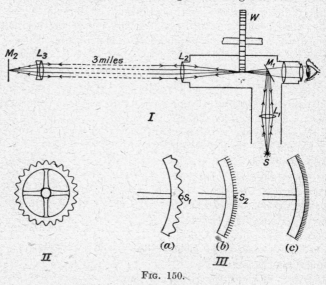

Fig. 150.

in Fig. 150. A strong source of light is brought by means of a lens L_1 and plane mirror M_1 to a focus F between two teeth of a wheel W which can rotate in a vertical plane. F is situated at the principal focus of a telescope objective L_2 so that the rays from F will be rendered parallel after

assing through the lens. These parallel rays are then made
to fall on another objective L_3 after traversing about three
or four miles. A plane mirror M_2 is placed at the principal
focus of L_3 so that the rays will be reflected back along the
same path even if M_2 is not accurately set. The mirror M_1
is only partially silvered and therefore the eye is able to
see the image of S by means of the rays which return to F.

Now suppose W rotates. As long as the light can pass
from F to M_2 and back again before a tooth gets in the way the
image of S will be seen (Fig. 150, IIIb). If, however, the light
which passes through a space at F is reflected by M_2 and returns
to find a tooth blocking its path no image will be seen (Fig.
150, IIIc). As the speed of the wheel is increased from zero a
point will be reached when the time taken for light to travel
from F to M_2 and back is equal to the time taken for a tooth
to move the distance of a space between the teeth or half the
distance between the centres of two consecutive teeth. Thus
if d is the distance from F to M_2, N the number of revolutions
of the wheel per second, n the number of teeth on the wheel,
the time taken to traverse the distance 2d feet

$$= \frac{1}{2Nn} \text{second}$$

and therefore the velocity $V = 2d.2Nn = 4Nnd$ feet per sec.

The chief objection to this method is the difficulty of
knowing when to measure the speed of the wheel. The
image of the source does not vanish abruptly but gradually
dies away until the amount of light passing through is not
sufficient to excite the optic nerve at the back of the eye.

Cornu improved the apparatus considerably. The distance
was trebled and by means of electrical contrivances the speed
of the wheel at any instant could be measured. This enabled
him to observe carefully the time of disappearance and re-
appearance of the image : a mean was then taken. Both
Fizeau and Cornu tested their results by doubling and trebling
the speeds and thus getting multiple values of V.

Foucault's Method.—The original method was to allow
sunlight to pass through a rectangular aperture S, in the

middle of which was a fine vertical wire, and after reflection
by a half silvered mirror *mm* the light was made to converge
on to a second mirror MM (Fig. 151) situated so that its axis
of rotation contained the centre of curvature of a concave
mirror C. The mirror MM could be rotated at various speeds
about a vertical axis. Suppose it stationary—then an image
of S would be seen at A by means of the rays returning along
their original paths and coming to a focus after passing the
half silvered mirror *mm*. On rotating MM slowly, persistence
of vision enables the image still to be seen. On further
acceleration a speed may be reached at which the rays leaving MM strike the mirror C and return to find MM in
the position M'M'. The image will then be seen at A'.

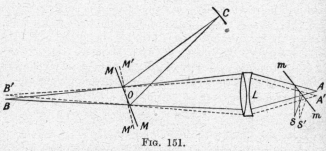

Fig. 151.

Moreover the student may remember (Chapter III) that the
angle through which the reflected rays are turned is twice
the angle through which the mirror has turned. The distance
AA' will give us the angle of deflection of the rays and consequently we can find the angle MOM' through which the
mirror has turned. Knowing the velocity of the mirror and
the distance between MM and C, we can determine the time
it takes for the mirror to turn through the angle MOM',
that is the time taken for light to travel from MM to C and
back, and so we can calculate the velocity of the light.

By using an air turbine, MM could be rotated at high speeds.
Even then the maximum deflection was only about 0·7 mm.
when OC was 20 metres. The fine wire in the aperture, however, enabled this deflection to be measured very accurately
when a micrometer eye-piece was used.

The method is useful for measuring the velocities of light in various transparent liquids. Long cylindrical tubes containing the liquid were placed between MM and C; it was in this manner that Foucault discovered that the velocity of light in water was less than in air.

Calculation in Foucault's Method.—Let a be the distance OA, d be the distance OC, x the amount of displacement AA', n the number of revolutions of MM per second; V the velocity of light. The time taken to travel the double distance OC $= \dfrac{2d}{V}$ secs. Therefore, the angle, α, through which the mirror turns in this time $= 2\pi n \dfrac{2d}{V}$ radians $= \dfrac{4\pi nd}{V}$ radians.

From previous knowledge the angle the reflected rays turn through has twice this value, i.e. $\dfrac{8\pi nd}{V}$ radians. When the light returns from C and impinges on M the pencils at AA' appear to come from BB' behind M so that OB = OB' = d. If the distances of the lens from the slit and revolving mirror are l and L, we have, since $<$ALA' is small, $\dfrac{AA'}{l} = \dfrac{BB'}{L+d}$ and BB' = $2d\alpha$.

Hence
$$x = \frac{2d\alpha l}{L+d} = \frac{8l.\pi nd^2}{v(L+d)}$$

$$\therefore V = \frac{8\pi lnd^2}{x(L+d)}$$

Michelson's Method.—In its original form Foucault's method had several drawbacks, which made earlier workers prefer Fizeau's method. Apart from the time measurement, it requires a measurement of the very small displacement of the image and this could only be increased by increasing the path of light, since the speed of rotation is limited by mechanical difficulties. However, the apparatus was not adapted to any great increase in the distance the light travels owing to the decrease in the intensity of the image. This is clearly so since the rotating beam from M (Fig. 151) is returned from C only during the small fraction of time that it is sweeping

o

across C, and this is evidently less the greater the distance between M and C. Michelson overcame the difficulty by choosing a lens of great focal length and placing it between M and C in such a position that its focal plane was a little behind M; the concave mirror C was replaced by a plane mirror. In this arrangement all rays striking the lens are brought to a focus on the mirror and the intensity of the image is determined by the aperture of the lens and not that of the mirror, which even for very great distances need not be greater than that of the lens.

Another improvement adopted by Michelson and Newcomb was to replace the plane mirror M by a prism having four or more reflecting surfaces, which again increased the brightness of the image.

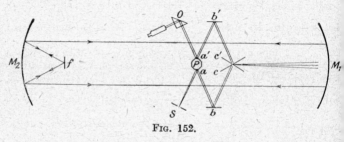

FIG. 152.

In 1926 Michelson carried out a wonderful series of measurements using a still further improved form of Foucault's method. The optical arrangement is shown in Fig. 152. As a rotating mirror he used an eight-faced prism P maintained in rotation about its axis (perpendicular to the diagram) by an air-driven turbine. The light from an arc lamp is focused on a slit S and then falls for the first time on one face a of this rotating prism. By means of the two small plane mirrors b and c it then reaches the concave mirror M_1 whence it is reflected as a parallel beam to the second concave mirror M_2, a distance of 22 miles away. This forms at its focal plane an image of the slit and a small plane mirror placed there sends back the light along the same path. By means of mirrors c' and b' it again reaches the rotating prism at a', passing thence by the reflecting prism O into the measuring eye-piece. The mirror was driven at such a speed that during the time taken by the light to make the trip there and back (0·00023 sec.) the mirror turned through exactly one-eighth of a revolution, so that the image of the slit was in the same position as when P was at rest. It was found that the required speed was about 528 rev./sec.

Direct Measurements in Vacuum.

In all the terrestrial experiments mentioned it is, of course, the velocity V in air that is directly measured. From this the velocity in vacuo c is calculated from the relation $c = \mu V$ where μ is the refractive index of the air.

Michelson's experiments were so excellent that it was found that the accuracy of the calculated value of c was limited by the fact that the exact conditions of pressure and temperature of the air between the two stations were not known, and the value of μ obviously depends upon these conditions. Michelson, therefore, planned an experiment to measure the speed in a vacuum. The experiment was begun in 1929 with Pease and Pearson and was not completed until after Michelson's death in 1931.

The method was similar to his previous one, except that the path of the light was inside a long evacuated pipe. The pipe was made of iron 3 feet wide and a mile long, its joints being so carefully sealed that it was possible to maintain a pressure as low as half a millimetre. The mean value obtained from nearly 3000 observations was 299,774 km./sec.

A Modern Version of Fizeau's Method.   Use of Kerr Cells.

A very remarkable modern development of Fizeau's method is provided by the measurements made in 1925 by Karolus and Mittelstaedt. Their method was similar in principle to Fizeau's, differing from it only in the method of interrupting the beam of light. Instead of using a mechanical shutter—the cog wheel—they used an electrical one—the Kerr cell, of which great use is made in television. We need not here consider the mode of action of the cell; all we need realise is that it will interrupt a beam of light. The cell consists of a small glass vessel, provided with two parallel metal plates connected to wires sealed through the walls and filled with nitro-benzene. The arrangement is shown in Fig. 153. N_1, N_2 are two Nicol prisms (cf. page 302) crossed so that in the absence of K_1 no light from the source S will emerge through N_2. If now K_1 is placed between N_1 and N_2 it is found that when a high voltage is applied across the plates of K_1 light passes through N_2; but, when this is switched off, the passage of the light is again prevented by N_2. Thus with the strong electric field between the plates the light can pass through the arrangement $N_1 - K_1 - N_2$; that is, the light valve is open; whereas with no field the valve is closed and no light can pass.

The light from N_2 is collimated by L_2, travels to the mirror M where it is reflected to L_3 and then refracted through a second

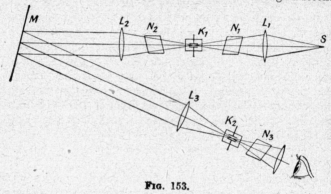

Fig. 153.

cell K_2 to a nicol N_3 and then through the lens to the eye. The light which emerges from N_2 is plane polarised (cf. page 299) and since N_3 is crossed with N_2, the light will be stopped by it unless the electric field exists between the plates of K_2.

Suppose Now K_1 and K_2 are connected to an oscillator by means of which an alternating field of high frequency can be applied synchronously; that is, the two light valves are made to open and close together. If this frequency is high enough it is clear that even for a relatively short distance L_2ML_3 it may be that by the time the light which has passed through N_2 arrives at K_2 the field is zero and, hence, no light passes through N_3. This is precisely what happens in Fizeau's experiment when the light is stopped by the next cog. But in Fizeau's experiment it was only possible to interrupt the light some 50,000 times a second, whereas this electrical shutter can be opened and closed millions of times a second.

Karolus and Mittelstaedt used a path of about 300 metres and starting with a low frequency, at which of course the light was seen, they were able by steadily raising the frequency to make the light pass through a series of minima and maxima, exactly as in Fizeau's experiment.

QUESTIONS. X.

1. Write an essay on the determinations of the velocity of light.

2. How did Roemer estimate the velocity of light from observations on Jupiter's satellites ?

3. Explain how the aberration of light was used by Bradley to determine the velocity of light.

4. Describe any terrestrial method of finding the velocity of light (a) in air, (b) in water.

CHAPTER XI

THE MEASUREMENT OF LIGHT. PHOTOMETRY

Introductory.—The question of the measurement of light has taken on a greatly increased importance in recent years. We are realising more than ever before the importance of adequate illumination and the extent to which our health, efficiency and happiness depend upon it. To cope with the many problems involved, a new branch of applied physics, that of illuminating engineering, is being developed and a very important section of this is concerned with the measurement of light.

Until recently all light measurements depended upon the eye, just as the earliest heat measurements were based on our sense of hotness. In the development of heat the inadequacy of this sense as a basis of measurement was soon realised and physical instruments such as thermometers, in no way dependent on our senses, were invented. In the case of light, however, our special sense organ, the eye, has remained the basis of all measurements. In some respects this is understandable since in dealing with light we are primarily concerned with its effect on the eye ; but it is none the less true in this case also that the eye is a very unsuitable measuring instrument. Its indications vary from one individual to another and even for a given person they change from day to day depending upon circumstances. For this reason a good deal of research work is being given to the problem of devising some physical instrument whose action is not directly dependent upon the eye and by means of which measurements of light can be made with the same accuracy and simplicity as we measure temperature, electric currents, etc.

Photometric Quantities.—If we replace a candle in a room by an electric lamp we know that the lamp sends out a more copious stream of light than the candle. In more technical terms we say that the lamp produces a much greater *luminous flux* than the candle. Moreover, with the electric lamp as our source the amount of light falling upon everything in the room is greater ; that is, the *illumination* is increased. Again, if our electric lamp has a " pearl " bulb and has no reflecting filling, the light will be emitted more or less uniformly in all directions, whereas if we fit a suitably shaped reflector behind it we can arrange that the light is concentrated, say, downwards in a cone. In this way we have not altered the total flow of light from the lamp, but have merely redistributed it, so that now very much more light is emitted in certain directions than in others. Putting it in technical speech again, we say that the source (i.e. the lamp and fitting) gives a greater *luminous intensity* in some directions than in others.

Suppose we take two lamps of the same power, one having a clear glass bulb and the other a pearl bulb ; these both give approximately the same amount of light ; but, looking at them, we notice that the glowing filament of the one has a much greater *brightness* than the translucent surface of the other. In the latter the same amount of light is emitted from a much larger surface and it is clear that the brightness depends upon the relation between the intensity of its light emission and its area.

The four terms introduced above, namely luminous flux, luminous intensity, illumination and brightness are the four most important photo-metric quantities. We shall now proceed to deal with them in detail. Before doing so it is recommended that students not familiar with solid angles should read the following note :—

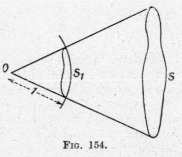

Fig. 154.

Note on Solid Angles.— The definition of this is arrived at by a simple generalisation of the method used to define a plane angle in circular measure. With O as centre (Fig. 154) describe a sphere S_1 of unit radius. The lines joining O to each point of the edge of the surface S will describe on S_1 a certain figure. The area ω of this figure is a measure of the solid angle subtended by S at the point O. The unit solid angle is sometimes called the *steradian*.

Since the total surface area of S_1 is 4π it is clear that the solid angle corresponding to the whole space surrounding O will be 4π.

It is useful to obtain an expression for the small solid angle subtended at a point by a small element of surface. Let S (Fig. 155) be the small plane area situated at a distance r from the point O and having its normal Pn inclined at an angle θ to the radius OP. It is assumed that S is so small that its linear dimensions are negligible compared with r. Then, if we describe a spherical surface, centre O and radius $r = OP$, the cone subtended at O by S will cut off on this sphere a small region of area $s \cos \theta$ (this is the apparent area of S seen from P). The

FIG. 155.

area cut off on a spherical surface S_1, centre O and radius unity will thus be

$$\frac{s \cos \theta}{r^2}$$

so that the small solid angle ω is given by

$$\omega = \frac{s \cos \theta}{r^2}.$$

Luminous Flux.—Since a beam of light is a stream of energy it seems natural to speak of the luminous flux as the rate of passage of energy. But it must be remembered that light sources send out a good deal of radiation, e.g. infra-red and ultra-violet, to which the eye is not sensitive at all. Moreover, the sensitivity of the eye is very different for different parts of the visible spectrum (cf. page 150). As it is obvious that we are only concerned with the visual effect of the radiation, the mere statement of the energy transferred by the source is insufficient. The definition of *luminous flux* adopted by an international convention is " *the rate of passage of radiant energy evaluated with reference to its visual effect.*"

Luminous Intensity.—If luminous sources all emitted light equally in all directions we could specify the light-giving power of any source by simply stating the total luminous flux it provided. But this is most often not the case and so it is desirable to have some means of specifying the rate at which a given source is producing light in any given direction. It is for this purpose that the quantity luminous intensity is introduced. The definition of this may be understood in the following way :

Let O be a small source of light and around OP (Fig. 156) as axis suppose a cone of small solid angle ω is constructed. Let the luminous flux of O within this cone be E. Then if

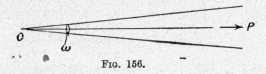

Fig. 156.

the cone be sufficiently small we may take it that the flux is uniformly distributed within it so that the ratio $\dfrac{F}{\omega}$ is a measure of the light-giving power of O in this particular direction. This ratio is called the luminous intensity of O in the direction OP. That is, the luminous intensity of a source I in any specified direction is the flux per unit solid angle emitted in the given direction. If a given source has the same intensity for all directions within a solid angle Ω the total flux it emits within this solid angle is given by

$$F = I\Omega.$$

If it emits with the same intensity in all directions it is called a uniform source and the total flux F_0 is given by

$$F_0 = 4\pi I.$$

Units of Intensity and Flux.—We have considered the idea of flux first and explained that of intensity in terms of it ;

this is the better order of dealing with the relation of the ideas. When, however, we come to the question of setting up suitable standards of measurement it is more convenient to begin with luminous intensity. This is done by specifying in detail a certain source of light and taking as the unit of intensity the intensity of this source in a particular direction.

In the early days of photometry it was agreed to take as the standard source a candle of specified materials and dimensions, burning at a specified rate. With growing accuracy of measurement it was found that this candle was not sufficiently constant in its rate to act as a good standard and it was replaced by the Vernon-Harcourt Pentane lamp. This lamp

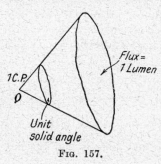

Fig. 157.

has no wick, the source of light being a pentane flame. Under defined conditions it provides a very constant source. The flame was made fairly large so as to give an intensity in a horizontal direction of approximately that of 10 candles. From this lamp the International Standard Candle was defined as the intensity of a source having $\frac{1}{10}$th the intensity in a horizontal direction of this pentane lamp burning under specified conditions.

At the present time for the sake of greater convenience the standard is maintained in terms of a group of electric filament lamps kept at the various standardising laboratories. There is no need to go further into this question here ; it is sufficient to realise that we have a certain source of light whose intensity in a given direction is the agreed unit of luminous intensity. The luminous intensity of any source measured in terms of this unit is called the International Standard Candle-Power or briefly the *Candle-Power of the source.*

Having fixed the unit of luminous intensity we can define the unit of luminous flux in terms of it. Thus, let O (Fig. 157) be a point source of uniform intensity equal to one candle-

power. The flux emitted by this source within a cone of unit solid angle is taken as the unit of luminous flux, and is known as one *lumen*. That is, the lumen is the flux, or quantity of light per second emitted by a uniform source of one standard candle-power within a cone of unit solid angle. It is clear that the total flux emitted by this source in all directions will be 4π lumens, and the total flux F_0 emitted by a uniform source of intensity I will be given by

$$F_0 = 4\pi I \text{ (lumens)}.$$

Illumination.—The third quantity, illumination, is defined as the total flux received or intercepted by the surface per unit area. If the surface is so lighted that the same amount of light falls per second on every equal little bit of the surface (e.g. on every sq. mm.) it is said to be uniformly illuminated, and the value of the illumination E is equal to the total flux F falling upon the surface divided by the area. That is,

$$E = \frac{F}{A}.$$

It should be noted that in this definition we have to consider the total flux falling on the surface, quite independently of the direction in which it reaches the surface. Furthermore, we are *only* dealing with the flux which the surface *receives* and not with what happens to the light when it reaches the surface. Thus, it may all be reflected regularly or in various directions, or it may be all or partly absorbed or transmitted. These differences will, of course, greatly affect the appearance of the surface or its *brightness*. A piece of black velvet lying on fresh snow may well have the same illumination as the snow, but its brightness will be widely different. This important distinction between illumination and brightness should be noted ; it is often misunderstood.

The Fundamental Photometric Relation.—A constantly occurring problem in photometric work is the calculation of the illumination produced at any place by a given arrangement of lamps or other sources of light. The basis of all these calculations is the expression for the illumination produced at any point of a surface by a single point source of light.

Let O (Fig. 158), be a point source having a luminous intensity I in the direction OX and let a be a surface the plane of which is perpendicular to OX ; that is, the light from O falls

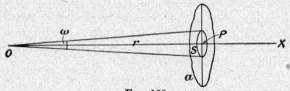

FIG. 158.

perpendicularly on the surface at P. In order to determine the illumination, consider a small area s with P as its centre. This will subtend a small solid angle at O given by

$$\omega = \frac{s}{r^2}.$$

The flux F emitted by O within this cone will be

$$F = I\omega$$

and, hence, the illumination of the small area at P will be given by

$$E = \frac{F}{s} = \frac{I}{r^2}$$

that is, the *illumination varies inversely as the square of the distance.*

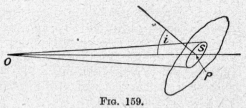

FIG. 159.

Consider next a surface turned about P as fixed point until a normal to the surface at P makes an angle i with the light from O (Fig. 159). The point P is still at the same distance from O, but the light is no longer incident normally but at an angle i. The illumination at P is now lower than before and it is easy to see that a small area s around P subtends a smaller angle at O given by

$$\omega = s \; \frac{\cos i}{r^2}.$$

The flux emitted by O within this small angle is given by $F = I\omega$ and hence the illumination at P is given by

$$E = \frac{F}{s} = \frac{I \cos i}{r^2}.$$

That is, for light incident at an angle i the illumination is reduced by the factor $\cos i$ as compared with the illumination when the light is incident normally.

Units of Illumination.—From the definition of illumination as flux incident per unit area, it is natural to take as the unit of illumination that which is obtained when unit flux (one lumen) falls on unit area. There will be several units according to the unit of area adopted. The common units are lumen per square metre, or the *lux* as it is sometimes called, and lumen per square foot. These two are often called the *metre candle* and the *foot-candle* respectively; these terms arise in the following way.

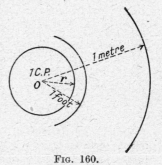

Fig. 160.
(not to scale.)

Let O be a uniform point source of *one* standard candle. Imagine a sphere of radius r drawn with O as centre. The total flux emitted by O is 4π lumens and this flux is distributed uniformly over the spherical surface so as to produce a uniform illumination given by

$$E = \frac{4\pi}{4\pi r^2} = \frac{1}{r^2}.$$

Thus the unit of illumination is given by the illumination produced at the surface of a sphere of unit radius by a uniform point source of one standard candle placed at the centre. The lux is clearly the illumination at the surface if the radius is one metre ; that is, it is the illumination produced by a source of one candle-power at a surface one metre away, the light being incident normally to the surface. In the same way an illumination of one lumen per square foot is equal to that produced on a spherical surface of one foot radius with a source of one standard candle at the centre ; that is, the illumination due to one standard candle on a surface one foot away when the light is incident normally.

It is preferable to use the term " lumen per square foot " since this gives direct expression to the proper definition of illumination as flux per unit area.

Brightness.—This is the last of the four fundamental quantities. As we have seen above, the illumination of the surface is determined by the light *received*. Brightness, however, is concerned with the light *emitted* by the surface.

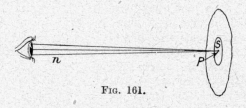

Fig. 161.

Suppose we are looking at a point P (Fig. 161) on an illuminated surface, or a self-luminous surface, along a line Pn perpendicular to the surface. A small bit of the surface of area s, around P may be regarded as a point source of light. If its intensity in the direction Pn be I_0, then the ratio I_0/s, or the candle-power per unit area, is called the brightness B of the surface at P in the direction Pn.

The *unit of brightness* is thus *candle-power per unit area.*

Some idea of the brightness obtained from various sources is indicated in the table below :—

Sun's disc .	.	.	165,000 candles per sq. cm.
Moon's disc	.	.	0·5 candles per sq. cm.
Incandescent filament of			
electric lamp .	.	.	600 candles per sq. cm.

Surface of opal bulb of
   electric lamp .   .   1·7 candles per sq. cm.
Crater of arc   .   .   16,000 to 17,000 candles per sq. cm.
Paper suitable for read-
   ing.   .   .   .   0·001 to 0·002 candles per sq. cm.

Comparison of Luminous Intensities.—We can now
turn from the consideration of fundamental principles to the
question of measurement, and since it is a standard of intensity
which is the basis of all measurements we shall begin with the
comparison of the luminous intensities of two sources.

It is important to realise that the eye cannot make any
direct numerical comparison of intensities. In fact, the only
thing the eye can judge is brightness, which we have seen is a

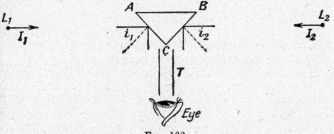

Fig. 162.

very different thing from luminous intensity. Moreover, we
cannot by the eye alone give any quantitative comparison of
different brightnesses; that is, the eye is not capable of
determining for example that one surface is twice as bright
as another. In this respect it is like our other senses; we
cannot tell by our hotness sense how much hotter one body
is than another. However, we find that the eye can judge
with considerable precision when two adjacent surfaces are
equally bright, provided they appear the same or nearly the
same colour, and this power of the eye forms the basis of visual
photometry.

Let L_1, L_2 (Fig. 162) be the two sources whose intensities
I_1 and I_2 are to be compared. Between them is placed a
wedge ABC of Plaster of Paris such that the surface AC is

illuminated by L_1 and BC by L_2. These two surfaces are observed simultaneously through the tube T. By moving the wedge or one of the sources it is possible to find a position such that the two surfaces appear equally bright. Suppose this is so when the distances of L_1 and L_2 from the respective surfaces are d_1 and d_2. Then if i_1 and i_2 denote the angles at which the light is incident on the faces, the illuminations E_1 and E_2 produced on AC and BC are given by

$$E_1 = \frac{I_1 \cos i_1}{d_1^2} \text{ and } E_2 = \frac{I_2 \cos i_2}{d_2^2}.$$

Now, if the two surfaces are exactly similar in their reflecting properties, we may conclude that when they appear equally bright they must be equally illuminated. Hence, we have

$$\frac{I_1 \cos i_1}{d_1^2} = \frac{I_2 \cos i_2}{d_2^2}.$$

If, as would be usual, it is arranged that $i_1 = i_2$, we have

$$\frac{I_1}{I_2} = \frac{d_1^2}{d_2^2}.$$

It is rare that surfaces have exactly the same reflecting powers and, therefore, the assumption that equality of brightness means equality of illumination is not in general correct. One or two procedures may be adopted to overcome this difficulty. One is to interchange L_1 and L_2 or the two surfaces and to obtain a mean of the readings when balance is obtained. Another and easier way is to use a third lamp on one side at a fixed distance away and to obtain a balance first with L_1 and then with L_2. Then if d_1 and d_2 are the distances of L_1 and L_2 when balance of brightness is obtained, then clearly

$$\frac{I_1}{d_1^2} = \frac{I_2}{d_2^2}.$$

This is the so-called *substitution method*.

Any arrangement suitable for carrying out a comparison of candle-powers as in the above experiments is called a *photometer*. A great many have been devised and one or two will now be described.

The Bunsen Grease Spot Photometer.—This was the earliest form capable of any precision. It consists essentially of a sheet of white paper, forming the screen, in the middle of which a part is made translucent by means of paraffin. This translucent part may have any shape; but its edges should be sharply defined. The screen is held in a suitable box which has been blackened inside. The central part transmits more light than it reflects, while the converse is true for the surrounding part. There are various ways of using it, of which the most satisfactory is the substitution method. The disc is viewed from one side—as nearly normally as possible—and the position of the lamps adjusted until the boundary line between the centre and the surroundings can no longer be distinguished, the whole disc being of uniform brightness. The procedure is then repeated with the other source under test, keeping the comparison lamp fixed at the same distance from the screen and moving the other lamp. Then it follows as before that

$$\frac{I_1}{I_2} = \frac{d_1^2}{d_2^2}.$$

It is usually impossible to obtain exact equality of brightness on both sides of the photometer screen simultaneously. An alternative procedure, sometimes adopted, is to adjust the position until the two sides show an equal *contrast* between the spot and the surrounding part. To facilitate this, two inclined plane mirrors are arranged behind the disc so that the two sides can be viewed at the same time.

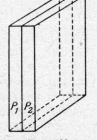

Fig. 163.

Joly Photometer.—In this form the photometer head consists of two rectangular blocks of paraffin wax or opal glass placed side by side and separated by a sheet of tin foil (Fig. 163). Light from the two sources falls normally upon the sides of the block which appear suffused with light. Adjustment is made until the two edges P_1 and P_2 have the same brightness. When

ᵱ

balance is nearly obtained it is found that the less brightly illuminated side has a grey band near to the central line. As the balance point is passed this band moves across the line so giving a sensitive indication of the precise point of balance.

The Lummer-Brodhun Photometer.—This is the most satisfactory type and is used in all precision measurements. The distinguishing feature of the arrangement is the Lummer-Brodhun cube C (Fig. 164). This consists of two rectangular prisms whose hypothenuse faces are polished and are optically plane. The outer part of this face of one of the prisms A is

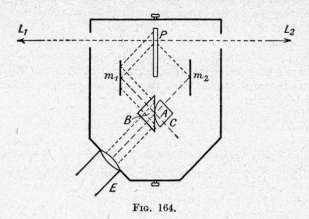

Fig. 164.

etched away leaving a sharply defined circular central part untouched. The prisms are then pressed together as shown so that where their polished faces are in contact light can pass through unweakened by any reflection. On the other hand, light entering one of the faces of B is totally reflected at the annular surrounding part. The general arrangement should be clear from Fig. 164. Light from L_1 and L_2 falls upon opposite sides of the screen P which is made of some white diffusing substance, usually Plaster of Paris. The light scattered from these surfaces is reflected by the mirrors m_1, m_2 on to the cube. A microscope E is focused on to the hypothenuse face of the latter and the centre of the field of view is illuminated only by light from L_2 while the outer part receives light only from L_1. Thus if the left-hand side of P is brighter than the right, then the field of view has the outer part brighter than the centre ; if the reverse is the case the centre part appears brighter. When the field of view is uniformly bright, that is when no dividing line between the centre and the surroundings is visible, the two sides of P must be equally bright, and hence if they have the same reflecting properties they must be equally illuminated. Since the two sides may in fact differ, it is preferable to use the substitution method.

Candle-power measurements of the type described above may be used to determine the fraction of incident light which is transmitted by a thin sheet of material or the fraction reflected by a mirror.

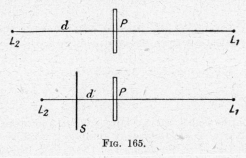

FIG. 165.

(1) *Transmission Factor of a Thin Sheet*.—The method should be understood from Fig. 165. Lamps L_1 and L_2 are arranged to give a photometric balance at the photometric screen P. The distance of L_1 from P is measured (d). The thin sheet of material S is then interposed between L_2 and the photometer head. Since only a certain fraction of the light incident on S is transmitted it will be necessary to move L_2 nearer to P in order to obtain once more a balance. Let the new distance be d'. If the candle-power of L_2 is I and its effective candle-power with the screen interposed is I', it is clear that

$$\frac{I}{d^2} = \frac{I'}{d'^2}.$$

The ratio I'/I gives the fraction of light transmitted by the plate ; this is called the transmission factor.

(2) *Reflection Factor of a Mirror.*—The procedure here is indicated in Fig. 166. Suppose balance is obtained with L_2 at A ($AP = d$), the mirror M being removed. Then with M placed at say 45° to the axis of the bench, L_2 is moved to position B such that its image in the mirror is at B′. Then it is as though P were illuminated from the left by a source of candle-power I′ ($= rI$) at B′ where I is the candle power of L_2 and r is the required

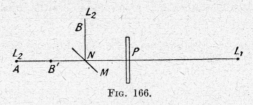

Fig. 166.

Reflection Factor. If the distance B′P (that is, $BN + NP$) for which balance is again obtained is d' we have

$$\frac{I}{d^2} = \frac{I'}{d'^2}$$

and hence

$$r = \frac{I'}{I} = \frac{d'^2}{d^2}.$$

It should be noted that the same side of L_2 must be directed along BN as is directed along AP since, in general, the candle-power will vary with direction.

Measurement of Total Luminous Flux.—While the measurement of the candle-power of a source in any direction is a fundamentally important measurement, we are more concerned in modern lighting practice with the total light flux given by any lamp. With the development of the diffusing globe and the use of reflecting shades so as to get the best distribution of light for a given purpose, it has become customary to specify lamps by stating their total light output. Hence it has become necessary to devise means of measuring this quantity. We could, of course, calculate it if we first measured the candle-power in a large number of directions, but this would be a laborious business and, to avoid it, methods

have been developed for determining the total flux by direct experiment. Photometers for this purpose are called *integrating photometers*, and are based on the following principle :—

If a source of light is placed inside a hollow sphere whose wall is perfectly diffusing, it can be shown that *the illumination of every part of the surface due to light scattered from the remainder is the same and is proportional to the total flux emitted by the source.* This was first recognised by SUMPNER (1892), but was first applied by ULBRICHT in 1900. It is now extensively used in all lamp works.

The procedure is to introduce the lamp into a sphere, the wall of which is coated with a suitable diffusing paint. The sphere is fitted with a window W (Fig. 167) made of opal glass and a small screen S protects W from direct light from L. Then according to the above principle, a given flux from L, regardless of the direction in which it is emitted from the lamp, produces the same illumination on the window W. The illumination on W is thus simply proportional to the total flux from the lamp. The bright-

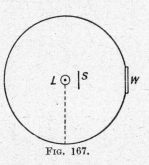

FIG. 167.

ness of the window with the test lamp L in the sphere is then compared with that obtained with a lamp, the total flux from which has been determined by measuring the candle-power in all directions.

Measurement of Illumination.

So far we have been concerned with measurements made on sources of light—their candle-power and total flux. It is often, however, more important to measure the illumination at a given place without regard to the particular sources of light that produce it. In planning the lighting of a factory or a schoolroom, for instance, what we are primarily concerned with is to produce sufficient illumination where it is required —on the workbench or desk as the case may be—and it is important to have some ready means of measuring this quantity directly. Portable instruments for doing this are called *Illumination photometers* and many different kinds are now available.

The underlying principle is the same in all of them. A white diffusing surface is placed in the position at which the illumination is to be measured and its brightness is compared with that of another surface contained in the instrument, the

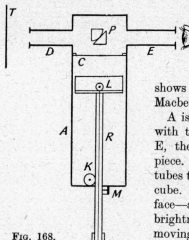

brightness of which can be varied in some convenient way. The illumination is then read off on a calibrated scale. Fig. 168 shows one particular form, the Macbeth Illuminometer.

A is a tube fitted at one end with two short side tubes D and E, the latter carrying an eyepiece. At the crossing of the tubes there is a Lummer-Brodhun cube. C is the comparison surface—a sheet of opal glass, the brightness of which is varied by moving the small lamp L fixed to the end of the rod R. The latter is provided with a scale and

FIG. 168.

is moved in and out by the knurled knob K, its position being indicated by the mark M. In making a test the axis of the side tubes is directed towards the test-plate T—placed in the required position—and the Lummer-Brodhun cube is observed through E.

The outer part of the field is illuminated by C and the centre by the test-plate. The position of L is then adjusted until the two parts have equal brightness, and the corresponding value of the illumination is read off on the scale.

The calibration of the scale is obtained by finding the position of the lamp for balance when T is exposed to various

known values of illumination. This can conveniently be done
by the subsidiary apparatus shown in Fig. 169.

The tube A, fitted at one end with lamp L of known C.P.,
is placed with the other open end on the test-plate. The
photometer is directed on to T through
the side tube H. If the intensity of L is
I, the illumination on T is $E = I/d^2$. The
photometer is balanced and the scale
marked with the corresponding value of E.

It is necessary, of course, that the lamp
L shall have the same C.P. during the
test as during the previous calibration.
To ensure this, it is desirable to make
frequent checks of the instrument with
the test-plate exposed to a known illumination. Also, it is very important that the
test-plate P should be carefully preserved
so that its reflection characteristics are not altered.

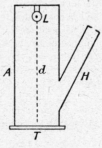

Fig. 169.

Lights of Different Colours.—In all the preceding experiments we have assumed that the surfaces whose brightness we
were comparing appeared to the observer to have the same
colour. When this is not so, great difficulties arise. It is found
that the results obtained differ not only from one observer to
another, but for one and the same observer under varied conditions
of test. The establishment of the electric lamp substandards
make comparisons easier than if we use the reddish pentane
standard, but even with these we are faced at the present time
with the rapid development of electric discharge lamps, such as
sodium vapour, mercury vapour, etc., whose colours are very
different from those of our standards.

A great deal of research work is being carried on with some
measure of success. One method of approach is to make use of
suitable filters by means of which the colour differences are
reduced. The transmission characteristics of the filters have, of
course, to be separately investigated and allowed for. Another
method is to divide the colour difference into a number of steps,
employing intermediate series of lamps whose colour differences
are small. A third procedure is provided by the flicker photometer.

The Flicker Photometer.—The principle of the method is to expose to the eye alternately in rapid succession the two surfaces to be compared. It is found that a frequency can be obtained for this alternation for which the colour difference disappears, the two blending into some intermediate hue, while the flicker due to differences of brightness still remains. The photometer head is then adjusted until this brightness flicker disappears also or is reduced to a minimum. A large number of different forms of photometer have been developed on this principle. A simple type is shown diagrammatically in Fig. 170. One comparison surface C is fixed and the other AB has the form of a disc of the shape shown (b). When AB is rotated about K as axis an eye observing through the tube F sees first B illuminated by one source L_2 and then C illuminated by L_1 in rapid succession.

Research on the method has shown that results can be obtained

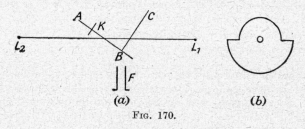

(a)　　　　　　　　　　　　　　(b)

Fig. 170.

in close agreement with other methods provided certain conditions are observed. In particular it is found that (1) the field of view should be small so that only the central part of the retina is used, (2) the illumination of the two parts of the field should be high, and (3) the comparison field should be surrounded by a region of about the same brightness. These requirements are met in the modern form of instrument due to Guild. This is shown diagrammatically in Fig. 171.

S is a disc which has the form shown. It rotates about the axis K parallel to the photometer bench L_1L_2 and is illuminated by the source L_2 to the right. The other comparison surface F is at right angles to K and receives light from the other source L_1 by means of the totally reflecting prism P. The observer looks along the line EH. R is a box the inner surface of which illuminated by the lamp Q provides the suitable bright surrounding of the photometer field.

In ordinary practice the difficulties connected with coloured
light are often avoided by using as a comparison source a
standardised lamp of similar colour to the one to be tested.

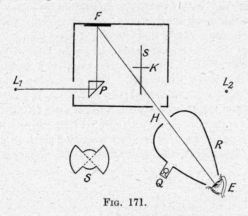

Fig. 171.

Physical Photometry.—All the measurements so far considered depend upon the judgment of the eye as to the brightness of some surface. This has been the standard procedure
ever since the pioneer work of Bouger and Lambert at the
end of the eighteenth century, and it leads to satisfactory
results so long as we are concerned with sources of light of
the same or nearly the same colour. But, as we have noted
in the last section, these visual methods are much more difficult
and less satisfactory when we have to deal with lights of
widely different colour. For this reason efforts are being made
to develop methods of measurement which do not depend
upon the eye. At present probably the most successful is
the so-called " *barrier-layer* " *photo-electric cell*, the principle
of which is illustrated in Fig. 172. The essential part consists
of a " sandwich " composed of a disc of metal, usually copper,
covered with a layer of semi-conducting material on the top
surface of which is spattered a very thin transparent film of
some metal, usually gold or platinum. The semi-conductor is
either copper oxide or selenium ; the latter is used, for
instance, in the Weston Photronic cell. The top film and the

lower plate are connected through some current measuring instrument, A. The action of the cell depends upon the fact that when light falls upon the top surface it causes electrons to pass from the semi-conductor through a so-called barrier layer into the metal film ; thus a current is indicated by A.

Now it is clear that if this effect is to serve our purpose its magnitude (i.e. the current produced) must depend upon the wave length of the radiation in the same way as the visual effect on the eye (cf. page 150). That is, it must not respond at all to infra-red and ultra-violet radiation, but must have its maximum sensitiveness for a wave-length of 5540 Å, and so on. It is found that the cell does not quite behave like this, but if a suitable filter—a sheet of a special greenish glass—is placed in front of it, the total effect of the radiation is very

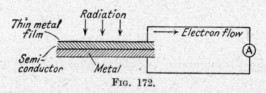

Fig. 172.

closely similar to the response of the average eye. Thus, the current produced gives a direct measure of the visual effect of the radiation, or its lighting value which is what is required.

Various manufacturers are now producing cells of this type and their use is revolutionising the commercial measurement of illumination.

Brightness of Images.—It is of interest in connection with optical instruments to consider some points concerning the illumination and brightness of images formed by a lens. Let A′ be the image of a surface A formed by the lens L (Fig. 173). Consider a small patch ab of the object A of area s, the image of which is the small patch $a'b'$, of area s'. Let the brightness of ab in the direction of the lens be B ; this means that it radiates light towards L like a source of intensity I equal to Bs. Hence if the lens L subtends at O a solid angle ω the luminous flux collected by the lens from the small area ab is given by

$$F = I.\omega = B.s.\omega.$$

Some of this light will be reflected from the lens surface and some may be absorbed, so that a reduced amount, say F′ ($<$ F) is transmitted. This is spread over the patch $a'b'$ of the image and hence the illumination is given by

$$E' = \frac{F'}{s'}$$

and hence $E' \leqslant \dfrac{F'}{s'}$ or $E' \leqslant \dfrac{B.s.\omega}{s'}$

the equality sign only holding if there is no appreciable loss of light in transmission through the lens.

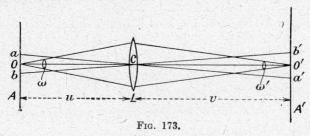

FIG. 173.

Since $\dfrac{s}{s'} = \dfrac{u^2}{v^2}$ and $\omega = \dfrac{A}{u^2} = \dfrac{\pi d^2}{4u^2}$

where A and d are the area and diameter of the lens respectively, we have

$$E' \leqslant \frac{B.\omega.u^2}{v^2} \quad \text{or} \quad E' \leqslant \frac{B.A}{v^2} \quad \text{or} \quad E' \leqslant \frac{\pi}{4}.B.\left(\frac{d}{v}\right)^2.$$

We see, therefore, that the illumination of the image of the surface is proportional to the brightness of the surface and the aperture A of the lens.

In a camera it is clear that for very distant objects the illumination of the image formed on the plate will be given by

$$E \leqslant \frac{\pi}{4}.B.\left(\frac{d}{f}\right)^2.$$

The quantity d/f is the aperture ratio (cf. page 154).

In the case of the eye, we may regard v as a constant so that the illumination of the image formed on the retina is proportional simply to the brightness B of the surface and the aperture A of the pupil of the eye. In particular we note that it does not depend on the distance of the surface from the eye. As it is the illumination of the retinal image that determines the *apparent brightness* of the surface, we see that the latter is independent of the distance of the eye from the surface.

It is important to observe that this argument is only true for a surface source. If the source is so small that it may be regarded as a point and its image on the retina is so small that it covers no more than one of the elements of structure of the retina, then the apparent brightness is directly proportional to the total luminous flux that the eye collects from the point source. Hence, a point source will appear fainter as it recedes from the eye because the amount of light entering the eye from it will diminish.

The above considerations apply to the illumination of a screen on which the image is formed. Suppose, however, no screen is used and the aerial image $a'b'$ is observed by an eye looking towards the lens. The luminous flux coming from the small area $a'b'$ will be F' and this will be contained within the solid angle ω'; hence this bit of the image will act like a source of intensity $I' = \dfrac{F'}{\omega'}$; that is, the brightness of this image in the direction CO' produced, will be given by

$$B' = \frac{I'}{s'} = \frac{F'}{s'\omega'}$$

i.e.

$$B' \leqslant \frac{B.s.\omega.}{s'\omega'}$$

and since clearly $s.\omega. = s'\omega' \left(\text{for } \omega' = \dfrac{A}{v^2} \right)$

we obtain the result $B' \leqslant B$.

That is, the brightness of the image $a'b'$ can *at most* be equal to that of the object ab and is in general less owing to the loss of light in transmission.

Summarising our results, we see that the apparent brightness of any surface is governed by the illumination of the retinal image, and this depends only upon the area of the pupil opening and the brightness of the surface under observation. Also, we have shown that the brightness of the image of any surface formed by a lens (or a system of lenses) cannot exceed—and in general is less—than the brightness of the surface itself. Hence, it follows that the apparent brightness of the image of any surface seen through a telescope cannot be greater than that of the surface seen by the eye.

On the other hand, if the source is a point, the apparent brightness depends simply on the light collected by the eye from the point. With a telescope, provided that all the light collected by the objective enters the eye, this brightness is increased in the ratio A_0/A_e where A_0 is the area of the objective and A_e that of the pupil. It follows, therefore, that more stars are visible in a telescope than with the naked eye. The brightness of the background is not increased since this is a surface source, but the stars being point sources have their apparent brightness increased greatly—about 200 times with a 4-inch objective.

Sources of Light.—By far the most important practical sources of light are provided by incandescent solids. These emit light solely because of their high temperature, the energy needed for the production of the light being derived from the thermal motions of the molecules. Flames, gas mantles, electric arcs and filament lamps are all of this type.

The earliest and for a long time the only sources of artificial light were flames, in all of which the greater part of the light is emitted from particles of carbon heated to incandescence. Through the long ages of their use many forms were tried, but it was not until 1884 that the first important scientific improvement was made, when Argand obtained a greatly improved light by using a tubular wick and surrounding it by a chimney, thereby producing an upward draft of air which caused better combustion. Coal gas was first introduced on a commercial scale in 1792 by Murdoch and in 1810 it was used for the first time for street (Pall Mall, London) illumination. The real development of gas lighting, however, awaited the introduction of the incandescent mantle by Welsbach in 1893. This consists of cotton or silk fabric impregnated with a mixture of the oxides of thorium (99 per cent.) and cerium (1 per cent.) from which the organic material is burnt off leaving an ash skeleton of the mixture of oxides ; this gives a brilliant light when heated to incandescence in the flame. Clearly, in this case it is the heating power of the flame and not its own luminosity which is important. The great advance obtained by the use of the Welsbach mantle was largely due to the fact that in the spectrum of the oxide mixture a far greater proportion lies in the visible spectrum than is the case with carbon. The exact composition of the mixture is very important.

The first application of electricity to lighting was provided by the electric arc, discovered by Davy in 1810. He found that if two metal rods in contact were connected to the poles of a large battery and then drawn slightly apart, the current continued to flow, the gap between the rods being bridged by an arc of glowing gas. The most important type is the *carbon* arc, in which the ends of the carbons become intensely brilliant, though the flame between them is only slightly luminous. The positive carbon burns to a hollow " crater " which provides almost the whole of the light. As the carbons are gradually consumed, it is usual nowadays to provide means for automatic adjustment so that the rods are kept together. An important development was the introduction of the *flame arc*, in which the carbon rods were made with a special mixture of carbon and certain metallic salts. In arcs of this type the principal source of the light is the flame itself which is made intensely luminous by the vaporised salts. Because of the intense brightness of the positive pole, the arc has many applications in special directions, particularly for use in search-light projectors ; but its unsteadiness, its large size, the need for frequent attention and above all its high cost are dis-advantages which have almost eliminated it as a general source of light.

It is of interest to note a development of the arc provided by the Pointolite lamp. In this an arc is maintained between a small ball of tungsten forming the positive electrode, and a short length of tungsten wire. The arc is started in this case, not by bringing the electrodes into contact, but by heating the wire and thereby providing a copious shower of electrons in the intervening space. The glowing tungsten ball forms practically a point source and for this reason is often of great use in the laboratory.

Of all sources of illumination to-day, the most important

is the electric filament lamp. The first practical form of this, produced in 1879, by Edison in America, and Swan in England, consisted of a very thin filament of carbon contained in an evacuated bulb and heated to incandescence by an electric current. The light given by these early lamps was over-rich in yellow and was in many ways less satisfactory than the incandescent gas-mantle ; but as a result of a great deal of systematic research they have been so improved that the electric lamp is now unrivalled as a general illuminant. Every year the electric-lamp industry turns out more than a thousand million lamps of one type or another.

The whole development of the electric lamp has been directed towards the increase of its efficiency and it is of interest to consider it briefly from this point of view ; that is, as a device for converting electrical energy into light. It is usual to express its luminous efficiency by giving the total luminous flux in lumens per unit electrical power supplied, measured in watts. The electrical energy used in maintaining a flow of current through the lamp is converted into heat in the filament, which causes the temperature of the latter to rise rapidly until a point is reached at which the rate of heat production is just balanced by the rate at which it is lost from the filament. This loss occurs partly in the form of radiation, and partly owing to conduction and convection. The radiation forms a continuous spectrum (see Fig. 240, Chap. XVII). Unfortunately only a small part of the radiated energy falls in the visible region where we need it, much the greater part being in the longer wave infra-red region. In order to increase the amount of energy radiated within the visible part of the spectrum, the temperature must be raised. With the early carbon filaments the maximum temperature that could be used was limited by the fact that the filament was easily volatilised and deposited on the glass of the bulb. Despite various improvements in the method of manufacture efficiencies of the order of 3·5 Lm/watt were all that could be obtained. In the first decade of this century considerable improvements were obtained by using various metals with high melting-points for the filament instead of carbon.

Osmium and tantalum were used for some time, but eventually these were discarded in favour of tungsten which at the moment has still no rival. The tungsten lamps of 1911 had an efficiency of about 10 Lm/watt ; they were all of the vacuum type in which as before volatilisation trouble limited the temperature that could be used if the lamp was to have a reasonable life. One way of reducing this evaporation of the filament is to fill the bulb with some inert gas, but by so doing the rate of loss of heat by convection is very much increased, and hence far more energy would be needed to keep the filament at a given temperature. The problem was to find some way by which the advantage of gas filling could be made to outweigh the disadvantage. The solution was found in 1913—largely due to the work of Irving Langmuir—by making the filament in the form of a closely wound coil. By this means the area of surface from which the filament radiates is made large, while the convection losses, which depend only on its length (coiled) are kept small. At first it was only found possible to apply this with advantage to the larger-sized lamps, but recently by again coiling the coiled filament —(the coiled-coil lamp)—the efficiency of the smaller lamps has also been appreciably improved up to approximately 15 Lm. per watt.

It is clear that the struggle to increase the efficiency of the electric lamp is a hard one, and despite brilliant research work the results are still very low. The basic reason, of course, is that the production of light by heating a solid is a thoroughly inefficient process as a great part of the radiation poured out is worse than useless. Experiment shows that if 1 watt of electrical power could be completely converted into light of wave length $0.55 . 10^{-4}$ cm. (for which the eye is most sensitive, see page 150) it would produce a flux of 620 lumens, and even if it were distributed uniformly over the whole visible spectrum, it would still give about 250 lumens. This shows how far short we are of the ideal. The glow-worm and firefly manage things far better ; their radiation is confined entirely to the visible. The question therefore arises as to whether it is possible to devise practical sources of light which do not epend on incandescences.   Great strides have been made in his direction during recent years by the development of the o-called gas-discharge lamps.   It has long been known that he passage of an electric current through a gas often produces beautiful luminous effects, a well-known example being he so-called Geissler tubes often used in spectroscopic work. These are made in a great variety of forms, one of which is ndicated in Fig. 174.   A glass tube is fitted with two electrodes E, E—usually of aluminium.   The tube contains a gas t a low pressure, and when a high electrical potential difference is applied to the electrodes e.g. by connecting them to the secondary terminals of an induction coil) the insulation of the gas is broken down and a luminous glow fills a arge part of the tube.   This is in no way due to heat ; the tube remains quite cool.   The light rises as a result of the bombardment of gas toms by electrons which are swept along in the ube by the electrical forces between the electrodes.   (More details about this mode of producing light are given in Chap. XVII.)   Practical pplication of this phenomenon was first made by Moore (in 1895) and to-day it is familiar to all ecause of its wide use in advertisement signs ; hese may be regarded as large Geissler tubes, and y using different gases and coloured glasses for the ubes, a large variety of colours can be obtained.

FIG. 174.

hus, neon gives a red colour ; argon, blue ; carbon ioxide, white (nearly like daylight, but the gas requires requent renewal) ; mercury vapour in brown glass, green ; elium in yellow glass, yellow, etc.

Gas-discharge lamps of this kind need high electrical pressures of the order of 10,000 volts for their operation ; their fficiency is low and their chief use is to serve as luminous eatures rather than sources of illumination.   However, in the ast few years physicists have obtained a far deeper insight into he processes by which light is produced, and this has led to he development of gas-discharge lamps of very remarkable

properties—for example, the sodium vapour and mercur
vapour lamps with which we are becoming familiar to-day i
street lighting, etc. In these "hot cathode" lamps th
negative electrode—i.e. the cathode—is heated (either by a
external battery or by the discharge itself) so that it become
the source of a copious stream of electrons, just as the filamen
does in a wireless valve. The discharge in these cases is a
arc and the lamps work at ordinary supply voltages. In th
case of the sodium lamp, the greatest part of the energ
emitted is in the form of the familiar yellow light, and sinc
this is near the maximum of the luminosity curve of the eye
the efficiency is relatively high, approximately 35 Lm. pe
watt. These gas discharge lamps all give coloured light, an
though for many purposes—lighting of streets, railway yard
etc.—this is not of great importance, it would preclude the
use for purposes where a white light is essential. In thi
connection it is interesting to note a recent development i
which the phenomenon of fluorescence is applied. By coatin
the glass of a mercury vapour discharge tube with suitabl
fluorescent materials which absorb the plentiful supply
ultra-violet radiation produced by this lamp and re-emi
the energy as visible light, the efficiency of the lamp ha
been greatly increased and values of 60 Lm. per watt hav
been attained. In addition a much whiter light is produced

QUESTIONS. XI.

1. Distinguish between luminous flux and luminous intensity. Ho
are they related and in what units are they measured ?

2. How would you show that illumination varies inversely as th
square of the distance ?

3. In what units is illumination measured ? What is the essentia
difference between illumination and brightness ?

4. How would you compare the luminous intensities of two source
of light by the aid of a grease-spot photometer ?

5. Two lamps L_1 and L_2 give equality of brightness in a photomete
when their distances are 50 cm. and 100 cm. respectively. A plan
mirror with its plane perpendicular to the axis of the bench is place
10 cm. from L_1 further from the photometer head. L_2 has then to b
moved 10 cm. to restore the photometric balance. Calculate th
percentage of light reflected normally by the mirror.

6. Prove that the solid angle θ of a circular cone of semi-vertical angle is given by $2\pi(1 - \cos \theta)$.

Calculate the luminous flux emitted within a cone of semi-vertical angle 60° by a small source giving a constant intensity of 10 C.P. for all directions within this cone.

7. A uniform source of C.P. 1000 is used in a searchlight and by means of a suitable mirror 25 per cent. of the total flux from the surface is concentrated in a conical beam of semi-vertical angle 2°. Calculate the luminous intensity in the direction of the beam.

8. A small source is placed at a height of 100 cm. above a horizontal surface. Plot a curve showing the variation of the illumination it produces at points along a line on the table through the point vertically below this source. Take the C.P. of the lamp to be 50 for all directions concerned.

9. Describe some form of photometer which is independent of the eye.

PART II

CHAPTER XII

THE WAVE THEORY OF LIGHT

Wave Motion.

Let A,B,C,D—W (Fig. 175) be particles moving in simple harmonic motion about the mean positions Abcd—w. Let us suppose that these mean positions are equally spaced out along a straight line as illustrated. If the amplitudes and the periodic times are all equal, and the phases vary regularly from particle to particle, we may find at some given instant

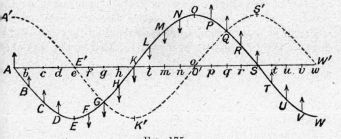

Fig. 175.

that the particles are in the position shown by the full curve. A is moving upward from its mean position. B, C and D are likewise moving upward. E is momentarily at rest, and on the point of ascending. K is in its mean position but is descending. O is at rest and ready to move downwards, and S is exactly in the same phase as A. Each consecutive particle differs in phase by a definite amount $\left(\dfrac{\pi}{8}$ in diagram$\right)$ from the one before it as we proceed along the curve. When we arrive

229

at S we find the conditions beginning to be repeated. Hence
the curve A,B,C,D—S is called a complete wave and the
distance Abcd—S is the *wave length*.

Consider the position of the particles a quarter of a period
later. A will be at A', E at E' and so on, as represented by the
dotted line. Thus the crest of the wave, which was at O, has
now moved to S'.

If we examine the state of affairs after another fraction of a
period has elapsed, we shall find that the crest is still further
to the right. In other words, the vibration of the particles in
the manner described has produced a wave motion, the motion
being in a direction at right angles to that of the particles producing it. The *velocity of propagation* of the waves is the
velocity with which the crests or troughs move along. If
we examine the diagram we shall see that the distance from
crest to crest or trough to trough is the same as the distance
A—S, which is the wave length. Using the notation V for
velocity of propagation, λ for the wave length and T for the
periodic time, we can find a relation between these terms.

It will be seen in the figure that the wave has travelled a
distance OS' in a quarter of a period. That is, the wave has
travelled $\frac{1}{4}\lambda$ in $\frac{T}{4}$ secs., or its velocity $V = \dfrac{\frac{1}{4}\lambda}{\frac{T}{4}} = \dfrac{\lambda}{T}$

therefore $\lambda = VT$.

The student will be reminded of the formation of waves
similar to the above by reference again to Chapter II. A rope
or rubber band is stretched out and fastened at one end. The
other end is jerked sharply at right angles to the direction of
the band. The result of the jerk is to send a wave along the
rope. The reason for this will easily be seen from the diagram
(Fig. 176). The rope is originally as in position I. On moving
A quickly into the position A_1, the neighbouring particles are
dragged along with it, but on account of the flexibility of the
rope and its inertia the action is sluggish, and the consecutive
particles lag more and more behind one another as the distance
from A increases. The second downward movement produces

positions III and IV. Finally, when the complete jerk or one oscillation has been given to A, the rope has the appearance shown in position V. This disturbance will travel along to B.

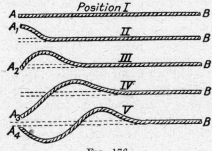

Fɪɢ. 176.

The type of wave motion which has been considered is known as *Transverse Wave Motion* and for reasons given later, is believed to be the way in which light energy is transferred. Sound, on the other hand, is propagated by particles of air or matter vibrating longitudinally, that is, in the same direction as the wave is travelling. This is called *Longitudinal Wave Motion*.[1]

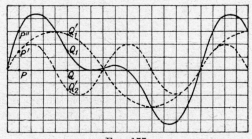

Fɪɢ. 177.

Waves Superposed.—Later on in the book we shall find many examples of the superposition of wave disturbances. It will be well therefore at this point to consider the effect pro-

[1] Cf. Barton's *Sound*.

duced on particles by the action of two or more simple
harmonic disturbances.

The dotted curves in the diagram (Fig. 177) represent two
harmonic waves differing in amplitude and wave length but
travelling in the same direction. The resultant motion is
represented by the full curve, and is obtained by finding the
effect on each separate particle of the two waves combined.
For example, the particle whose mean position is P has a
displacement equal to PP′ for each wave. Its total displacement is therefore PP″. Again, the particle Q is displaced
QQ′$_1$ by one wave in an upward direction, and QQ′$_2$ by the
other wave in a downward direction. Its resultant displacement is therefore the algebraic sum of these two, that is QQ$_1$.

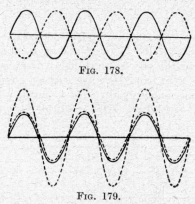

FIG. 178.

FIG. 179.

If we take the simple case of two harmonic disturbances of
equal amplitude, wave lengths and periodic times, but differing
in phase by π we shall see that one disturbance annuls the
other (Fig. 178). If, however, the two waves represented by
full and dotted lines respectively (Fig. 179) are together in
phase, they reinforce each other, and produce a disturbance
with double the amplitude.

The so-called interference of light phenomena which is discussed in a later chapter illustrates the above two examples of
wave motion in a beautiful manner.

The Wave Theory.—The wave theory of light was founded
by HUYGENS in 1678. The conception of it is said to be due
to Aristotle ; he, however, was not an experimentalist in the
true sense, and consequently he made no effort, as far as we
know, to test his theory. Newton, who might have helped to
establish the wave theory if he had so willed, preferred his
corpuscular theory. Reference was made in Chapter I to this
theory and an indication was given as to why Newton's theory
was untenable. It will be remembered that for refraction to
occur, the " light particles " must be attracted when they
approach the surface of a transparent medium : that is, their
velocity must be increased by this " easy fit of refraction " (as
Newton called it). Foucault, however, showed that the velocity of light was less in its passage through water or any
highly refracting medium, and consequently Newton's theory
cannot hold. In 1690 Huygens published a book on light
which put forward the theory that " light is a wave motion
propagated in the ether, the ether being a continuous medium
in which matter exists and which fills all space."

The medium mentioned by Huygens cannot, of course, be
perceived, but its properties may be ascertained by studying
the character of the waves which pass through it. We know
that light possesses a finite velocity and that it is a form of
energy. Thus the medium must be capable of transmitting
energy. If this energy is transmitted in the form of waves
as is assumed in the Wave Theory, the ether appears to
possess (1) density : that is, it is capable of acquiring kinetic
energy when in motion, and (2) elasticity, or the property of
acquiring potential energy.

Let us examine this statement a little more closely. In
Chapter II we illustrated wave motion by jerking a thick
rubber band. An effort was required to do this jerk or, in
other words, the band offered a resistance to the movement.
Further, as the disturbance moved along the band, each portion of the substance resisted this distortion and tried to
recover its original position. The energy required to jerk the
band was transferred to the material particles constituting the
band. These acquired kinetic energy or energy of motion.

Two quantities are associated with this type of energy—mass and velocity.

Again, suppose we only raise the end of the band a little and hold it there. The portion out of alignment is in a state of strain, and it is only the force of the hand which keeps the portion from moving. In other words, a certain length of band has acquired potential energy or, we may say, it possesses elasticity. If the force is removed the length falls, and some of the potential energy becomes converted into kinetic energy. We may, therefore, according to the Wave Theory, consider that the ether possesses some of the properties of an elastic solid. The student, however, is warned not to push the analogy too far.

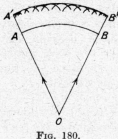

FIG. 180.

In his book, Huygens assumed that the property of the ether is the same in all directions. He then showed that if the position of a wave front (that is, the plane where all the ether particles are in the same phase of vibration) is known at any time, its position can be determined at any other time.

AB (Fig. 180) is shown as part of a wave front due to a source of light placed at O. All the particles of ether in this wave front are in the same phase of vibration. According to Huygens' theory each point on AB is considered to be the centre of a disturbance, and these, in some time t, send out secondary waves of radius Vt (where V is the velocity of light) which will all touch a curve A'B'. Consequently A'B' becomes the new wave front.

When the distance of the wave front from the source of origin is very great, as is the case of light which comes from the stars, the wave front becomes plane if considered in small portions. This follows from the fact that a plane is a portion of a sphere of infinite radius.

So far, Newton quite appreciated Huygens' theory. What led him to abandon it in favour of the corpuscular theory was the fact that sound—a wave phenomenon—could bend round corners whilst light was propagated in straight lines. The corpuscular theory easily accounted for rectilinear propagation; the wave theory apparently did not. It remained for Fresnel, by using Huygens' theory together with the idea of interference introduced by Young, to give a satisfactory explanation of this behaviour of light. He showed that light does in fact bend round obstacles (this is dealt with in more detail in a later chapter), but, owing to the extreme smallness of the wave lengths of light, this bending is very small and, hence, it appears to travel in straight lines.

Very simple experiments with ripples on water are sufficient to show clearly that the extent to which waves bend round the edge of an obstacle depends very much on the relation between the wave length and the linear size of the obstacle. Figs. *a* and *b* of Plate I illustrate this point. In each case parallel straight line ripples are produced and a barrier is laid containing an opening which is small in (*a*) and large in (*b*). It is seen that in the first case the waves spread out widely beyond the opening whereas in the second (*b*) the spreading is much less, the waves travelling on in a rather definitely limited beam. Had the waves been still shorter the difference would have been still more pronounced.

The Rectilinear Propagation of Light.—Fresnel explained his theory in the following manner :—Suppose that a source of light *s* is sending out energy into the surrounding ether in all directions, and suppose AB is a wave front of disturbances at any instant. (Figs. 181*a* and 181*b* represent a plane and spherical wave front respectively.) Every point in this wave front, according to Huygens, will be setting up secondary disturbances, which will in time affect the ether at a point O farther from the source. The disturbance from Q will arrive at O later than that from P : the one from R will arrive still later, and so, by considering all the various secondary wavelets in the wave front, we can find the resultant effect on the ether at O.

If the waves from P and Q are of the same amplitude and the difference in the distances OP and OQ is half a wave length, the waves at P and Q will differ in phase by π when they arrive at O, and, consequently, will destroy each other's action. Let the distance OP be a, the wave length of the light be λ, then with centre O and radii equal to $a + \dfrac{\lambda}{2}$, $a + \lambda$, $a + \dfrac{3\lambda}{2}$ etc., divide the surface of AB into zones (as in Fig. 181a).

It will be seen that

$$OQ - OP = OR - OQ = OS - OR = \ldots = \frac{\lambda}{2}.$$

In the first zone which lies between P and Q the phases of the wavelets arriving at O differ by less than π from the one from P. In the second zone, that is, the annular space

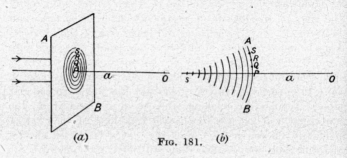

Fig. 181. (a) (b)

between Q and R, the wavelets arriving at O differ by varying phases between π and 2π from the wavelet arriving from P. Similarly, for the third zone, the phase differences are between 2π and 3π. Without much error we may assume that the average phase at O of the wavelets from the first zone is $\dfrac{\pi}{2}$ ahead of the phase of those that left P and for the second zone the average is $\dfrac{3\pi}{2}$ ahead, thus giving an average difference of phase π for these two zones. Similarly, for any pair of consecutive zones, the difference will be π. For alternate zones the difference will be 2π. It should be clear then that the 1st, 3rd, 5th, 7th, etc., zones tend to assist each others' action at O whilst the others combine to oppose these effects.

Now let us consider the amount of energy passing through these zones : this is necessary if we wish to know the resultant effect at O, for if the second zone receives more energy than the first it may not only kill the action of the first, but may have enough energy left to cause illumination. The amount of energy passing through a zone will depend on the area of that zone and on the amplitudes of the waves which pass through it. Consider the areas :—

It is assumed that Q, R and S are very near to the pole P and therefore $PQ^2 = OQ^2 - OP^2$ (exactly in (a) and nearly so in (b)).

$$= \left(a + \frac{\lambda}{2}\right)^2 - a^2$$

$$= a\lambda \ (\lambda \text{ is very small and so } \frac{\lambda^2}{4} \text{ is neglected})$$

consequently the area of the 1st zone is $\pi a\lambda$.

With the same reasoning $PR^2 = 2a\lambda$, and therefore the area of the second zone is $2\pi a\lambda$ minus the area of the first $\pi a\lambda$.

Thus the area of the second zone is $\pi a\lambda$.

Similarly, it may be shown that the area of the third zone $= \pi a\lambda$.

It will be noticed that the zones are all very nearly equal in area although there is a gradual increase as they recede from P. It can be shown, however, that the amplitudes at O of the wavelets from the various zones get smaller and smaller as the distances of the zones from O increase, thus balancing the increase in area ; consequently the resultant effects [1] of these zones become more and more nearly equal as we recede from P. In fact, the zones situated at a very small distance

[1] If d_1, d_2, d_3 etc. represent the disturbances due to the 1st, 2nd 3rd etc. zones

Resultant Disturbance $= d_1 - d_2 + d_3 - d_4 + d_5 \ldots$

$$= \frac{d_1}{2} + \left(\frac{d_1 + d_3}{2} - d_2\right) + \left(\frac{d_3 + d_5}{2} - d_4\right) + \ldots$$

$$= \frac{d_1}{2} \text{ (since other terms vanish)}$$

i.e., Resultant Displacement is equal to half that due to wavelets from the first half period zone.

from P destroy each others' effects with the result that we are left with the action of the few in the immediate vicinity of P.

In other words, if the wave length is small, the light from the source s will travel in a straight line from s to O. The wave length of the middle of the spectrum is about $\dfrac{1}{20,000}$ cm. long and so satisfies our condition. A small obstacle will easily block the passage of the few zones immediately surrounding the light and as the effects of the remainder cancel each other, no light is visible.

Reflection and Refraction will now be explained according to the wave theory and the principle laid down by Huygens.

Reflection of Waves at a Plane Surface.

(a) **Plane Waves.**—Suppose abc (Fig. 182) are rays representing a plane wave travelling towards a plane surface CE

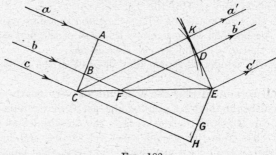

Fig. 182.

separating two different media.[1] It will be remembered that rays are merely normals to the wave, consequently the rays a, b and c are all parallel to each other and are perpendicular to the wave front AC.

According to Huygens, when the wave reaches the surface, secondary wavelets immediately form at the points touched. Thus, every point along CE in turn becomes a centre of disturbance which is sent back into the medium. The first

[1] AC and CE are sections of planes at right angles to the plane of the paper.

THOMAS YOUNG

After a painting by SIR THOMAS LAWRENCE

point at which the wave front AC touches the surface is C, and the last point is E. During the time that it takes for the part A of the wave AC to travel from A to E (a time t say) a secondary wavelet has spread out from C, a distance equal to Vt (when V is the velocity of the wave in the medium). In a similar way a wavelet spreads out from F as soon as the disturbance from B reaches the surface.

We shall now show that these secondary disturbances all touch a plane KE at some given time after reflection and consequently KE becomes the reflected wave front. (KE will be the section of the plane at right angles to the plane of the paper.)

To obtain the new wave front construct a sphere with centre C and radius Vt. Draw a tangent plane EK to this sphere : this will be the reflected wave front if all the disturbances between C and E touch this plane. If no surface existed the wave front AC in time t would be in the position EH. The point G in EH corresponds to the point B in AC : thus FG is the radius of the wavelet starting at F. Draw CK, FD perpendicular to KE. Then, in the $\triangle$'s CKE and CHE it easily follows that $\angle$ CEK = $\angle$ CEH and, therefore, in the $\triangle$'s FDE and FGE we have FD = FG. But FG is the radius of the wavelet from F, and consequently the wavelet touches KE at D. In a similar manner we can show that all the disturbances which begin along CE due to the wave front AC touching the surface, at some subsequent time touch a plane KE. Thus KE is the reflected wave front. It will be easily seen that as EH is a parallel plane to AC, and as $\angle$ KEC = $\angle$ HEC, the plane wave fronts are equally inclined to the surface. Moreover, from our definitions $\angle$ ACE = $\angle i$ and $\angle$ KEC = $\angle r$ and consequently the angle of incidence is equal to the angle of reflection.

Again, AC, CE and KE are all sections in the plane of the paper of planes at right angles to the plane of the paper, and so the normals to these all lie in the same plane. As the normals to AC and KE are the incident and reflected rays respectively we may state that the incident and reflected rays together with the normal to the surface at the point of incidence all lie in the same plane.

R

(*b*) **Spherical Waves.**—AB (Fig. 183) is a section of a plane surface at right angles to the plane of the paper. A source of light O sends out disturbances in the manner shown and *ab*, *cd*, *ef*, etc. represent the wave fronts at different distances from O. If OP is perpendicular to AB, the wave front *gh* will be touching AB in one point only, the point P. From

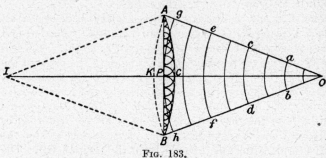

FIG. 183.

P a disturbance starts, and in time *t* (the time taken for the wave front *gh* to be in the position AKB if no surface were present), this secondary wavelet will have a radius equal to PC or PK. In turn each point in the wave front *gh* reaches the surface and sets up disturbances. It should be fairly clear that these wavelets will all touch the sphere ACB where ACB is of equal radius to AKB but opposite in direction. That is, the reflected wave front is ACB and it is such that it appears to have diverged from a point I, the image, situated at a distance IP equal to OP the distance of the object from the reflecting surface.

Refraction of Waves at a Plane Surface.

(*a*) **Plane Waves.**—In this case the diagram (Fig. 184) represents a plane wave incident at the surface of separation of two media X and Y. Suppose the velocities of light in the two media be V_1 and V_2 respectively, we can imagine the wave front ABC first of all incident at the point C and lastly at the point E. The section only is shown as in the case for reflection : that is, ABC and CE represent planes at right angles to the plane of the paper.

As the surface [1] CE is successively disturbed from C to E, wavelets will be developed and will spread out into the medium Y; but because the velocity of light is different in this medium from what it is in X, the wave front, after some time t say, which would have been at EGH had the medium not changed, will be in some such position as KDE. To find this position, with centre C and radius $CK = V_2 t$ describe a sphere. Draw EK a tangent plane to this sphere at right angles to the plane of the paper. Then EK will be the refracted wave front if the spheres of wavelets from CE all touch the plane EK at some given instant, that is for example if FD is the radius of the wavelet developed at F when the surface is affected by the wave front ABC. Draw FD perpendicular to EK. Then obviously $CH = V_1 t$ and $CK = V_2 t$.

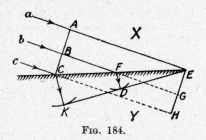

FIG. 184.

$$\frac{CK}{CH} = \frac{V_2 t}{V_1 t} = \frac{V_2}{V_1}.$$

Again, from similar triangles

$$\frac{FD}{CK} = \frac{EF}{EC} = \frac{FG}{CH}.$$

consequently,

$$\frac{FD}{FG} = \frac{CK}{CH} = \frac{V_2}{V_1}.$$

But the $\dfrac{\text{radius in medium X}}{\text{radius in medium Y}} = \dfrac{V_1}{V_2}$

and FG is clearly the radius of the wavelet if the light had not changed media. Thus FD is the radius of the wavelet in medium Y, and as it was drawn perpendicular to the plane EK, the wavelet must touch this plane. Similarly we can

[1] By the surface we mean the ether just below the surface

show that all other wavelets developing in CE will touch the plane EDK.

CK and FD are obviously refracted rays, since they are normal to the plane KE, and cC, bBF the incident rays, being normals to the wave front ABC. It should follow then from previous reasoning on reflection that the *incident and refracted rays together with the normal to the surface at the point of incidence all lie in the same plane.*

In order to prove Snell's law, we observe that the angles $\angle$ACE and $\angle$CEK are incident and refracted angles respectively, since they are complements of the angles the rays make with the surface.

$$\therefore \quad \frac{\sin i}{\sin r} = \frac{\dfrac{AE}{CE}}{\dfrac{CK}{CE}} = \frac{AE}{CK} = \frac{V_1}{V_2} = \text{a constant, } \mu.$$

This result is very valuable, for we see that according to Huygens' theory the index of refraction of two media is the ratio of the velocities of light in the two media.[1] This is borne out by experiment.

(*b*) **Spherical Waves.**—The diagram (Fig. 185) illustrates

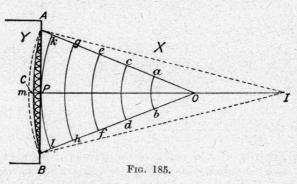

Fig. 185.

a spherical wave diverging from a luminous source O. The wave fronts at different instants are given by *ab*, *cd*, etc.

[1] Cf. page 233.

When the wave reaches the boundary of separation AB of two transparent media X and Y, we may suppose secondary wavelets to develop in turn as the wave passes over it. AmB would be its position at some subsequent time t if the wave had continued in the same medium. Its velocity, however, has altered from V_1 to V_2 and consequently whilst the point k moves to A the wavelet at P has only spread out to C.

It is easy to see that the curvature of the wave front in the medium Y has altered from AmB to ACB : that is, waves in the second medium now appear to diverge from I the image.

Assuming that the refracted waves may be regarded as spherical, which is true for a small region round P, we have approximately rectangle $CP.2PI = AP^2$

$$\text{and} \quad \text{,,} \quad mP.2PO = AP^2.$$

Using the usual notation of u and v but ignoring signs

$$CP.2v = mP.2u$$

therefore,

$$\frac{v}{u} = \frac{mP}{CP} = \frac{V_1 t}{V^2 t} = \frac{V_1}{V_2} = \mu.$$

Consequently $\mathbf{v} = \boldsymbol{\mu}\ \mathbf{u}$ a relation we have already met in Chapter V.

Reflection and Refraction of Spherical Waves at Spherical Surfaces.

Now that we have explained fully the principles of reflection and refraction, we propose to deal briefly with the reflection of a spherical wave at the surface of a concave mirror and the refraction of such a wave by a convex lens. In both cases all distances will be positive since we are dealing with real images. The second radius r_2 of the lens, however, is negative in accordance with the conventions given on page 98.

(a) Concave Mirror.

It is easy to see that the wave from O will strike the mirror at two points such as A, B before the central portion has reached the pole P. If we assume that the radius of curvature of the mirror is large compared with its diameter, then while the central point L travels on to P the new wavelets at A and B have travelled to D and E respectively. Thus the reflected wave front is DPE, which we shall assume is spherical.

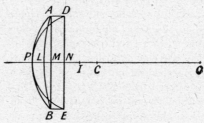

FIG. 186.

With the usual notation of u, v and r we have

$$OP = u, \quad CP = r \text{ and } IP = v.$$

Also we have approximately, $AM^2 = 2 \, OL.ML$

and, therefore, $ML = \dfrac{AM^2}{2u}$ approx.

Similarly, $NP = \dfrac{DN^2}{2v} = \dfrac{AM^2}{2v}$, and $MP = \dfrac{AM^2}{2r}$.

But $PL = MN$, and therefore, $ML + NP = 2 \, MP$.

Hence $\dfrac{1}{v} + \dfrac{1}{u} = \dfrac{2}{r}$.

(b) *Convex Lens.*

In this case the central portion of the wave strikes the lens

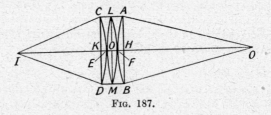

FIG. 187.

first, but since the secondary disturbances travel slower in the more dense medium, the wave from A reaches C in the time that the wave from F takes to arrive at E. The new wave front which is assumed to be spherical is CED with its centre at I.

Now $AC = \mu EF$

or $(HF + FO + OE + KE) = \mu \, (FO + OE)$

Let $CK = LO = AK = y$, and with the usual notation of u, v, r_1 and r_2 and the usual sign conventions, we have by geometry (cf. (a) above)

$$HF = \frac{y^2}{2u}, \; FO = \frac{y^2}{2r_1}$$

$$KE = \frac{y^2}{2v}, \; OE = \frac{y^2}{-2r_2} \; \text{(since r_2 is negative)}$$

Hence $$\frac{y^2}{2u} + \frac{y^2}{2v} = (\mu - 1)\left(\frac{y^2}{2r_1} - \frac{y^2}{2r_2}\right)$$

or $$\frac{1}{u} + \frac{1}{v} = (\mu - 1)\left(\frac{1}{r_1} - \frac{1}{r_2}\right).$$

QUESTIONS. XII.

1. Give an account of the corpuscular theory and wave theory.
2. Write a short essay on the ether.
3. How did Fresnel explain the Rectilinear Propagation of light on the basis of the wave theory ?
4. Show how laws of reflection and refraction may be deduced from the wave theory.
5. Describe the manner in which spherical waves are reflected and refracted. What deductions are possible ?
6. Show how on the wave theory a real image of an object is obtained by using a concave mirror and convex lens.

CHAPTER XIII

INTERFERENCE OF LIGHT

History.—It was first pointed out by Huygens that the passage of a beam of light through an aperture was quite independent of the presence or otherwise of other beams. For example, when a person watches a football match he is receiving hundreds of small pencils of light from all directions. Many of these must cross each other when they enter the eye, but no blurring is observed by the onlooker. The first to state clearly the principle on which this everyday phenomenon depends was Thomas Young, and as the whole development of the Wave Theory rests on this it will be of historical interest if we quote the scientist's own words as they appear in a paper read before the Royal Society in 1801.

" *Proposition 8. When two undulations from different origins coincide either perfectly or very nearly in direction, their joint effect is a combination of the motions belonging to each.*"

" *Since every particle of the medium is affected by each undulation wherever the directions coincide, the undulations can proceed no otherwise than by uniting their motions so that the joint motion may be the sum or difference of the separate motions accordingly as similar or dissimilar parts of the undulations are coincident.*"

From this statement it should be clear that if two waves of the same amplitude, same wave length and of equal frequency move in the same direction, but one wave differs from the other in phase by π, the one wave will completely annul the other.

In 1807 Young published a paper containing experimental details of this interference. Critics were dubious, however as to the interpretation of results obtained.

Fresnel (1788–1827), a short time afterwards completely

248

removed these doubts and showed by means of his celebrated bi-prism that interference was an established fact.

The Principle of Superposition.—Since interference is only a particular case of superposition, we see that if two sources of light X and Y supposed near to each other are vibrating in phase and emitting continuously waves of a single wave length λ, then at any point equidistant from X and Y the waves always arrive in the same phase. At some other point P say (Fig. 188), where XP and YP are not equal, there will be a difference in phase which will depend upon the distance YP − XP, provided the waves do not alter in any way. If YP − XP is a multiple of the wave length λ, that is an even multiple of $\dfrac{\lambda}{2}$, it is clear that these waves will arrive at

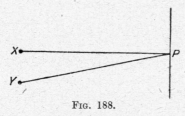

Fig. 188.

P in the same phase and therefore, according to Young, will reinforce each other and produce more intense illumination (i.e. compared with one source alone). When, however, YP − XP is an odd multiple of $\dfrac{\lambda}{2}$, there will be a constant difference in phase of π at P between the two separate wave trains and the result is interference. At points between the two we have mentioned, there is a continuous change of illumination.

For experimental purposes it has been found impossible to obtain two sources of light which will produce interference. This is because it is impossible to maintain a constant phase relation between the two sources owing to the very rapid and sudden changes of phase which take place in a source of light. If, however, two interfering trains of waves are both derived from the same source, any change in the one will be repeated in the other so that their phase relationship is unaltered. The method adopted by Young was to have one small source and two narrow apertures.

Young's Experiment.—Young admitted a beam of sunlight through a slit S into a darkened room (Fig. 189a). The beam was then allowed to fall on to a screen containing two pinholes A and B. The effect on a screen CD was the result of the interference of waves from "two sources" A and B, oscillating in the same phase. A series of coloured bands in directions at right angles to AB was observed: these diminished in width as the distance AB was increased, until finally the bands disappeared. (Plate I c, p. 234)

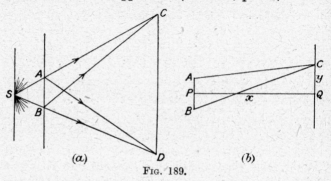

(a)   (b)

FIG. 189.

To understand the positions in which these bands are formed consider Fig. 189b. Let AB = 2d so that AP = d, and let x be the distance from the sources to the screen. If a point C is chosen such that CQ = y and y is very small compared with x, we can find an approximate value for BC − AC.

$$BC^2 = x^2 + (y + d)^2 = x^2 + y^2 + 2yd + d^2$$
$$AC^2 = x^2 + (y - d)^2 = x^2 + y^2 - 2yd + d^2$$
therefore $BC^2 - AC^2 = 4\ yd,$

therefore $\quad BC - AC = \dfrac{4yd}{BC + AC} = \dfrac{4yd}{2x}$ approx.

$$= \dfrac{2yd}{x}$$

From previous reasoning there will be brightness or darkness at C according as BC − AC is equal to an even or an odd multiple of $\frac{\lambda}{2}$. That is, for *bright bands*

$$\frac{2yd}{x} = 2n\frac{\lambda}{2}, \text{ giving } y = \frac{xn\lambda}{2d}$$

and for *dark bands*

$$\frac{2yd}{x} = (2n+1)\frac{\lambda}{2}, \text{ which gives } y = \frac{x\lambda(2n+1)}{4d}.$$

Thus the distance ω between consecutive bright or dark bands is given by, $\omega = \dfrac{x\lambda}{2d}.$

When monochromatic light is used, alternate bright and dark bands are produced. In the case of white light we find

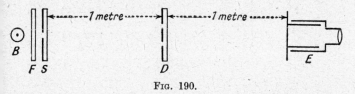

FIG. 190.

that the central band only remains white ; the others are coloured and ill-defined owing to overlapping.

It is interesting to note that even with monochromatic light, if a broad slit is used, overlapping takes place with consequent loss of definition.

An excellent method of viewing Young's interference bands is one proposed by Meier. A motor-car headlight bulb B is put close to a single slit S, which is turned until it is accurately parallel to the straight filament. If monochromatic light is required, a filter F should be placed between the bulb and the slit. Fig. 190 shows the arrangements in plan. A good form of slit can be made by ruling a sharp line on a photographic plate which has been exposed to light, developed, washed, fixed, washed again and dried. The line is best drawn by means of a used gramophone needle. Two parallel lines are drawn on a second plate D and these also are adjusted to be parallel with S and the filament. The bands are viewed in the eye-piece E.

Another good method suggested by S. E. Sands is the arrangement shown in plan (Fig. 191). The method gives a wide field and can be done in a fairly light room.

An ordinary clear domestic bulb B is used as the source of illumination. C is a cardboard screen. The slit S is fairly broad and can be made by cutting it out of a stiff piece of cardboard. A test-tube T, containing copper nitrate solution mixed with strong potassium dichromate solution and acidified with nitric acid, serves as a good filter for monochromatic green. A double slit D, as in Meier's experiment, and an eye-piece complete the apparatus.

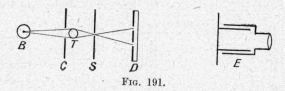

FIG. 191.

If a sodium arc is used in place of the lamp and test-tube, brilliant monochromatic yellow bands are produced.

Fresnel's Bi-prism.—Fresnel adopted two methods of procedure : (a) reflection, using two inclined mirrors, (b) refraction, by the aid of a bi-prism. The principle was the same in each case : that is, two vertical images of a narrow slit were used as two virtual sources of light. The bi-prism is the one commonly used for experimental purposes on account of its simplicity. It is, as its name suggests, a combination of two prisms with their bases joined and their two faces making an angle of nearly 180° (Fig. 192). In actual practice it is found more convenient to grind the prisms from the same piece of glass. If an illuminated slit S is placed symmetrically behind the two prisms, the light which is incident on the prism forms two images of the slit S in the manner shown, that is, by refraction through the two prisms A and B. The effect of making the angles at A and B very small is to bring S_1 and S_2 near together. Light from these produces interference bands on a screen XY. (See Plate II a, p. 274.)

As in Young's experiment the distance ω between consecutive bright bands is given by $\omega = \dfrac{x\lambda}{2d}$ where $x = $ SP and $S_1S_2 = 2d$.

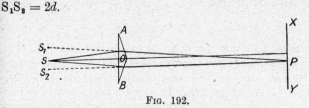

FIG. 192.

To find the Wave Length of Light.

The bi-prism provides a ready means of finding the wave length of light of a particular colour. Arrange the bulb, filter and slit [1] as in Young's experiment. The filter F chosen should be one which provides the colour whose effective wave length is required. Place a convex lens L (Fig. 193) a short distance from the slit S and adjust a positive eye-piece

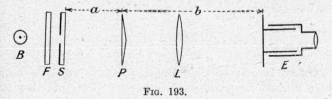

FIG. 193.

E until an image of the slit is focused in the middle of the eye-piece scale. The plane of the eye-piece should be perpendicular to the bench and of the same height as the slit. Remove the lens and introduce the bi-prism P. The angle of the bi-prism should not be more than 1°. Adjust the prism until the bands are clearly defined. It will be noted that, superimposed on these at the edges are other bands; these,

[1] It is preferable to use a slit whose width may be varied.

which are due to diffraction (see Chapter XV) are clearly evident on Plate II. The eye-piece and bi-prism should now be arranged by a motion perpendicular to the bench so that no transverse movement of the band takes place when the eye-piece is moved along the bench. Measure ω, the mean width of a fringe (i.e. the mean distance between consecutive bright bands). Then from above, we have:

$$\omega = \frac{(a+b)}{2d} . \lambda \quad \cdots \cdots \quad (1)$$

We must now find the value $2d$ or the distance S_1S_2 (Fig. 192). Keep the slit and bi-prism fixed. Introduce the convex lens between the eye-piece and bi-prism, and move the lens until two positions are found in which a sharp pair of images of the slit are formed. Note the distances between the images in each case. Let these distances be y_1 and y_2. Then, with the usual notation, the first magnification $\dfrac{y_1}{2d} = -\dfrac{v}{u}$.

On moving the lens to the second position the values of v and u interchange and

$$\frac{y_2}{2d} = -\frac{u}{v}.$$

Consequently $\dfrac{y_1 y_2}{4d^2} = 1$ or $2d = \sqrt{y_1 y_2}$.

Hence from (1) $\lambda = \dfrac{2d\omega}{a+b} = \dfrac{\omega\sqrt{y_1 y_2}}{a+b}$.

Other Interference Methods.—Various methods have been devised for producing interference effects but they do not all lend themselves as readily to experiment as Fresnel's bi-prism. Two or three will now be described briefly.

Fresnel's Double Mirrors.—Two mirrors OA and OB (Fig. 194) are inclined to each other at nearly 180°. A source S is arranged so that the images S_1 and S_2 formed in the two mirrors are very near to each other. Then it follows from the usual construction for such images that $S_1O = SO$ and $S_2O = SO$ and consequently S_1 and S_2 are equidistant from O. Thus S_1 and S_2 act as two similar sources, and if a screen is placed

at right angles to OP, they will interfere and produce interference bands on the screen.

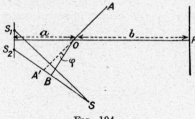

FIG. 194.

A little reflection on the part of the student will show him
that $\angle S_1OS_2 = 2\angle BOA'$ (i.e. twice the angle ϕ), and therefore $S_1S_2 = 2a\phi$.

The calculation is now the same as in the bi-prism experiment. Thus $\lambda = \dfrac{2a\phi}{a + b} \cdot \omega$, where

FIG. 195.

ω is the width of a fringe.

A simple device for obtaining
two mirrors inclined at such a large
angle is to use two right-angled
prisms which have been optically
worked and to insert a piece of
cardboard as shown (Fig. 195). The prisms and cardboard
are then clamped together.

The Bi-plate and Billet's Half Lenses.—Both these
methods are quite ingenious, although no new principles are

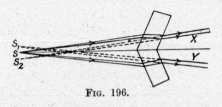

FIG. 196.

introduced. In the first (Fig. 196) two glass plates cut from
the same piece are inclined at an obtuse angle. This leads, as

shown in the figure, to two identical virtual images S_1 and S_2, which may be made to form real images by allowing the rays represented by X and Y to fall on a convex lens (not shown). The light from these real images produces interference bands.

The second (Fig. 197) due to Billet, makes use of two parts of a convex lens to form the two images. The distance

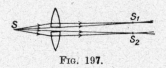

FIG. 197.

between S_1 and S_2 may be made to vary by adjusting the space between the two halves of the convex lens. This will enable varying widths to be obtained in the interference bands.

Lloyd's Single Mirror.—A very interesting method was proposed by Dr. Lloyd in 1834.

A narrow slit S (Fig. 198) was placed parallel to a plane mirror MM and very near to its plane. Thus the light from S fell at almost grazing incidence on the mirror and produced

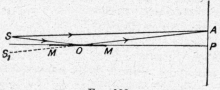

FIG 198.

an image S_1, very near to the source S. Interference is therefore produced on a screen at A by light direct from S to A and by reflected light viâ SOA (Plate Id, p. 234). The interest of this experiment lies in the unexpected. It is found that at those points where we should expect from previous considerations a maximum of illumination, we obtain minima. This leads us to the conclusion that the direct and reflected light differ in phase by π. In other words, the *effect of reflection on a light vibration from air to glass is to alter its phase by π*.

To understand this more clearly and fully, let us consider a mechanical analogy. Suppose a very heavy railway wagon is standing in a station siding and a number of lighter trucks are being connected to the first by the usual method of shunting. As the light truck strikes the heavy stationary wagon, it rebounds and starts to move off in an opposite direction to that before impact, whilst the heavy wagon moves slowly in the direction in which the shunting occurs. Now consider the wagon and truck to change places at the beginning; that is, the light truck is stationary and the heavy wagon impinges on it. Both are seen after impact to be moving in the same direction.

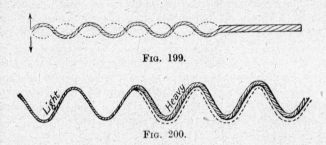

Fig. 199.

Fig. 200.

In the former case we may say that the velocity of the impinging-body has changed " sign," that is, the body has a velocity in an opposite direction after impact. In the second case no change in sign has occurred.

Again, suppose we have two ropes tied together, one heavy and the other light. If a wave is sent along the light rope by a quick up and down jerk of the end portions it will be reflected back when it reaches the heavy rope in such a way (Fig. 199) that the reflected wave differs in phase by π from the original wave.

If, however, the wave is sent along the heavy rope (Fig. 200) when it reaches the junction two waves are formed, one carrying on the disturbance in the light rope and a reflected one (dotted) returning in the same phase along the heavy rope. We see then that if a light wave is travelling in air and is incident at the surface of a more optically dense medium such as glass, the reflected wave will suffer a change in phase by the amount π. This is reflection *with* a change in sign. If, however, the wave impinges on the boundary of a less optically dense medium such as glass to air, no change in sign occurs.

Lloyd's single mirror experiment is easy to perform if a car bulb, filter and slit are used as in previous experiments. Plate glass or, better still, an optically worked glass surface will act as an effective mirror, and this should be slightly inclined at a short distance from the illuminated slit. The eye-piece should be adjusted to receive the bands.

General Observation.—At first thought it might appear that in producing interference bands we are destroying light energy. This is no more true than the statement that by using a system of pulleys a person minimises the expenditure of energy. The light which vanishes in the dark regions appears in the bright with the result that the bright bands are more intense than they would be if uniform illumination prevailed. All that we do is to direct the waves from a source to a screen in such a way that waves from a point of the source reach a point on the screen by different paths.

QUESTIONS. XIII.

1. What do you understand by the term interference of light ? Give any historical facts connected with this discovery.

2. Give an account of Young's experiment on interference and indicate clearly any experimental details necessary for its success. How may Young's interference bands be examined ?

3. What is a bi-prism and how has it been used for determining the wave length of monochromatic light ?

4. Compare the interference bands obtained by (*a*) a single mirror, (*b*) a double mirror.

5. What is a bi-plate and how has it been used to produce interference bands ?

CHAPTER XIV

INTERFERENCE EFFECTS OF THIN FILMS

We have all watched the delight of a child who, regardless of the fact that his feet are getting wet, persists in pressing a piece of orange peel into a puddle of water in order to " make colours " on the surface of the water. The oil from the peel forms a thin film on the water and this produces colours by the interference of light from the upper and lower surfaces of the film. Soap bubbles, glass blown by amateurs, and oil films by leaks from motors are other examples of everyday effects which illustrate interference phenomena by thin films. There are two types—interference by " reflected " light and interference by transmitted light.

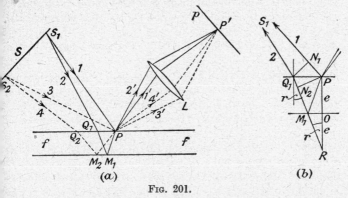

FIG. 201.

Interference by Reflected Light.—In order to understand clearly how these interference effects are produced, let us consider Fig. 201. S represents a broad source of light such as a sodium flame, ff a thin film and L a lens which forms an image of a patch of the film on a screen p. The lens and screen, of course, may be replaced by the eye.

It will be remembered from the previous chapter that in order to obtain observable interference effects it is necessary for the two interfering trains of waves to emanate from the *same* source of light. Let P′ be the image of a point P of the film; that is, all the light from P collected by the lens is brought together at P′. Let S_1 be a point of the source from which light reaches P by the two paths S_1P, that is direct, and $S_1Q_1M_1P$, that is by refraction at Q_1 and then reflection at M_1. These two parts of the same wave from S_1 then proceed from P in the slightly different directions 1′ and 2′ and are brought together at P′. Their combined effect there will depend on their phase difference on arrival.

The phase difference at P′ will be the same as at P, since none is introduced between these points; we have, therefore, simply to find the phase difference at P.

Now the light from S_1 travelling in the direction 2 will take a longer time, say t secs. more, to reach P than the part travelling along 1. Let us calculate this time retardation due to the difference of paths. Draw Q_1N_1 (Fig. 201b) perpendicular to S_1P, PN_2 perpendicular to Q_1M_1, and let Q_1M_1 produced meet the normal through P at R. Then, remembering that the thickness of the film is very small so that PQ_1 will be very small compared with S_1P, it is clear that S_1Q_1 can be put equal to S_1N_1. That is, Q_1N_1 may be regarded as a portion of a plane wave falling on the film, and PN_2 will be the corresponding refracted wave. Hence the light travelling along 2 will be at N_2 at the instant that the light travelling along 1 is at P; so that the time retardation, t, will simply be the time taken by the light to travel the path $N_2M_1 + M_1P$ in the film. From the figure, it is clear that this distance is equal to $N_2M_1 + M_1R$; that is, $2\,e\cos r$, where e is the thickness of the film, PO, and r is the angle of refraction. Hence, if V is the velocity of light in the film, the time retardation t is given by

$$t = \frac{2\,e\cos r}{V}.$$

From this it would appear at first sight that if e were negligibly small, so also would t be, and hence for an infinitesimally thin film the time retardation would be zero and the two parts of the wave would reinforce each other. But, *exactly the reverse takes place.* The explanation follows at once if we recall the remarks on the Lloyd's mirror experiment. We saw there that when light is reflected at a boundary the reflection may be accompanied either with no change of phase or a change corresponding to half a period. The first occurs when the light is reflected at the boundary of a less dense medium and the second when the reflection is at the surface of a denser medium. Now, in our case, the light reflected at P will undergo a change of phase equal to half a period, while that reflected at M will suffer no change. Hence the effective time retardation due to differences in path and circumstances of reflection will be

$$\frac{2\,e\cos r}{V} + \frac{T}{2}$$

where T is the period of vibration. If this amounts to an integral number of periods the two wave trains 1' and 2' proceeding from P will be in phase and we shall get reinforcement at P'; while if it is equal to an odd multiple of half-periods the two trains of waves will be in opposite phase at P (and, hence, also at P') and will, therefore, annul each other there (completely if their amplitudes are equal).

That is, we have maximum disturbance at P' if

$$\frac{2\,e\cos r}{V} \pm \frac{T}{2} = nT, \text{ or } \frac{2\,e\cos r}{V} = (n \pm \tfrac{1}{2})T$$

and minimum disturbance there if

$$\frac{2\,e\cos r}{V} + \frac{T}{2} = (n + \tfrac{1}{2})\,T, \text{ or } \frac{2\,e\cos r}{V} = nT.$$

If we multiply these equations through by V_0, the velocity of light in air, we note since $\frac{V_0}{V} = \mu$ and $V_0 T = \lambda$ that the conditions for interference of reflected light in thin films are :—

Max^m. $2\,\mu\,e\cos r = (n \pm \tfrac{1}{2})\lambda$ . . . . (1)

Min^m. $2\,\mu\,e\cos r = n\lambda$ . . . . . (2)

Generalising, we may say that *any thin film situated between two layers of the same material will produce interference if the optical length* [1] *of the difference of the paths of two waves is equal to nλ and will produce reinforcement when the difference is equal to an odd number of half-waves.*

When white light falls upon the film, as is the case in the natural phenomena mentioned in the first paragraph, only some of the colours will interfere, since the optical differences in path vary for the different colours. Consequently, the light which reaches the eye is coloured. The varied nature of the colours should be easily understood since the obliquity of the light and the thickness of the film may be different at every point.

It is important to notice why the film must be thin for inter-ference effects of this type to be observed at P'. Referring again to Fig. 201, we see that the lens L will collect other pairs of rays, such as 3', 4', originating in some other point S_2 of the source and reaching P' by the slightly different paths S_2P and $S_2Q_2M_2$P. For such a pair the total time retardation will be

$$\frac{2\,e\cos r'}{V} + \frac{T}{2}$$

where r' is the corresponding angle of refraction in the film. If the lens L is small so that it only subtends a small angle at P, it follows that the values of r and r' can only differ slightly ; hence, when e is small the retardation for all these pairs will be practically the same. Thus, if there is a maximum at P' due to one pair there will be a maximum for all such pairs. If, on the other hand, e is large we may have one pair such as 1' and 2' producing a maximum at P', while another such as 3' and 4' gives a minimum there, and this overlapping would obliterate the effect. It also follows that the wider we make the aperture of the lens—that is, the greater the range of values of r which it collects from P—the smaller must be the value of e in order that overlapping should not take place. If the eye lens is used the range of possible values of r is small

---

[1] For a ray path of length l in a medium μ, the value μl is called the optical length.

and consequently it is easy to detect interference effects if the film is not too thick.

Interference by Transmitted Light.—In this case (Fig. 202) the source S and the point P are on opposite sides of the thin film. Light from a point of S will reach P by the paths S R P and S Q M N P. The ray S Q M N P is reflected twice (at M and N) at surfaces of less dense media and, therefore, there will be no change of phase. The retardation is merely due to the extra length of path, which is clearly the same as in the case of reflected light. Thus, the total time retardation is given by

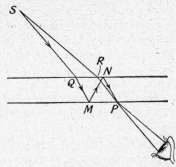

$$\frac{2\,e\cos r}{V}.$$

Fig. 202.

This, as we should expect from energy considerations, leads to conditions of maxima and minima which are just the reverse of those for reflected light : that is,

Max^m. $\qquad 2\,\mu\,e\cos r = n\lambda$ . . . . . . (3)

Min^m. $\qquad 2\,\mu\,e\cos r = (n \pm \tfrac{1}{2})\lambda$ . . . . (4)

Generalising, we may say that *a thin film of finite thickness situated between two substances of the same material and viewed by transmitted light will produce interference if the optical length of the difference of the paths of two waves is equal to $(n \pm \tfrac{1}{2})\lambda$ and reinforcement if it is equal to an even number of half wave lengths, i.e. $n\lambda$.*

It easily follows that since the conditions for maxima and minima are opposite in the two cases of reflected and transmitted light, if white light is observed the colours will be complementary when viewed by reflected and transmitted light respectively.

Equal Thickness Fringes.—If the lens L (Fig. 201) is at a considerable distance from the film as in the case, say, of an eye observing P at its nearest distance of distinct vision, the value of r will be approximately the same for any point of the film in the neighbourhood of P ; hence, the effect observed will depend simply on the thickness e. If this is the same over the whole patch of the film and we are using monochromatic light we shall see in the case of reflected light a bright patch if (1) holds and a black patch if (2) holds. The reverse will be the case for transmitted light ((3) and (4)).

If the value of e varies from point to point we shall have a bright patch traversed by dark fringes, the latter passing through those points for which (2) holds. By varying the thickness in a regular and gradual manner, as for example in a wedge-shaped film or a film lying between a convex lens and a sheet of plane glass, it is possible to obtain a regular pattern of interference fringes. The latter method is the one adopted by Newton and the fringes are called Newton's Rings.

Newton's Rings.—Although named after Newton they were first mentioned by Hooke in 1665 so that they constitute one of the earliest observed interference phenomena. Newton studied them very carefully and his results were explained by Young.

The experiment consists of laying a convex lens of large radii of curvature on to a piece of plane glass and illuminating the air film immediately surrounding the point of contact by either reflected or transmitted light. At the point of contact the film is infinitesimally thin, but as we slowly move away from this central spot we gradually increase the thickness of the film. Since the lens is a portion of a sphere, concentric circles may be drawn, each of which is the locus of a point whose distance from the plane glass is a constant. Consequently we shall have a series of circular interference bands produced by the difference in the paths of waves reflected at the top and bottom of the air film.

To measure the Wave Length of Sodium Light by means of Newton's Rings.—The usual method adopted is to lay a plano-convex lens L_2 (Fig. 203) of known large radius of curvature on to a piece of plate glass G in the manner illustrated, and by means of another piece of plate glass P waves of sodium light coming from a source S, situated in the focal plane of a lens L_1, are reflected on to the central portion of the air film. The interference rings are examined through a microscope M. The lens L_1 should be adjusted until the rings are very distinct.

The diameters of the nth and $(n + m)^{th}$ ring should then be measured.

In order to make use of our measurements for finding λ consider the diagram (Fig. 204). The convex lens is part of a sphere and consequently we have $BO^2 = BA(2R - BA)$ where BA is the thickness of the air film and R is the radius of curvature of the convex surface. Moreover, BA is small compared with R.

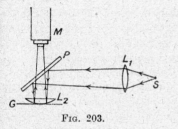

FIG. 203.

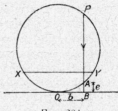

FIG. 204.

Hence if e is the thickness of the film BA at a distance b from the central spot O, we can put

$$b^2 = 2Re \quad \cdot \quad \cdot \quad \cdot \quad \cdot \quad \cdot \quad (1)$$

It will be seen that b is the radius of any ring considered. Moreover as the rays fall almost perpendicularly on to the air film the retardation between any two rays which produce interference or reinforcement is equal to $2e$. This follows from the fact that one ray is reflected at A and the other is reflected at B, the latter being retarded by the amount 2AB.

It will be remembered that O, the central spot, is dark by reflected light, and that B is dark if 2AB is equal to $n\lambda$. Again for a bright ring to appear at B we must have $2AB = (n + \frac{1}{2})\boldsymbol{\lambda}$. Combining this with equation (1) we have

$$b^2 = R(n + \frac{1}{2})\lambda.$$

In other words the radii of the bright rings are equal to

$$\sqrt{R(n + \tfrac{1}{2})\lambda}.$$

and the radii of the dark rings are equal to $\sqrt{Rn\lambda}$.

Suppose r_n is the radius of the nth bright ring and r_{n+m} the radius of the $(n + m)$th bright ring

$$r^2_n = R(n + \tfrac{1}{2})\lambda$$

and

$$r^2_{n+m} = R(n + m + \tfrac{1}{2})\lambda.$$

therefore

$$r^2_{n+m} - r_n^2 = Rm\lambda$$

and

$$\lambda = \frac{r^2_{n+m} - r_n^2}{Rm}$$

$$= \frac{d_2{}^2 - d_1{}^2}{4Rm}$$

where d_1 and d_2 are the measurements of the two diameters.

The reason for measuring the diameters of two rings rather than their radii is because the central spot is rarely well defined. A better procedure would be to measure a large number of rings and plot d^2 against n.

Newton experimented with white light under similar conditions. No pure colour was observed, however, as there was too much overlapping of the spectra. A very pretty illustration of the colours formed when white light is used is obtained by *Boy's Rainbow Cup*. It consists of a brass ring fixed horizontally and capable of being rotated about a vertical axis. A soap film is stretched across the ring which is then rapidly rotated. The effect of this is to cause the film to thicken at the edges at the expense of the central portion which gets thinner the more rapidly the ring is rotated. In time the thickness of the centre becomes small compared even with the wave length of light and consequently a black spot is observed when reflected light is used to illuminate the film. Around this spot can be seen beautifully coloured rings which change continually as the speed is varied.

The Wedge.—Let the wedge consist of two glass plates enclosing a liquid of refractive index μ and slightly inclined to each other at an angle θ. We shall consider the case where the film is illuminated by reflected light.

It will be seen from Fig. 205 that at a distance x from the edges of contact, the thickness e of the film will be given by $e = \theta x$, since θ is very small. If we assume that the light falls normally on the film we have, as a condition of *darkness*,

$$2 \mu e = n\lambda, \text{ or } 2 \mu \theta x = n\lambda.$$

and for *brightness*, $2 \mu e = (n + \tfrac{1}{2})\lambda$, or $2 \mu \theta x = (n + \tfrac{1}{2})$.

The distance $x_2 - x_1$ between the nth and the $(n + m)^{\text{th}}$ dark band is given by:

$$\frac{(n + m)\lambda}{2\mu\theta} - \frac{n\lambda}{2\mu\theta} = \frac{m\lambda}{2\mu\theta}.$$

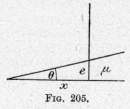

FIG. 205.

This result provides a means of finding (1) λ if μ and θ are known, (2) μ, given θ and λ and (3) θ given μ and λ.

We arrive at the same result in the case of transmitted light.

Other Applications of Interference.

Fizeau applied Newton's rings to measure coefficients of expansion of substances in the form of crystals. The crystal was cut into the shape of a cube which rested on a plane metal disc DD (Fig. 206). The disc was supported by three screws passing through it near the circumference. On the screws rested a lens G which could be brought as near to the upper edge of the crystal as was desired. When light was allowed to

FIG. 206.

fall on G, Newton's rings were formed owing to the thin film of air between C and G. As the temperature rises the thickness of the air film changes by an amount which can be deduced from the alteration in the rings. Knowing the alterations which occur in the refractive index of the air, the length of the screws and the lens, it is possible to find the increase in the linear dimensions of the crystal.

Rayleigh tested the accuracy of a plane surface of glass by placing it horizontally under water and examining the interference fringes when the water surface and glass were parallel.

Any slight defect in flatness produces a curvature in the
straight bands. The experimental difficulty is that of avoiding
tremors on the water. The general method is to use what is
already known to be an optically plane piece of glass in place
of the water surface, and then to examine the bands produced
by a thin film of air in between the two surfaces.

One of the most useful applications is the instrument known
as the *Refractometer*. The earliest form was one adopted by
Fresnel and Arago for measuring the difference between the
refractive indices of dry and of moist air. Two parallel tubes
containing first dry air in both and then one dry and the other
moist, were placed in the paths of waves which would produce
interference fringes. The displacement of the fringes owing
to a change in the optical lengths of the paths served as a means
of calculation. The full theory need not be discussed here, but
the student will remember that a length d *in vacuo* becomes an
optical length μd in a substance of refractive index μ, and,
consequently, if the central band of the second takes the place
of the nth band of the first, the difference of the paths,
$\mu_1 d - \mu_2 d$, may be measured in terms of $n\lambda$.

In *Jamin's* form of refractometer (Fig. 207) two blocks of
glass of equal thickness and cut from the same material, each
having one surface silvered, are fixed to a groove (not shown)
in such a way that they lie with their faces parallel. Screws
$S_1 S_2$ permit the blocks to be rotated until both are parallel,
as in the diagram. When this is the case, a narrow pencil
of light incident on the surface ab is both reflected and refracted. If we consider that the reflected beam after traversing a cylinder X is incident on the surface cd, some of it will
be reflected by CD and will emerge to join the portion which
has passed through the cylinder Y and has received reflection
at cd. It is clear that the two beams travel the same optical
length of path always provided that X and Y contain the same
substance and that the blocks Ab and cD are parallel. By
rotating cD slightly about a vertical axis, a system of interference bands is observed by an eye placed at S′ and looking
towards cd, owing to the difference produced in the two paths.
If then we keep a vacuum in X and fill Y with various gases

a displacement of these bands will occur and by measuring the amount of this displacement in each case we can obtain the values of the indices of refraction. The amount of displacement is usually measured by means of a " compensator "

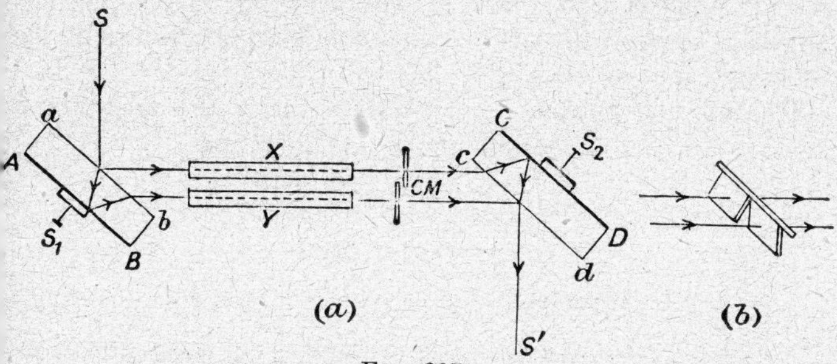

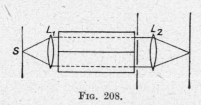

FIG. 207.

CM (Fig. 207), which consists of two plates of glass capable of independent rotation round a horizontal axis. One plate receives the beam of light which passes through X and the other that which passes through Y. An alteration in the angle of tilt produces a change in the thickness of glass to be traversed. The null method is adopted : that is the plates are rotated until the central band occupies its original position.

Using this form the thickness of soap films of the order 10^{-5} mm. has been determined.

FIG. 208.

Rayleigh's Refractometer was specially designed for experiments on the refractive index of gases and was based on Fresnel's original form of apparatus. The light from a slit S is made parallel by a lens L_1 and then after passing through two brass tubes, soldered together and containing the gases, passes through two more slits whence it is brought to a focus by a second lens L_2. The two slits act as two sources as in Young's experiment and consequently interference bands are produced in the focal plane of the lens L_2. The displacement of the bands is again used to determine the changes in the length of the optical paths and so to obtain the values of the refractive indices.

This method is used in practice to detect the presence of small quantities of carbon monoxide in mines.

QUESTIONS. XIV.

1. Show how interference may be produced when light is reflected from a thin film.

2. Compare the colours produced by reflected and transmitted light when thin films are used.

3. What are Newton's rings and how are they obtained ?

4. Describe a method of measuring the wave length of light by the use of Newton's rings.

5. Two glass plates in the form of a wedge enclose a liquid of refractive index μ. Light falling upon the wedge shows interference effects. If the angle of the wedge is θ, find an expression for the wave length of the light in terms of μ and θ.

6. Give a description of some form of refractometer. For what purpose may it be used ?

CHAPTER XV

DIFFRACTION

Historical Introduction.—Newton's objection to the Wave Theory lay in the fact that light travels in straight lines and does not, as in the case of sound, bend round corners. Fresnel, however, proved conclusively that light *does* bend round corners and that the comparison with sound is merely a matter of degree. The wave length of sound is something like 10,000,000 times as large as the wave length of light, and whereas a beam of light is blocked out by a small obstacle, a " beam " of sound of a similar " intensity " would require an obstacle 10,000,000 times as large to obstruct its passage. The fact that sound can be cut off by large obstacles is well known. The phenomenon dealing with the bending of light round the edge of an obstacle is called *Diffraction*.

GRIMALDI in 1665 was the first to point out that when light from a small aperture falls on an obstacle the edges of the shadow which is produced are never perfectly defined no matter how sharp the edges of the obstacle may be ; in other words, we never obtain a true geometrical shadow, that is a shadow which would be formed if the paths of the rays were always straight lines. Suppose a very narrow slit is placed parallel to the straight edge of an obstacle and a screen is put immediately behind the obstacle in order to receive the shadow, then it will be noticed that some of the light is making its way into the geometrical shadow. Further, several dark bands appear *outside* the geometrical shadow and these gradually get nearer together as we get further and further away from the edge until they fade away into uniform illumination.

Both the physicists Hooke and Newton had observed this phenomenon but the explanations they gave were all based on the corpuscular theory. Young tried to explain them as interference effects produced by the direct light near the edge of the obstacle and the light reflected at grazing incidence.

Fresnel also started with this idea but was compelled to abandon it after making investigations with different edges. He found that the sharpness of the edges and the type of material used had no effect whatsoever on the bands. A round edge had the same effect as a sharp one, which would certainly not be the case if the phenomena depended on reflection. The true explanation, which he verified shortly afterwards by mathematical calculation, was that interference took place between the secondary wavelets from the *same wave front*.

Diffraction at a Straight Edge.—Suppose we consider light from a slit S illuminating a screen XY (Fig. 209). If an

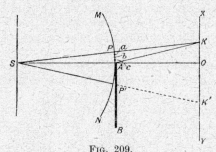

Fig. 209.

opaque obstacle AB is put in the way of this light, a shadow will be cast on the screen and the part beginning at O and stretching towards Y will be the geometrical shadow. Adopting Fresnel's modification of Huygen's reasoning we may consider at any instant a wave front MPAN setting up secondary disturbances, the combined effect of which at some point K determines the illumination at K. According to this theory (Chapter XII), the effect at K is only dependent on the zones immediately in the vicinity of P and, therefore, if the point P is at some distance from the obstacle, the illumination at K will not be interfered with. Suppose, however, P is very near to the obstacle; some of those zones will be blocked out and the effect at K, according to Fresnel, will be that due to the remaining zones. Divide the arc MPAN into zones such that $Ka - KP = Kb - Ka = Kc - Kb \ldots = \dfrac{\lambda}{2}$.

These zones into which a wave front is cut are sometimes called *half-period elements* with respect to K because the vibrations they send to K differ by half-periods. Thus, as we learned in Chapter XII, two consecutive zones send, on the average, vibrations which differ in phase by π; or we have the 1st, 3rd, 5th, etc., half-period elements on either side of P assisting each other at K, and the 2nd, 4th, 6th, etc., tending to destroy this effect.

If therefore P is so near to A that only the 1st half-period element is in action on one side, K will be brighter than it would be if the obstacle were removed. If two elements are free they will tend to destroy each other and K will be darkened. For three elements K becomes bright again and so *outside the geometrical shadow the condition for maximum brightness is*

$$KA - KP = (2n + 1)\frac{\lambda}{2}$$

and for *minimum brightness*

$$KA - KP = n\lambda.$$

Now let us examine the conditions *inside* the geometrical shadow OY. If P′ is some distance from A, all the effective elements will be completely cut out by the obstacle and consequently K′ will be dark. When P′ approaches very close to A and, say, only the 1st half-period element is cut out, K′ receives the combined effects of parts of the 2nd, 3rd, 4th . . . elements. Detailed investigation shows that the 1st one has a greater influence at K′ than any other and that the resultant illumination of the remainder of the wave front is not large. In fact there is a continuous and rapid decrease in intensity as we pass into the geometrical shadow. Fig. 210 and Plate II*b* represent the results of experiment. The ordinates represent the illumination and the abscissæ the position in the pattern measured along the line XY. O denotes the edge of the geometrical shadow. The horizontal line through N represents the normal illumination, that is the uniform illumination which would be produced with the screen

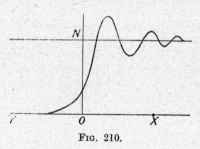

removed. It will be observed that the distance between successive maxima decreases as we move outwards from O. The illumination extends only a short way into the geometrical shadow, the brightness falling off rapidly without alternations of intensity.

Fig. 210.

Diffraction by a Narrow Obstacle.—Let AB (Fig. 211) be an obstacle, say a narrow piece of wire placed in the path of a beam of light from a slit S so that the sides of the wire are parallel to the sides of the slit. OL will represent the geometrical shadow of AB.

Outside the geometrical shadow diffraction bands will be formed by the edges A and B (see Plate IIc). From O towards K the visible bands will be due to the edge A alone, on account of the obliquity of BK. Overlapping might occur

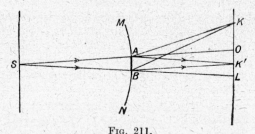

Fig. 211.

if AB were extremely narrow, but otherwise the effect of the wave front BN at K is negligible compared with the effect of AM.

Inside the geometrical shadow, on the other hand, we do get a combined effect of the elements at A and B and bands are

PLATE I

 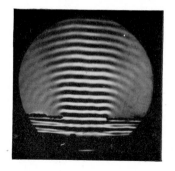

(a) (b)

RIPPLE-TANK PHOTOGRAPHS.
(*Cottingham*)

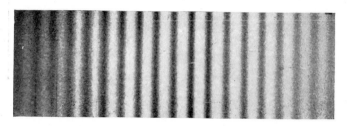

(c) YOUNG'S INTERFERENCE FRINGES.
Poynton)

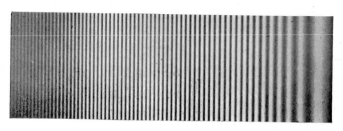

(d) LLOYD'S MIRROR INTERFERENCE FRINGES.
(***Poynton***)

PLATE II

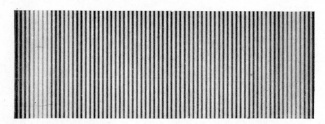

(a) FRESNEL'S BIPRISM INTERFERENCE FRINGES.

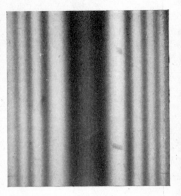

(b) DIFFRACTION AT A STRAIGHT
EDGE.

(c) DIFFRACTION ROUND A THIN
WIRE.

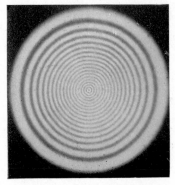

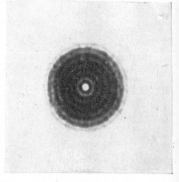

(d) DIFFRACTION THROUGH A
CIRCULAR APERTURE.

(e) DIFFRACTION ROUND A
CIRCULAR DISC.

Photographs by F. Y. Poynton, at the Northampton Polytechnic.

FRESNEL INTERFERENCE AND DIFFRACTION PATTERNS

ormed. The bands cannot be due to diffraction since we saw that an edge merely gives a falling off in intensity in the geometrical shadow. They must therefore be interference bands brought about by the action of two identical sources at A and B, and we must consider a point K' as receiving light from a few half-period elements of A and B by two paths, AK' and BK'. If the difference of the two paths is equal to an odd number of half wave lengths interference occurs ; if an even number, we get reinforcement. Thus, unlike the diffraction bands, we get a system inside the geometrical shadow of equal width and equal distances apart. From Young's experiment we see that if x is the distance of the obstacle from the screen and b the breadth of the obstacle, the distance ω between the interference bands is given by

$$\omega = \frac{x\lambda}{b}.$$

Diffraction by a Narrow Rectangular Aperture.—
When Newton was experimenting on the nature of white light he noticed that coloured bands were formed on the screen when his illuminated aperture was very narrow. This phenomenon is evidently complementary to that of the narrow obstacle.

The details of the pattern obtained depend greatly on the width of the slit. If the slit is very narrow (Fig. 212a) there will be a broad flat maximum at the centre, the illumination remaining considerable far out into the geometrical shadow on each side, since only far in the region of the geometrical shadow is there any possibility of destructive interference between

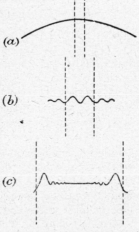

Fig. 212.—Dotted lines represent edges of slit.

disturbances due to different parts of the slit. If the slit is wide (Fig. 212c) there will be only very minute variations of intensity in the middle part of the pattern, the variations increasing as we approach the edges of the geometrical shadow. The wider the slit, the more nearly will the pattern approach that of two straight edges independent of one another. For a slit of intermediate width (Fig. 212b) there will be fringes both within and outside the geometrical shadow, but there will be no marked transition (as for a narrow obstacle) between the internal and external fringes. It may be noted that in this case there may be a maximum or a minimum in the centre of the pattern according to the width.

Diffraction through a Pinhole or Circular Aperture.— When the pinhole camera was discussed in Chapter II it was

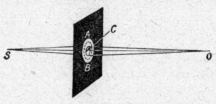

Fig. 213.

stated that no advantage was obtained by diminishing the size of the hole indefinitely. The reason given then was that the small amount of light which could pass through the hole when the latter was very small prevented good definition. This, however, is not the only reason for having a limiting size.

Suppose a very small hole AB [1] (Fig. 213) be made in some solid opaque object, such as a plate of tin, and a source of light be placed on one side of this at S say. If this hole is viewed through a lens at O, it appears as a bright spot surrounded by beautiful coloured rings (Plate IId). These vary in a remarkable manner as the distance between the eye and the hole is varied. In fact the whole phenomenon bears a close resemblance to the colours obtained by thin films.

In order to investigate it let SCO be a line drawn through

[1] The size is exaggerated in Fig. 213 for the sake of clearness.

the centre of the hole AB from the source to the screen. As in previous cases divide the wave which arrives at the hole into half-period elements. The effect at O will be the sum of the effects of these zones. Remembering that consecutive zones destroy each other (page 236), O will be bright or dark according as the number of zones transmitted is odd or even. Thus as O approaches AB the number of zones transmitted through the aperture will diminish and hence there will be seen a succession of alternate brightness and darkness. By reducing the pinhole to such a size that it only contains a fraction of the first zone with reference to a point on the axis the light will spread far outside the geometrical image of the pinhole. This should be clear if we consider how great a distance it will be necessary to move the point from the axis before the difference between the distances from the nearest and farthest extremities of the pinhole constitutes half a wave length. Reducing the hole below the first half period is therefore valueless.

Experiments on Fresnel Diffraction.

Most of the preceding examples of diffraction can easily be demonstrated experimentally by means of a car bulb, a filter

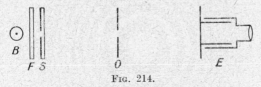

Fig. 214.

and a single slit together with the obstacle or hole and an eye-piece. The slit should be constructed as before from a fogged plate, but in these experiments it is desirable to adjust the slit at *right angles* to the filament in order to obtain a good point source of light.

Fig. 214 shows the apparatus in plan. B is the bulb, F the filter, S the slit, O the obstacle or hole and E the eye-piece.

A good circular aperture can be obtained by piercing a thin piece of zinc foil with holes of different sizes. The best size should be found by trial.

There are two or three good means of obtaining circular obstacles :—(1) a small ball bearing, (2) a tiny drop of mercury on a glass plate and fixed in position by shellac, (3) a photographic plate on which a drop of mercury has been allowed to fall before exposing and developing ; the positive gives a circular obstacle.

A large-scale method of demonstrating diffraction is the following :—Remove the objective lens and slide carrier from a magic lantern. Focus the arc light by means of the condenser on to a hole in a brass sheet (the size of the hole should be found by trial). No eye-piece is required ; a frosted glass screen or even a white sheet of cardboard will suffice. The obstacle or hole should be at least 10 feet from the lantern, while the screen may be a further 20 or 30 feet away.

Zone Plates.—A rather interesting verification of the preceding theory is the zone plate. As the consecutive zones in

Fig. 215.

AB (Fig. 213) destroy each other it should be possible by covering up alternate zones to obtain very bright illumination at O. It will be remembered that these zones are approximately of equal area and therefore their radii will be proportional to the square roots of the natural numbers, i.e. 1, $\sqrt{2}$, $\sqrt{3}$, $\sqrt{4}$, etc.

To construct a zone plate take a piece of white paper and describe a series of concentric circles with radii proportional to the numbers just given. Cover the alternate annuli, i.e. the 2nd, 4th, 6th, etc., with some opaque substance (Fig. 215). The plate is now required in miniature and this is best done by photographing it on a plate of thin glass. If this glass zone plate is now placed in the path of a beam of white light it will be found to give the same result as a convex lens although the actions are entirely different. The circles on the plate are half-period elements with respect to some point O on the diameter and consequently this point will act as a focus and will be very brightly illuminated. Each colour will have its own separate focus [1] as in a lens, but with this difference, the red will be nearer C than the violet. In the case of a lens the reverse takes place, for the red is less refrangible than the violet and consequently comes to a focus farther away from the lens.

The Opaque Circular Disc.—Although merely the reverse of the circular aperture its investigation by POISSON, after Fresnel's memoir was presented to the French Academy, led to what appeared an absurd conclusion, viz. :—*that the illumination at the centre of the shadow of the disc should be the same whether the disc were present or not.* He reasoned in this manner. The illumination at any point is due to the resultant effect of the half-period zones into which a wave front may be divided. In ordinary wave propagation the resultant displacement is equal to half that due to wavelets from the first half-period zone (cf. page 237, footnote). If the first zone is missing the resultant is due to half that of the second, and so on. Thus the effect of cutting out one or two of the zones should make very little difference to the illumination as the resultant from the remaining zones will be nearly the same as if all the wavelets were present. It only remained to verify this reasoning by experiment and fortunately for Fresnel,

[1] There are a number of foci for each separate colour corresponding to the different " orders."

Arago was successful in rediscovering an experiment which had been recorded by DESLISLE in 1715, but which had subsequently been forgotten on account of the lack of an interpreter. Arago used a thin circular copper disc 2 mms. diameter and observed the bright spot at the centre of the shadow. If a small coin is hung up by means of thin thread at about 18 to 20 feet from an illuminated pinhole the shadow cast at about the same distance on the other side gives a clearly defined illuminated centre (Plate II*e*).

Fraunhofer Diffraction Patterns.—So far we have been concerned with a type of diffraction phenomena associated with the name of Fresnel. There is another distinct class of diffraction effects named after the great German optician, Fraunhofer, who was largely responsible for their earlier investigation. This group of diffraction phenomena is of great importance in connection with the theory of optical instruments.

Rectangular Slit. —Consider first the case represented in Fig. 216. O is a very narrow slit perpendicular to the plane of the drawing. L′ is a lens, placed so that O is in its first focal plane; thus the light from O gives, after passing through L′, a plane wave front. S is a screen with a rectangular aperture of width AB and having a great length perpendicular to the plane of the diagram. The light after

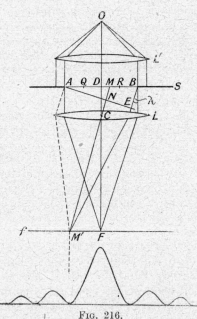

FIG. 216.

passing through this aperture falls on a second lens L, the axis of which is perpendicular to the screen.

The question now is :—What is observed in the focal plane f of this lens ? From the geometrical optics of lenses which we have dealt with in an earlier chapter, our answer would be this :—If the lens is perfect, that is, free from aberrations such as spherical aberration, etc., we should get a perfect image of the slit O. That is, we should have a brightly illuminated strip of light with sharp edges, the width being easily found when we know the width of the slit and the power of the lenses. The finer we make the slit O, the finer will be the image at F ; the size of the aperture AB does not appear to enter into the problem. But our previous study of lenses was based on the idea that light travels in straight lines : this we have seen is only partially true. Light is a wave motion which spreads into regions where we should not expect it if the straight line law were exactly true, and therefore it will not surprise the reader to find that the simple laws of geometrical optics do not give the whole story.

If we examine carefully the appearance in the focal plane, we find that instead of a sharply defined image there is a pattern of illumination which consists of a central bright strip flanked symmetrically on both sides by a series of dark and bright fringes (a picture of such a diffraction pattern is shown in Plate IIIa). The distribution of illumination in this pattern is shown graphically in the curve at the bottom of Fig. 216 ; the intensity (ordinates) is plotted against the position (abscissæ) in the pattern. The scale of the abscissæ is very much greater in the figure than in the actual case.

In order to explain the formation of these fringes, we imagine secondary wavelets to be originated at the aperture AB. The part of each wavelet which travels in the direction CF is brought by the lens L to the point F (principal focus) where all the contributions arrive in phase, so that we get a strong maximum there.[1] The light from each point which travels

[1] We may note that in this respect it contrasts with the Fresnel diffraction pattern for a slit (no lens), for which the centre of the pattern may be a maximum or minimum depending on the width of the slit.

in a direction parallel to MCM', inclined at a small angle to CF, will be brought by the lens to a focus at M', but the contributions from the different parts of the wave front AB will not now arrive at M' in phase.

The phase differences between the contributions can easily be calculated. Draw ANE perpendicular to the direction MCM', cutting the rays from M and B in this direction, in the points N and E. Then the phase difference at M' between the contributions due to the wavelets from A and, say, M is simply that corresponding to an extra path difference MN, and between those from A and B that due to path difference BE, and so on. This follows since the time taken to travel from A, N, E and all points in this plane to M' through the lens is the same.

Suppose we now consider the effect in such a direction that BE is exactly λ. It is easy to see that in this direction the resultant effect at M' will be zero. For we can imagine the aperture divided into two halves and it follows that the wavelets from corresponding points in each half will differ in phase on arrival at M' by $\lambda/2$ and will hence annul each other. Thus the effect of the wavelet from A will cancel that of the wavelet from the mid-point D, that from such a point as Q will just cancel that from R, where AQ = DR, and so on.

Hence we see that the *first minimum* will occur in a direction given by :—

$$BE = \omega \sin \phi = \lambda \quad . \quad . \quad . \quad . \quad (1)$$

where ω is the width of the aperture,
or, since ϕ is usually very small, this may be written

Direction of First
Diffraction Minimum $\quad \phi = \dfrac{\lambda}{\omega}.$

Succeeding minima will also occur whenever BE is an integral multiple of λ. It is not difficult by similar reasoning to show that a series of maxima will be obtained when, approximately,

$$BE = \frac{\lambda}{2}, \frac{3\lambda}{2}, \text{ etc.}$$

The intensity of these lateral maxima is much less than that of the central maximum and rapidly diminishes as we move outwards (Plate IIIa).

The student should note that if ω is wide, ϕ is very small, that is the central maximum is very narrow and we have a close approximation to a perfect image of the slit. On the other hand, if ω is narrow the first minimum will lie far out, the central maximum will be broad and flat and there will not be the perfect image which geometrical optics would indicate.

It is interesting to observe the effect obtained with two similar slits, parallel to each other and at a slight distance apart. An example of the pattern obtained is shown in Plate III*b*. We notice that the same diffraction pattern as for a single slit is produced ; but superimposed on it is a system of interference fringes due to the superposition of wavelets from corresponding parts of the two slits. The separation of these fringes is determined by the distance apart of the slits.

Circular Aperture.—The same question arises if we consider O (Fig. 216) to be a point source of light and S a screen with a circular aperture. Ordinary considerations of geometrical optics would indicate that a point image of O would be formed by the lens at F, but here again what we actually find is a pattern consisting of a central disc surrounded by a system of bright and dark rings. These are known as Airy rings (Plate III*c*). The exact mathematical evaluation of the radii of the dark rings is very difficult, but from analogy with the previous case of a slit, we should expect the first minimum (dark ring) to subtend at C an angle approximately equal to $\dfrac{\lambda}{D}$, where D is the diameter of the aperture (corresponding to ω for the slit). Mathematical analysis shows that this is nearly the case ; the first minimum occurs for an angle ϕ given by :—

$$\phi = 1{\cdot}22 \,\frac{\lambda}{D}.$$

Thus for a lens of focal length f, the radius of the central disc of the pattern is given by :—

$$r = \phi f = 1{\cdot}22 \,\frac{\lambda . f}{D}.$$

Gratings.—If a number of obstacles of equal widths are arranged parallel and at equal distances from one another, the arrangement is called a grating. We owe most of our knowledge of gratings and their diffraction effects to Fraunhofer. His first effort was to produce a grating with 340 obstacles to the inch ; this was done by straining fine wire over screws. Subsequently, he ruled gratings on a layer of gold leaf attached to glass, and again by attacking glass wire a diamond point. The latter method was by far the most successful and by its use he determined the wave length of the principal Fraunhofer lines in the spectrum of the sun (cf. page 334). Soon afterwards many improvements were introduced into the construction of gratings. Rutherford, an amateur astronomer, in 1880 ruled gratings on metal by means of an automatic dividing engine. It was found that metal did not have the wearing effect on the diamond that glass had. Rowland (1848–1901) was probably the most successful of all. He concentrated on the perfection of the screw and managed to obtain as many as 20,000 obstacles or lines to the inch. Moreover, in 1883, he described a method of ruling them on concave mirrors. Previous to that date the grating was used in the same manner as a prism on a spectrometer ; the advent of the concave grating did away with the need for a collimator and telescope. Nowadays, it is usual except in special work, to use either photographic reproductions or else replicas of celluloid ; original gratings with many lines to the inch are very expensive.

R. W. Wood of John Hopkins University, who ruled the first large grating on aluminium for use on the 100-inch telescope at the Mount Wilson Observatory, has found recently that aluminised Pyrex glass does away with many of the difficulties experienced in the construction of special large gratings. He is also trying to develop a technique for constructing gratings by a moulding process involving the use of modern plastics. If this process is successful it should place good concave gratings within the means of every school.

For ordinary school purposes Meier has used with good effect a copper sieve––300 to the inch. A bit of this is placed between two lantern-slide plates and is fixed with the usual slide paper. The very large spacing produces many overlapping spectra which may easily be seen. A piece of Dufay colour film is useful for demonstration purposes.

Elementary Theory of the Plane Transmission Grating.—Let the grating consist of a series of very narrow parallel slits in an opaque screen. Let N be the total number of slits and let the distance between corresponding points of adjacent slits be g. Suppose plane waves of monochromatic light of wave length λ fall normally on the grating and the diffracted light falls on a lens L and is focused in the focal plane. We want to know what is the pattern of illumination produced in this plane.

The general character of the pattern is shown graphically in the lower part of Fig. 217a. We note that (1) there are a number of very marked peaks called the *principal maxima*, and (2) between these there is a set of much smaller *subsidiary* maxima and minima. To explain this we again suppose each point of all the apertures to be the origin of a Huygen's wavelet. If we assume that the slits are exceedingly narrow, we may look upon each slit as giving rise to a single wavelet, so that if we had only one slit the distribution of illumination would be somewhat as indicated by the curved line (a) (cf. page 275). With a number of slits, however, in order to obtain the illumination at any point, we have to find the sum of the contributions arriving there from the various slits, taking careful account of their phase differences on arrival. This phase difference may be obtained as for a single slit. Thus, consider the light from each slit travelling in a direction parallel to CP_1, say. Draw BE perpendicular to CP_1, cutting the ray from A in this direction in the point E. The phase of the wavelet arriving at P_1 from A is retarded relative to that from B by an amount corresponding to the path difference AE, that is, AB sin θ, where θ is the angle ABE which is the same as the angle P_0CP_1. The path difference for two wavelets from adjacent slits would be $g \cdot \sin \theta$. Let this be p. Now it is clear that if this latter quantity is an integral number of wave lengths, all the wavelets from the slits will arrive at the corresponding point in the focal plane *in phase*, and we shall, therefore, obtain strong illumination. The position of these *principal maxima* is thus given by

$$\mathbf{p} = \mathbf{g} \sin \theta = \mathbf{n}\lambda \quad (n = 0, \pm 1, \pm 2) \quad . \quad . \quad . \quad (1)$$

This is the so-called "*grating law*" and it shows that the

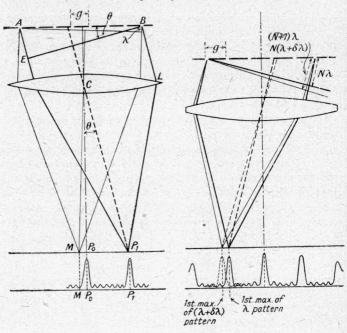

Fig. 217.

directions in which the principal maxima occur depend only on g and λ and not on the number of slits in the grating.

The reason for the subsidiary maxima and minima is very similar to that for the lateral maxima and minima in the case of a single slit. Thus, consider a point M such that the disturbances reaching it, viâ the lens, from two adjacent slits have a path difference $p = \dfrac{\lambda}{N}$, so that the path difference be

PLATE III

(a) SINGLE SLIT.

(b) DOUBLE SLIT.

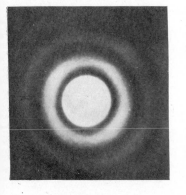

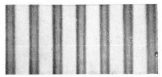

(d) THREE SLITS.

(c) CIRCULAR APERTURE
(AIRY'S DISC).

(e) FOUR SLITS.

Photographs by F. Y. Poynton, at the Northampton Polytechnic.

FRAUNHOFER DIFFRACTION PATTERNS

PLATE IV

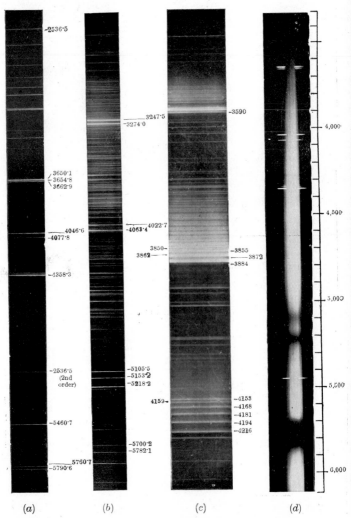

Photographs by C. V. Jackson, in the Clarendon Laboratory at Oxford.

(*a*) Quartz Mercury Vapour Lamp. (*b*) Copper Arc in Air. (*c*) Fluted Spectrum of Carbon Arc burning in air. (*d*) Absorption Spectrum of an alcoholic solution of Neodymium Nitrate. (The bright lines on the edge of the continuous spectrum are lines of mercury used for determining wave-lengths.)

SPECTRA

tween wavelets from the extreme points A and B is λ. Just as in the very similar case of the rectangular aperture already treated, we see that the wavelets originating in the left-hand half of the grating will just cancel, in pairs, those originating in corresponding slits in the right-hand half. Thus, the first subsidiary minimum near the central principal maximum will occur at an angle θ given by

$$p = g \sin \theta = \frac{\lambda}{N} \quad \cdots \cdots \quad (2)$$

Similar minima will occur when the path difference for consecutive slits is $\frac{2\lambda}{N}$, $\frac{3\lambda}{N}$, and so on. It can be shown that for a grating with N slits there would be $(N - 2)$ subsidiary minima between each pair of consecutive principal maxima. Plate III (d) and (e) show examples of this for the cases where N = 3, 4 respectively.

It is worth noting that the subsidiary minima next to the nth principal maximum will occur displaced from this by an angle corresponding to a change δp in the path difference, p, equal to $\frac{\lambda}{N}$. That is,

$$\delta p = \delta \, (g \sin \theta) = \frac{\lambda}{N}$$

or

$$g \cos \theta . \delta \theta = \frac{\lambda}{N}$$

or

$$\delta \theta = \frac{\lambda}{N \, g \cos O} = \frac{\lambda}{\omega'} \quad \cdots \cdots \quad (3)$$

where ω' is the width of the projection of the width of the grating on a plane perpendicular to the direction of the given diffraction maximum. This is analogous to the previous result for the single slit.

It will also be observed that the width of the principal maxima, that is, the angular separation between a principal maximum and its nearest subsidiary minimum, becomes smaller the greater the value of N. Thus with a small number of lines we get broad principal maxima, whilst with a very large number of lines of the same spacing we obtain the principal maxima in the same directions given by (1), but their widths are very narrow ; that is, each may be regarded as an image of the original slit.

The principal maximum corresponding to a path difference of $n\lambda$ between adjacent apertures is called the diffraction image of the nth order.

Determination of λ.—The diffraction grating is probably the simplest method of measuring the wave length of light of any given quality. For this purpose a spectrometer is used which is first of all set for parallel light. The grating is then fixed on the table with its lines normal to the table. This is carried out in a manner similar to that for a prism ; that is, the diffraction bands are all made to have the same height. The grating is then set normal to the incident light and the telescope is brought into the position of the nth image on either side of the central band. Half the difference between the telescope readings will give the angle of deviation of the nth image.

Then
$$\lambda = \frac{g}{n}.\sin \theta.$$

g is best obtained by measuring the number of lines per centimetre with the aid of a microscope.

Reflection Grating.—Reflection gratings may be made which will produce diffraction images similar to those of the transmission grating just described. A metallic surface is ruled with fine equidistant parallel lines so that waves falling on the reflecting portions separating the spaces are reflected in all directions. In certain of the directions the waves will tend to reinforce each other and in others to interfere. The greatest effect is obtained in the direction of direct reflection, for then all the reflecting portions act together.

Rowland's method was to rule a grating on a concave mirror with the lines at such distances apart that their projections on a plane were equidistant. In this way with a narrow slit at S (Fig. 218) placed on the circumference of a circle of which the diameter is equal to the radius of curvature of the mirror, he produced spectra of the source in different positions round the circumference. At I, for example, the image will be bright if SCI, SBI, SAI etc. differ by a constant multiple of a wave length.

In actual practice the diameter of the circle is 40 feet or more. The photographic camera which moves along XY is kept in position by an iron girder. At the opposite end of the girder is the grating. It was with this form of grating that Rowland carried out all his celebrated researches on the solar spectrum.

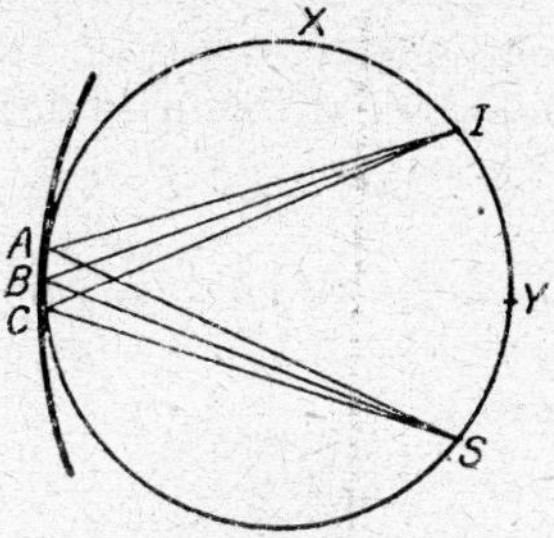

FIG. 218.

Mother of pearl is a natural curved grating, and this accounts for the beautiful colours that it produces by reflected light.

Resolving Power.—This term is used in connection with (1) spectroscopic apparatus, e.g. prisms, gratings, etc., and (2) lens systems, e.g. telescopes, microscopes, etc. For the first of these the resolving power is a measure of the power of the apparatus to separate two neighbouring lines in the spectrum, while for the second it is a measure of the power of the instrument to form separate images of two neighbouring object points.

We shall assume that the instruments are perfect, so that, from the point of view of geometrical optics, the image of a point or line source would be simply a point or line. But, owing to diffraction phenomena arising from the apertures through which the light must pass, instead of these sharp images we obtain diffraction patterns, the form of which depends on the shape and size of the apertures.

When two such patterns are formed close together there will be overlapping and the closer they are, the more difficult will it be to distinguish them as separate. The extent to which they can be separated by the eye will depend in some measure upon practice and the conditions. In order, therefore, to obtain a definite measure of the value of the resolving power,

U

Rayleigh suggested that two such patterns should be regarded as " separated " if the *central maximum* of one falls on the *first subsidiary minimum* of the other. We shall apply this condition to the grating, prism and telescope.

(a) *Grating.*—Consider the nth order image of the slit with light of wave length λ. We have seen that this occurs at such an angle that the path difference, p, for consecutive apertures is given by

$$p = g \sin \theta = n\lambda.$$

The adjacent subsidiary minimum occurs at an angular separation from this such that the path difference is changed by an amount δp given by

$$\delta p = \frac{\lambda}{N}.$$

Now if we consider light of wave length $\lambda + \delta\lambda$, the principal maximum will occur at an angle such that the path difference is given by

$$p + \delta p' = n(\lambda + \delta\lambda)$$

that is, the change in the path difference p in changing from λ to $\lambda + \delta\lambda$ is given by

$$\delta p' = n \, \delta\lambda.$$

If Rayleigh's condition is to be satisfied, that is, if the principal maximum for $\lambda + \delta\lambda$ is to fall on the first subsidiary minimum of the λ pattern, it is clear that we must have

$$\delta p' = \delta p$$

that is

$$n.\delta\lambda = \frac{\lambda}{N}.$$

So that, if the diffraction patterns in the nth order of two monochromatic wave trains of nearly the same wave length are to be separated, the wave lengths must differ by at least $\frac{\lambda}{nN}$.

The quantity $\frac{\lambda}{\delta\lambda}$ is defined as the resolving power. Denoting this by R we have

$$R = \frac{\lambda}{\delta\lambda} = nN.$$

This is illustrated for the 1st order spectrum in Fig. 217b.

(*b*) *Prism.*—Consider a parallel beam of light of wave length λ, produced say, from a slit S (Fig. 219) by a collimating lens L_1 and incident on the face AB of a prism at such an angle that

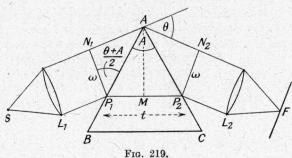

Fig. 219.

it passes through symmetrically. Then from page 70 we know that the following relation holds :—

$$\mu = \frac{\sin \frac{1}{2}(\theta + A)}{\sin \frac{1}{2} A}.$$

If the wave length changes slightly and becomes $\lambda + \delta\lambda$ then the index of refraction μ will change a little and will become, say, $\mu + \delta\mu$. Thus the change in deviation $\delta\theta$ will be given by

$$\delta\mu = \frac{\cos \frac{1}{2}(\theta + A)}{\sin \frac{1}{2} A} \cdot \frac{\delta\theta}{2}.$$

From the figure we see that $\sin\frac{1}{2}A = \dfrac{P_1 M}{A P_1}$

and $\qquad \cos \frac{1}{2}(\theta + A) = \cos A P_1 N_1 = \dfrac{P_1 N_1}{A P_1}.$

Hence, putting $P_1 P_2 = t$ and $P_1 N_1 = P_2 N_2 = \omega$

$$\delta\theta = \frac{t}{\omega}.\delta\mu.$$

Referring back, page 282, to the single slit, we realise that a parallel beam of light of wave length λ and width ω falling on the lens L_2 will not give a perfectly sharp line image at F but a diffraction pattern, the first subsidiary minimum occurring in a direction differing from that of the central maximum by an angle $\delta\theta' = \dfrac{\lambda}{\omega}$.

It is clear, therefore, applying Rayleigh's condition again, that if two components of wave lengths λ and $\lambda + \delta\lambda$ of the original beam are to give diffraction patterns that do not merge indistinguishably into one another, the wave length difference, $\delta\lambda$, must be at least enough for the centre of the $\lambda + \delta\lambda$ pattern to fall on the first subsidiary minimum of the λ pattern.

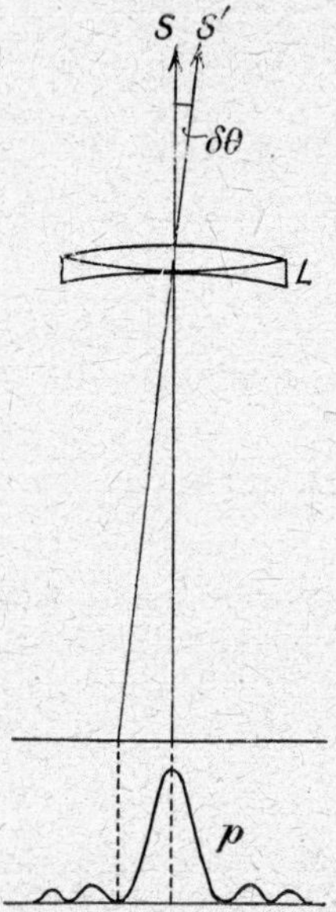

That is, we must have

$$\delta\theta' = \delta\theta$$

or, $$\frac{t}{\omega}.\delta\mu = \frac{\lambda}{\omega}$$

giving $$\delta\mu = \frac{\lambda}{t}$$

that is, $$\delta\lambda = \frac{d\lambda}{d\mu}.\delta\mu = \frac{d\lambda}{d\mu}.\frac{\lambda}{t}.$$

For the resolving power, R, we again take the ratio of the mean wave length λ to this limiting difference $\delta\lambda$.

Thus, $$\mathrm{R} = \frac{\lambda}{\delta\lambda} = t.\frac{d\mu}{d\lambda}.$$

Fig. 220.

(c) *Telescope.*—When a telescope objective L (Fig. 220) forms an image of a distant star, the supporting ring of the lens acts as a diffracting aperture. We have, in fact, the case of a circular aperture already briefly considered. Even though the lens is perfect in the sense of geometrical optics, the image of the star S—which we may regard as a point source giving waves which on arrival are plane—is not a point but a pattern, p, consisting of a central disc surrounded by a series of bright and dark rings. We have noted, page 283, that the first dark ring occurs at an angular separation from the mid-point of the central maximum given by :

$$\delta\theta = 1.22 \frac{\lambda}{D}$$

where D is the diameter of the objective lens ring, which here is the aperture. Now if there is another star S' so placed that it subtends with S at the telescope an angle equal to this $\delta\theta$. then the centre of its image pattern would fall on the first minimum of the pattern of S. Following Rayleigh, we may again take this as the limiting closeness of the two patterns if they are to be recognised as distinct. This minimum angular separation which two stars must have in order that their patterns shall not overlap so as to merge indistinguishably is called the resolving power of the telescope.

That is, $$R = 1.22 \frac{\lambda}{D}.$$

We see, therefore, in this an important reason why the diameter of the telescope objective should be as large as possible.

QUESTIONS. XV.

1. How did Fresnel account for the diffraction of light at a straight edge ?

2. Describe an experimental method of obtaining Fresnel diffraction patterns.

3. What is a zone plate and how is it constructed ?

4. What are Fraunhofer diffraction patterns ? Show that in the case of a rectangular slit the direction θ of the first minimum is given by $\theta = \lambda/\omega$ where λ is the wave length and ω is the width of the slit.

5. What is a grating ? Show that the direction θ of the principal maxima are given by $n\lambda = g \sin \theta$, where g is the distance between corresponding points of adjacent slits.

6. Account for the subsidiary maxima and minima in a grating pattern.

7. How would you determine the wave length of light with the aid of a grating ?

8. What do you understand by the term resolving power in the case of (a) a grating, (b) a telescope ?

CHAPTER XVI

POLARISATION AND DOUBLE REFRACTION

Longitudinal and Transverse Waves.—We have shown in previous chapters how it is possible to explain the phenomena of interference and diffraction by means of the Wave Theory and we have assumed that the waves are transverse. But there are two kinds of waves, longitudinal and transverse, and it remains to give reasons for the assumption that light motion is transverse as distinct from sound motion which is longitudinal. Before doing so, it will be useful to call attention to an important feature that distinguishes the two types of motion.

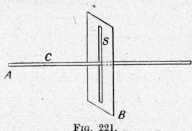

Fig. 221.

Any kind of longitudinal wave motion has the same properties with respect to any plane through its line of advance. In transverse wave motion, on the other hand, its behaviour may be different in different planes. A simple experiment will illustrate what is meant. Consider (Fig. 221) a stretched rubber cord C threaded through a narrow slit S in a card B. If a longitudinal wave motion is set up in C by moving the end A to and fro parallel to the length of the cord, it is clear that no matter how the card is turned about C as axis the passage of the waves through it is unaltered. Suppose, however, A is moved up and down in a vertical plane so that transverse waves pass along the cord, each point moving up and down as the waves pass. In this case it is obvious that if the slit S is vertical the waves will easily pass through, but if S is horizontal the waves will be stopped at the card. We see then that the fact that the particles all vibrate in a vertical plane through C singles out this plane as one with respect to which the waves have different properties as compared with other planes.

Another slightly more complicated model may be worth considering. Let B (Fig. 222a) be a board to which are attached

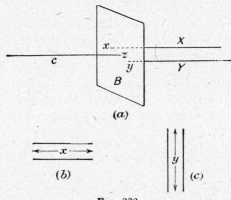

Fig. 222.

on the right-hand side two stretched cords X and Y, fixed to the board at points x and y. From a point z on the left-hand side a third cord c is attached stretching out to the left-hand side. Suppose that all three cords can transmit longitudinal or transverse waves, but that the cord X can only vibrate transversely in a horizontal plane while the cord Y is limited to such vibrations in a vertical plane. (The conditions might be produced as in Fig. 222b and c by confining X within two boards placed in a horizontal plane above and below it, and Y with boards in a vertical plane.)

If longitudinal vibrations are sent along c, the to-and-fro force produced on the board will set up longitudinal waves in X and Y. If, however, transverse vertical vibrations are transmitted along c we shall have transverse waves in Y but not in X. Similarly, with horizontal transverse vibrations along c, we shall have transverse waves in X but not in Y. If the vibrations in c are inclined at an angle θ say to the vertical, then waves will be set up along both Y and X, their amplitudes being in the proportion $\cos\theta : \sin\theta$, since the force F exerted on the board may be resolved into a force $F\cos\theta$ vertically and $F\sin\theta$ horizontally. It follows then that transverse vibrations in c in a definite plane will cause different actions in X and Y according to the angle this plane makes with the plane XY.

The question now arises :—Are there any experiments in which a beam of light shows different behaviour in different planes ? The first clear answer to this—and in the affirmative —was obtained as a result of some experiments carried out by Huygens on Iceland spar.

Double Refraction.—Before considering Huygens' experiments there are one or two important points to be noted about

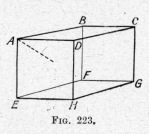

FIG. 223.

Iceland spar. It is a transparent crystal (chemical composition Ca_2CO_3) which occurs naturally in the form of rhombs (Fig. 223), each face being a parallelogram having angles of 77° and 102° nearly. At two opposite corners A and G the angles of the faces meeting there are all obtuse ; while at the others two are acute and one is obtuse. The material cleaves easily along planes parallel to these faces but not in other planes. The atomic architecture of the crystal is such that a certain *direction* in it is of special importance. This is called the *Optic Axis* of the crystal and it is parallel to a line through one of the blunt corners (e.g. A) making equal angles with the three edges meeting there. It should be noted that the optic axis is a *direction* and not a particular line. If the rhomb is cut so that its edges are equal, the optic axis will be parallel to the line joining opposite blunt corners (AG). A plane through the optic axis perpendicular to two opposite faces is called a *Principal Section*.

This crystal shows remarkable optical phenomena. Objects seen through it appear double. Thus, if it is placed over a dot marked on a sheet of paper, we see two images of the dot. If the rhomb is rotated on the paper one of these images remains stationary while the other revolves around it, the line joining the two being always parallel to the principal section. The stationary image appears nearer than the other. For this reason the crystal is said to be doubly refracting.

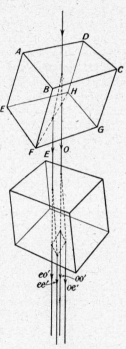

The phenomenon was first investigated by Erasmus Bartholinus in 1679. He showed that the stationary image was formed by rays which obeyed the ordinary law of refraction ($\mu = 1\cdot6$ approx.) while the other was formed by rays which behaved quite differently. Some twenty years later the matter was studied experimentally and more thoroughly by Huygens. One of his experiments is of particular importance to us in the present connection. A beam of light incident

Fig. 224.

normally on the face of a rhomb gives rise to two refracted beams, one travelling in the same line, the other deviated in the principal section towards the blunt corner (Fig. 224). The former behaves in accordance with Snell's law and is called the *ordinary ray* (or O) while the latter does not obey the law and is called the *extraordinary ray* (or E). At the second face E is again refracted and emerges parallel to O, If the crystal is thick enough, the two beams will emerge separated from one another. When the crystal is rotated around the original ray as axis, the *E* ray rotates round it, remaining in a principal section. The two beams are always of equal intensity.

Suppose now a second crystal is placed so that the two beams fall upon it normally and its faces are all parallel to corresponding ones of the first crystal. Each beam is then found to pass through the second crystal without further division ; the one which behaved in the ordinary way in the first rhomb continues to act in the same way in the second, that is it travels straight on, while the extraordinary beam is again refracted along the peculiar direction of an extraordinary ray. Now let us suppose that the second crystal is turned through 90° around the direction of the initial beam. This time we again find that there is no further division, but the ordinary and extraordinary rays change rôles ; the ordinary is refracted as an extraordinary ray and the extraordinary travels straight on and acts as an ordinary ray.

If the second rhomb is placed in any orientation other than these two (that is with principal section either parallel or perpendicular) we find that each of the two beams again produces two beams in the second crystal. Thus (Fig. 224) *O* gives rise to *oo'* and *oe'* lying in a plane parallel to the principal section of the second crystal, and similarly *E* gives rise to the pair *eo'* and *ee'* lying in a parallel plane. The intensities of these vary according to the orientation of the second rhomb. Starting with the principal sections parallel, we get only *oo'* and *ee'* ; as the angle between the two sections increases these two fade and *oe'* and *eo'* increase until when the sections are at right angles only the latter pair remain. On turning further, these fade and the other pair appear and increase until when the principal sections are parallel again we have only *oo'* and *ee'*.

It should be clear from our discussion on wave vibrations (page 294) that the above experiments with Iceland spar provide evidence that light waves are not longitudinal ; otherwise the two rays *O* and *E* on striking the second crystal would show no variation in their behaviour as the crystal was rotated. On the other hand, the view that the vibrations are transverse makes possible an easy explanation of the whole phenomenon. Suppose that in the ordinary beam O the vibrations are transverse and perpendicular to the principal section of the first rhomb, while in the beam E the vibrations are all parallel to the principal section. (This choice has been confirmed by other experiments.) Then we can explain what happens at the second rhomb in a way similar to that of our model, page 295. Consider the extraordinary ray only. Let Fig. 225 represent a plane parallel to the surface of the rhomb, and let OP_1, OP_2 be traces of the principal sections of the first and second rhombs. Let OA represent the amplitude of the vibrations in the E wave, that is, parallel to OP_1. Suppose that when this beam strikes the crystal it sets up vibrations of amplitude OM ($= OA \cos \theta$) parallel to OP_2 and ON ($= OA \sin \theta$) perpendicular to OP_2, and that the first of these gives rise to extraordinary waves and the second produces ordinary waves. Then it follows that the intensities of the two beams are in the ratio $\cos^2 \theta : \sin^2 \theta$ (since intensity $\propto$ amplitude²).

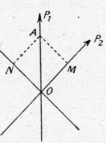

FIG. 225.

When the angle is zero we find only an E beam in the second crystal; when it is $\frac{\pi}{2}$, only an O beam is present, and so on. A similar explanation accounts for the behaviour of the O beam.

To explain why the original light always gives two equal beams, we need only suppose that in ordinary light transverse vibrations are present in all planes and that when the light is incident on the first crystal it is divided into two equal components, perpendicular and parallel to the principal section. These two components are said to be *plane polarised*; it is customary to speak of the ordinary beam as polarised in the principal section and the extraordinary beam as polarised at right angles to the principal section.

This simple explanation of double refraction was **not** evolved until the beginning of the nineteenth century, when

Young and Fresnel both became convinced of its truth at about the same time. Huygens confessed his inability to account for the phenomenon while Newton regarded it as a very strong reason against the view that light was a wave motion. Both of them were thinking of light as a longitudinal motion. The æther was regarded as something in the nature of " a rare and subtle gas " and it seemed impossible for such a medium to transmit transverse waves, just as air only transmits longitudinal waves.

Huygens' Construction for Double Refraction.—Although Huygens was unable to give any explanation of the physical behaviour of the two rays he was completely successful in explaining the rules governing the direction of the extraordinary ray. We have seen how he dealt with ordinary refraction on the wave theory by supposing that each point of the surface of the second medium became the centre of a secondary disturbance as the incident wave swept over the surface. In order to extend the idea to the case of double refraction it is necessary to assume that each point of the surface of the crystal becomes the centre of *two* wavelets travelling into the crystal. It is clear that the wavelets which give rise to the extraordinary beam are not spherical since they do not obey the ordinary law of refraction. Huygens therefore decided to try what spheroidal waves would do. He found that all the facts could be represented if it were assumed that from each point two secondary wavelets spread out as indicated in Fig. 226. The spherical one, of course, corresponds to the ordinary waves, while the spheroidal one gives the extraordinary wave. The axis of the spheroid is parallel to the optic axis of the crystal and the velocity of the two wavelets is the same in this direction. This corresponds with the experimental fact that for a ray incident normally on the crystal in a direction parallel to the optic axis there is no double refraction. In any other direction the E wavelet travels out faster than the O wavelet, the maximum difference being that for directions at right angles to the optic axis.

To understand how Huygens used this idea to find the

direction of the refracted rays let us consider several simple cases, Fig. 226.

(The differences are exaggerated greatly for the sake of clearness.)

(1) *Normal Incidence : the optic axis inclined to the surface* (Fig. 226*a*).—The dotted line represents the optic axis. The construction is similar to that given on page 243 except that

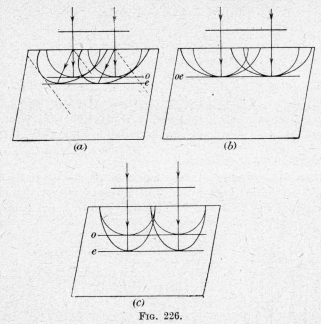

(a)   (b)

(c)

Fig. 226.

here we are dealing with two waves, one spherical and the other spheroidal.

(2) *Normal Incidence : the optic axis perpendicular to the surface* (Fig. 226*b*).—E and O waves coincide ; the rays travel in the same direction and at the same speed.

(3) *Normal Incidence : the optic axis is parallel to the surface and perpendicular to the plane of incidence* (Fig. 226*c*).—No separation takes place, but the velocities are different.

It is interesting to note that there are two types of crystals, one such as Iceland spar which has a wave surface for the extraordinary ray in the form of an oblate spheroid (commonly

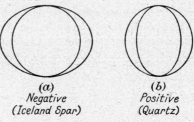

(*a*)
Negative
(Iceland Spar)

(*b*)
Positive
(Quartz)

Fig. 227.

known as a negative crystal) and the other such as quartz with a wave surface in the form of a prolate spheroid (a positive crystal). The two forms are illustrated in Fig. 227 (*a* and *b*).

Methods of Polarisation.

Nicol's Prism.—A very ingenious device for obtaining plane polarised light is the Nicol " prism," named after the inventor. A rhomb of Iceland spar is taken, and a prism obtained by cleavage along its natural planes. It is then

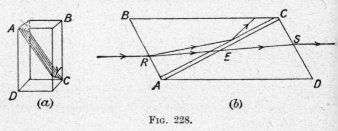

(*a*)

(*b*)

Fig. 228.

sliced along a plane XY (Fig. 228*a*), which is perpendicular to the principal plane and at an angle of 22° to the blunt edges (BC and AD). The cut faces are then polished and cemented together by means of a thin layer of Canada balsam. The velocity of light in Canada balsam being intermediate between

hose of the ordinary and extraordinary waves in Iceland spar,
he inclination of the plane XY (AC) can be such that for light
ncident on AB in the manner shown (Fig. 228b), the ordinary
waves will fall on the plane at an angle greater than the
ritical angle for the two media and will consequently be totally
eflected. The extraordinary rays will be incident at a
maller angle of incidence, pass through the prisms and emerge.

It is interesting to note that it is the extraordinary beam
which passes through the prism.

A modification of this prism was made by Foucault. In
lace of the Canada balsam is a layer of air ; the advantage
f this is that it enables the prism to be shorter and less
xpensive : the disadvantage is the loss of intensity of the
eam due to reflection. Hardly any loss of brightness occurs
1 the Nicol prism because the refractive index of the balsam
s nearly the same as that of the prisms for any extraordinary
ay entering it.

When the prism is used in order to obtain a beam of polarised
ght it is called a *polariser*. If it is desired to test a beam of
ght for polarisation the prism will act as an *analyser*.

ouble Image Prisms.

Rochon's Prism.—It is sometimes desirable to obtain two
mages of an object near together. Rochon's prism (Fig. 229)

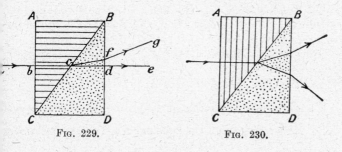

FIG. 229.   FIG. 230.

one method by which this may be done. It consists of
o prisms of quartz (say) ABC, CBD, with refracting angles

at C and B equal. One prism ABC has its optic axis parallel to AB so that a ray of light ab will pass through it undeviated. The other BCD is turned so that its optic axis is at right angles to the plane of the figure. Consequently, when the ray reaches c it is split up into two rays, the ordinary which passes on along the path cde without deviation and the extraordinary which is refracted along cfg.

Wollaston's Prism.—In this case (Fig. 230) the first prism has its axis parallel to AC, and therefore both rays receive equal amounts of deviation. The images are separated much more than in Rochon's prism.

A double image prism may be usefully applied to find the angular diameter of a planet. By inserting the prism in the telescope it can be so arranged that two contiguous images FI_1 and I_1I_2 (Fig. 231) are formed in the principal focal plane of the object glass O. That is, I_1 is the image of the

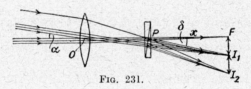

Fig. 231.

highest point of the planet as given by the undeviated rays and the lowest by the deviated rays.

The required angle α is the $\angle FOI_1$. Let the deviation of the prism, i.e. $\angle FPI_1$ be equal to δ, and the focal length of the object glass be equal to f. Let PF be equal to x.

Then $FI_1 = x \tan \delta = f \tan \alpha$

and, therefore, $\tan \alpha = \dfrac{x}{f}.\tan \delta.$

x is known from the position of the prism in the telescope and $\dfrac{\tan \delta}{f}$, which is constant, can be found in a separate experiment by finding the deviation corresponding to a known value of $\angle \alpha$. Thus the angular diameter can be found.

This principle was used by Cheshire during the Great War

for producing an ingenious pocket range-finder. A moving target, such as an aeroplane, was observed through the range-finder and the latter adjusted until the two images were in contact. The instrument was calibrated to read the distance directly.

Polarisation by Reflection and Refraction.—Another method of polarising light was discovered by Malus in 1808. If a beam of light is reflected at the surface of some transparent medium, a portion of the light is plane polarised. When the light is incident at a particular angle, called the Polarising Angle, it is found that almost all the reflected light is plane polarised. A good way of examining this phenomenon is to view the reflected light from a water surface through a plate of tourmaline. The tourmaline acts as an analyser, and if it is rotated, variations in the brightness of the beam are observed. It is rare that complete polarisation occurs on account of the surface of the transparent medium, which is often covered with a thin film of substance of lower refractive index. The effect of varying the refractive index of the medium is to vary the polarising angle. This was discovered by Brewster in 1815. The relationship, usually called *Brewster's law*, is given by the equation $\mu = \tan \theta$, where θ is the polarising angle, and the plane in which the light is polarised is the plane of incidence, or the plane of reflection. There will naturally also be a refracted beam, and the above equation leads to a further interesting result, for θ is the angle of incidence, $(\angle i)$, and therefore $\tan \theta = \tan i = \mu = \dfrac{\sin i}{\sin r}$ or

$$\sin r = \cos i$$
$$i + r = 90°.$$

Thus the reflected and refracted rays are at right angles to each other.

If the refracted beam is examined it will be found that this also is partially plane polarised, its plane of polarisation being at right angles to the plane of refraction.

Pile of Plates.—As a general rule the strength of the reflected polarised beam of light, discussed above, is very weak.

In order therefore to make reflection a practical method of obtaining polarised light, instead of using a single reflecting surface a much better plan is to use a number of very thin surfaces piled on top of one another. The beam of light is allowed to fall on the plates at the polarising angle, and reflection occurs from both back and front of each plate. Thus the waves which escape reflection at the first plate will have to run the gauntlet at each succeeding plate, and consequently with a reasonable number of plates it may be possible to reflect nearly all the incident light and so obtain a bright beam of polarised light.

Other Means of Polarisation.

Tourmaline is a doubly refracting crystal and, consequently, when a beam of light falls upon such a crystal it is split into two separate beams, ordinary and extraordinary. The ordinary beam, however, is absorbed if the thickness exceeds one millimetre, whilst the extraordinary beam is almost freely transmitted. This affords a ready method of obtaining plane polarised light.

Polaroid is a modern commercial means of obtaining polarised light. The medium consists of crystals of the organic compound iodosulphate of quinine, called herapathite, after Herapath who first produced and investigated the substance eighty years ago. Like tourmaline, only more so, these crystals absorb one component in quite a thin section and freely transmit the other. Herapath was only able to produce small crystals ; the modern development due to Land consists of making thin films of nitrocellulose filled with ultra-microscopic crystals of herapathite all having their axes parallel to the same direction. This uniform orientation of all the minute needle-like crystals embedded in the cellulose is achieved by slowly forcing the mixture of the cellulose and crystals through a narrow slit, the crystals orienting themselves in the flowing plastic material. By this means large sheets of polarising material can be prepared. The sheets are sold in the form of discs and can be used for such purposes as the conversion of instruments into polarising instruments, the study of optical properties of metals, the analysis of crystals, the control of light intensity, the production of non-glare surfaces on motor-car head lamps, and many other industrial requirements.

Elliptically Polarised Light.—It was discovered by Fresnel and Arago that two plane polarised beams of light coming from the same source could be made to produce fringes if they were polarised in the same plane. On the other hand, two such beams polarised in different planes would combine to produce an elliptic vibration. This is known as elliptically polarised light.

Blue of the Sky.—Brewster discovered that the light from the sky is polarised. Tyndall suggested that the light is scattered by the water molecules in the atmosphere and is thereby weakened. Rayleigh showed that the percentage of light scattered is inversely proportional to the fourth power of the wave length.

From Rayleigh's deduction it follows that the short violet and blue waves are scattered very much more than the longer red waves (about 16 times) so that the blue predominates. When we view the sky at a distance from the sun the waves have fallen obliquely on the particles in the atmosphere and, consequently, only the scattered light is visible. If the obliquity of the rays becomes very great, the scattered light is barely noticeable. This is what happens at sunset. The rays from the sun, which is low down on the horizon, have to travel a considerable distance through the atmosphere and then obliquity results in the diffracted light being lost. As this is chiefly the violet end of the spectrum only the red end is visible.

A very striking experiment was carried out by Tyndall in an effort to make artificial " sky blue " colour. Air was bubbled through butyl nitrite and then passed into an exhausted tube. This air was then brought into contact at low pressure with air which had been bubbled through hydrochloric acid. The cloud produced was then illuminated by a beam from an arc lamp. The effect of the beam was to bring about chemical action between the butyl nitrite and the hydrochloric acid with the formation of particles which gradually grew in size. When the particles were large enough to cause scattering of the light a beautiful azure colour was observed.

A variation of this experiment is to pass the beam through sodium thiosulphate contained in a glass tank, and then by the addition of a little dilute hydrochloric acid, particles of sulphur are formed which steadily grow in size. If the tank is long, interesting variations in colour take place. Inside the tank a pale blue is observed which gradually extends from the end nearer the source along the tank. The transmitted light first changes to yellow and then as the sulphur particles grow, it becomes more and more red until finally it is completely cut out. The scattered light ultimately becomes grey.

Optical Rotation.—If a beam of plane polarised light is

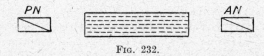

PN   AN

Fig. 232.

made to pass through certain substances it will emerge plane polarised but in a different plane from that of entry.

Suppose, for example, we fill a cylindrical tube with water and close the ends with glass plates (as in Fig. 232). If polarised light is allowed to pass through at one end, say by first transmitting a beam of light through a nicol, it will be possible by suitable adjustment of an analyser to stop further passage of the light at the other end. If the analyser is another nicol, and it is placed in a crossed position with reference to the polariser, no light will be visible. Without touching the nicols or altering the position of the tube in any way allow some sugar to dissolve in the water. On looking through the analysing nicol the light will be seen. By rotating the analyser in one particular direction extinction of the light may again be produced. This tells us that the effect of the sugar is to produce a rotation of the plane of polarisation. The amount of rotation depends upon the length of tube, the concentration of the sugar, the wave length of the light and the temperature. Two types of substances exist which might be termed optically active substances—those which produce right-handed rotation or, if we look towards the source of light, clockwise rotation, and those which turn the plane of polarisation in a left-handed direction or anti-clockwise.

If a quartz crystal is interposed between the two nicols considerable rotation may be produced. In this case the direction will depend upon the crystal : some quartz crystals produce left-handed and some right-handed rotations. In both cases the extent of the rotation will depend upon the thickness and density of the crystal, the wave length of the light employed and the temperature.

Specific Rotation.—In order to bring the rotation of all optically active substances into a comparable form we adopt the usual scientific method of standardising. Thus the term used, " specific rotation at a temperature t and wave length λ," is the amount of rotation (in degrees) produced by traversing a path of 10 centimetres length in a substance of unit density.

In equation form $S_{t\lambda} = \dfrac{10\theta}{l\rho}$

where $S_{t\lambda}$ = specific rotation at a temperature t and wave length λ

θ = actual rotation

l = length of tube or substance

ρ = density.

Measurement of Specific Rotation.—Of all the optically active substances sugar is probably the commonest, and it is often necessary to estimate the quantity of sugar in solutions. Commercially and for medicinal purposes the rotation produced affords a ready method of estimating these quantities. Instruments designed for this purpose are called *Polarimeters or Saccharimeters.*

The earliest and simplest form is the one described in the preceding discussion and was first used by MITSCHERLICH. Unfortunately it is difficult to locate precisely the position of the analysing nicol which will produce extinction of the light. The difficulty was overcome by LAURENT in the following manner :—

Laurent's Half Shade Polarimeter.—Light from a sodium flame falls on the polarising nicol PN (Fig. 233), but

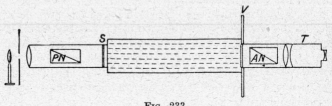

FIG. 233.

instead of passing immediately afterwards through the tube carrying the solution it is made to traverse a *Half Wave* plate S. It was this plate which enabled Laurent to make his polarimeter so successful.

The plate consists of a circle divided into two semi-circles, one made of glass and the other of quartz. (Fig. 234*a*). The

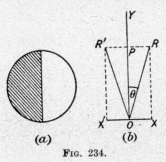

(a)   *(b)*

FIG. 234.

quartz is cut parallel to its axis, and is of such thickness that it produces a relative retardation of half a wave length in sodium light. In other words, the ordinary wave gains half a wave length on the extraordinary wave in passing through : that is, the two are made to differ in phase by π. The glass plate is of such a thickness that it transmits the same amount of light as the quartz. Let OY (Fig. 234*b*) be the direction of the axis in the quartz plate and let this make an angle θ with the principal plane of the polarising nicol. Then the principal plane of the nicol is parallel to OR, and consequently any vibrations which are incident normally on the plate will be parallel to OR. The plate splits up the vibrations into two components at right angles to one another (the ordinary and extraordinary waves), but when they arrive at the outside their difference in phase is π. Thus, if OP and OX represent the components of an original incident vibration given by OR, the emergent wave will be the resultant of OP and OX'. This follows from the fact that the vibration of OX relative to OP has changed phase by π and is therefore represented by OX'. Hence OR' is the direction of the emergent vibration and the effect of the quartz plate has been to rotate the plane by an angle 2θ.

From the explanation given it will appear that the light which passes through the polariser PN is divided into two halves, one which passes through the glass plate with no rotation and the other which receives an amount of rotation 2θ. When either half is viewed through the analyser, the intensity perceived will depend on the angle between the plane of polarisation of the light and that of the analyser. Thus, in general, the two halves will appear of different brightness. They will, however, be equally bright when the plane in which the light emerges from the analysing nicol is equally inclined to the planes of polarisation of the two beams ; that is, when the analysing nicol causes the emergent light to be in the plane OY. The slightest rotation of the nicol from this position produces considerable variation in the brightness of the two halves. This is where the advantage is obtained over the extinction method.

The analysing process is carried out by means of a nicol AN, and the light which comes through is examined by means of a Galilean telescope T. The position of AN can be adjusted by rotating the tube containing the nicol ; and the amount of rotation is measured by a vernier on a circular scale V attached to the movable table.

The Bi-quartz Polarimeter.—Earlier in this chapter it was stated that quartz may produce either clockwise or anti-clockwise rotation. Advantage is taken of this characteristic in the construction of a polarimeter. Two quartz plates each 3·75 millimetres in thickness and of opposite rotary power, are made into semi-circles and cemented together side by side so as to form a circle. This is then placed in the position occupied by the half wave plate of Laurent's apparatus. As the plane polarised light passes through each half it is rotated the same amount by each plate (about 90° for sodium light), but in opposite senses. A position may be found for the analysing nicol which will give the same appearance to the two fields.

A rather pretty effect is observed when white light is used with the quartz as thin as the above. If the analyser is set so as to extinguish the yellow rays a greyish violet tint called the *sensitive tint* is seen. The slightest rotation one way will change this tint either to blue or red. If, therefore, we wish to measure the specific rotation of a substance, the analyser is set so that the sensitive tint is observed in the two halves. In this way we can obtain the exact position of the plane of polarisation of the yellow rays.

Soleil's Polarimeter.—In commercial work where white light is desirable the use of the sensitive tint is very common.

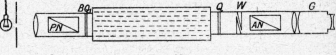

FIG. 235.

SOLEIL modified the above method by using a fixed analyser and two adjustable quartz wedges. The quartz produced an equal and opposite rotation to that of the solution.

The arrangements are shown in the diagram (Fig. 235). Light passing through the polarising nicol PN traverses a bi-quartz plate BQ_1 and then the tube carrying the solution. On emergence it is made to pass through a plate of right-handed quartz Q and then a double wedge W of left-handed quartz of variable thickness, after which it is received by the analysing nicol AN and Galilean telescope G. The nicol AN is set so as to produce the sensitive tint when the tube is empty and the thickness of the double wedge W equal to the thickness of Q. When the solution is put in, one wedge is screwed in or out, according as the rotation produced is right-handed or left-handed.

Use of Spectrometer in Polarimetry.—For very accurate working some modern instruments are provided with a spectrometer. The spectrometer is placed in front of the analyser and if a bi-quartz plate is used an image of this is made to fall on the slit of the spectrometer in such a way that two spectra are formed on top of each other. Whenever the analysing nicol is set so as to cut out light of a particular quality a dark band appears in the spectrum. In general these will occur at two different points in the two spectra. On rotating the analyser these bands will either approach each other or recede, and for a certain position will coincide one above the other. The light cut off is the sodium yellow, since the bi-quartz rotates the plane of polarisation 90° in each half. The plane of the analyser therefore must be at right angles to this. By finding the position of the analyser with and without the presence of solution the specific rotation is easily determined.

General Applications and Effects.

Glass under Compression.—If a block of glass is strained either by sudden contraction or some regular force, the glass becomes doubly refracting. Brewster suggested that this might be applied to calculating stresses in structures. In order to be able to make sufficient allowance for a safety margin, he proposed that a model of the structure required be made in glass and then the different parts under stress could be examined by polarised light. This would admit of more precision than in the usual calculations, which only give average values. Xylonite has now been substituted for glass, as it is more compressible and more easily worked.

Effects of Electricity—Kerr Effect.—In 1875 DR. KERR of Glasgow discovered that if dielectrics, e.g. glass and carbon bisulphide, are subjected to the action of an electric field they become doubly refracting, and act as if they are subject to stress. The method he adopted was to fix two terminals, one on either side of a slab of glass, and to connect them to a powerful Wimshurst machine or an induction coil. The glass was then placed between two crossed nicols, so that the field was dark when the current was off. On starting the coil, the field became bright and remained so, no matter what position the nicols were in. Kerr found that the best effect was obtained when the line joining the terminals was at right angles to that drawn through the centres of the nicols and at an angle of 45° with the principal sections of the nicols.

An extension of this effect is the modern Kerr Cell (cf. page 195) used largely in television. The cell contains nitro-benzene which is doubly refractive to light when placed in an electric field. A high-frequency alternating field enables the cell and its nicols to act as a very rapid shutter, so that the scanning of the object may be exactly reproduced at the receiver.

Magnetic Effect.—In 1877 Kerr showed that magnetism affected the plane of polarisation in certain cases. A beam of plane polarised light was allowed to fall on the polished pole of a magnet. When the light was polarised in or at right angles to the plane of incidence, the effect of the pole was to cause a slight rotation of the plane of polarisation.

QUESTIONS. XVI.

1. What evidence is there for the belief that light vibrations are transverse and not longitudinal as in the case of sound ?

2. What is plane polarised light ? Describe any methods of producing it.

3. How did Huygens explain double refraction ?

4. How may polarisation be brought about by reflection and refraction ? What do you know about light so polarised ?

5. How is it possible to account for the blue colour of the sky ?

6. Explain optical rotation. Define specific rotation and show how it can be measured.

7. Give a description of either Laurent's half shade polarimeter or Soleil's polarimeter.

8. Explain for what practical purposes polarisation can be utilised.

CHAPTER XVII

SPECTRA

We have so far been primarily concerned with questions relating to the propagation of light, e.g. reflection, refraction, interference, polarisation, and so on, and we have only briefly referred to the emission and absorption of light by matter. We propose now to give more detailed consideration to this topic, for it is in this part of the study of light that the greatest recent advances have been made.

The Complete Electromagnetic Spectrum.—We have noted in Chapter VII that the radiation from the sun and other luminous sources is not limited to the range of the visible spectrum, but includes waves of longer wave length—the infra-red—and of shorter wave length—the ultra-violet. It can be shown that these radiations are in no way essentially different from ordinary visible light except that the eye is not sensitive to them. Special methods have been devised for their study and their wave lengths have been measured by diffraction gratings and interference methods exactly as with visible light. As we have mentioned, the wave lengths of visible light range only from about $7 \cdot 10^{-5}$ cm. for the extreme red to about $3 \cdot 9.10^{-5}$ cm. for the violet ; but the infra-red radiation has been studied up to wave lengths as long as 10^{-2} cm., while in the other direction radiations with as short a wave length as 10^{-6} cm. have been detected and measured by the special methods of ultra-violet spectroscopy. We now know that even this extended spectrum is only a small part of a vast range of radiations of both shorter and longer wave lengths, all essentially resembling light in their physical nature. Thus, proceeding in the direction of shorter wave lengths we come to the X-rays. These are produced when electrons travelling with very high velocity strike a metal target. Their discovery by Röntgen in 1896 marks the beginning of a new epoch in the study of radiation. At first the nature of these rays was a matter of great controversy. Many investigators tried to devise experiments to show that they obeyed the same general laws as light, that they could be polarised, show interference effects and so on. But for a long time these efforts were unavailing and only showed that if X-rays *were* waves they must have exceedingly short wave lengths, in fact not much longer than the sizes of atoms themselves, that is of the order of 10^{-8} cm. Then in 1912 Laue, of Munich, hit on the brilliant idea that a crystal, consisting as it does of a regular arrangement of atoms, should act as a sort of three dimensional diffraction grating for waves as short as this. His idea was immediately confirmed by experiment and shortly afterwards Sir William Bragg and his son Professor W. L. Bragg, using a crystal of rock salt as a diffracting grating, obtained the first measurements of X-ray wave lengths. (It is of interest to note here in passing that in these experiments they also determined the exact structure of the rocksalt crystal and thus inaugurated the great stream of researches in which X-rays are being applied to reveal the detailed atomic architecture of crystalline materials of all kinds.) Since then, the technique of measuring X-ray wave lengths by means of crystals has been greatly developed and it has been shown that X-rays comprise a range of wave lengths of about 13 octaves extending from about $5 \cdot 10^{-7}$ cm. to about a thousand times shorter than this. In 1925 the essential similarity of X-rays and ordinary light was still more directly proved by an experiment carried out by Compton and Doan in which they succeeded in measuring the wave length of X-rays by means of a ruled diffraction grating as used in ordinary optics. Still shorter in wave length come the γ-rays, emitted by radioactive atoms, and the so-called cosmic rays. These also have been shown to be of the same kind as X-rays and their wave-lengths have been measured by crystals in the same way. They extend out to values some ten thousand times smaller than the shortest X-rays.

We find the same thing if we proceed from the infra-red to longer waves. The so-called " wireless " or " radio " waves with which everyone is now so familiar have exactly the same fundamental properties as light and all the typical phenomena such as polarisation, interference, reflection, refraction, etc., can be obtained with them. The waves used in ordinary broadcasting have a wave length of a few hundred metres, that is about a thousand million times longer than the waves of visible light. These radio waves are produced by oscillations of electricity in the transmitting aerial. They are electrical waves and their possibility was first predicted in 1865 by Maxwell from considerations of electrical theory. He showed that a circuit in which an electric charge oscillates should set up electrical waves in the surrounding ether, and he calculated the speed such waves would have. This turned out to be exactly the same as the speed of light and this fact led him to suggest (1873) that ordinary light was simply a particular kind of electrical wave. Maxwell's amaz-

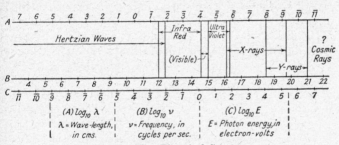

FIG. 236.—The Electrical Spectrum.

ing prediction was experimentally confirmed in 1888 by Hertz who, as we noted in Chapter I, was the first to produce such electrical waves and thus lay the experimental foundation of radio-communication. The waves produced and studied by Hertz had a wave length of the order of a few metres which is enormously greater than that of visible light. But in recent years this gap has been closed and now electrical waves have been produced having a wave length shorter than that of the longest infra-red waves produced and detected by ordinary optical methods. Thus, visible light is seen to be only a short section—less than an octave—of a vast continuous spectrum of electric waves extending over more than 70 octaves. Fig. 236 gives a summary of this complete spectrum. The scale of wave lengths is logarithmic, the numbers shown being powers of 10 and the unit wave length 1 cm.

Experimental Methods.—As most of the facts with which we shall be concerned in this chapter are obtained from a

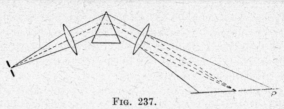

FIG. 237.

study of the infra-red and ultra-violet as well as the visible rays, it is of interest at this point to refer to common methods in use.

The *visible* spectrum is nearly always examined with a constant deviation prism which has already been referred to on page 182.

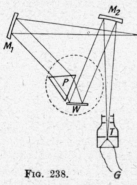

FIG. 238.

For experimental work in the *ultra-violet* it is impossible to make use of ordinary glass prisms and lenses since these would absorb the radiation. Quartz is therefore used instead of glass. Unfortunately, quartz produces optical rotation and so a special prism has to be used—called a Cornu prism —half of which produces left-handed rotation and half right-handed. The lenses are also of quartz, but they need not be achromatic as it is usual to receive the radiation on a plate of film P set at such an angle (Fig. 237) that the whole of the spectrum is in focus.

For examining the *infra-red* the prism is made of rock salt.

Stainless-steel concave mirrors M_1 and M_2 (Fig. 238) are used for collimating the radiation on to the detector T (a thermopile). The plane mirror W and P are fixed to the table which rotates.

Origin of the Quantum Theory.—After the work of Maxwell and Hertz the conception of light as a particular kind of electrical wave was developed by many scientists. It was found to be uniformly successful in explaining all the minutest details regarding the propagation of light, its polarisation, interference, diffraction and so on. It was natural, therefore, that attempts should be made to explain by its aid the processes by which light is emitted and absorbed by matter. It seemed reasonable to think that just as the long waves of radio are generated by the oscillations of electricity in the transmitting aerial, so the much shorter, but essentially similar, waves of light had their origin in the vibrations of electric charges in matter. The tremendously high frequencies of light vibrations suggested strongly that their origin must be looked for within the smallest parts of matter, the atoms and molecules themselves. Moreover, it was at this time—towards the end of the last century—that physicists were discovering many lines of evidence leading them to the view that the atoms of matter were electrical systems composed of particles of positive and negative electricity. In 1897 J. J. THOMSON, at Cambridge, had shown that negative electricity existed in the form of particles—electrons, as they are now called. These particles were found to be a constituent of all atoms and wherever they occurred they had the same charge ($1 \cdot 59 \cdot 10^{-19}$ coulomb) and mass about $\frac{1}{1800}$ of the mass of the lightest atom (hydrogen). These discoveries, together with the success of the electrical theory of light waves, filled the physicists of the time with lively hope that by applying the well-known laws of electrical theory to the motion of the electrons in atoms they would be able to understand the processes by which light was produced. Great efforts were made in this direction, but all of them failed. It became increasingly evident that despite the success of electrical theory in explaining the generation of ordinary large-scale electrical waves, it was quite inadequate to deal with the processes taking place in such minute regions as the interior of atoms. It was clear that the structure of atoms and the means by which they emitted and absorbed radiation were governed by as yet undiscovered laws. The first and fundamental step towards an understanding of these laws was taken in 1900 by PLANCK, Professor of Physics at Berlin. He made his great discovery in an attempt to explain the character of the radiation from a hot body.

If the radiation emitted by a hot body, for instance the incandescent tungsten filament of an electric lamp, is spread out into its spectrum by some form of spectrometer and the

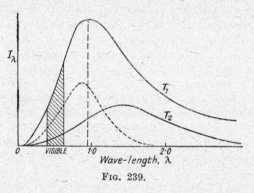

FIG. 239.

energy carried by the different wave lengths is measured, the results give a curve like that shown—dotted line—in Fig. 239. Here the abscissæ represent wave lengths (λ) and the ordinates (I_λ) are proportional to the intensity of the radiation for the different wave lengths. We see that the spectrum is a continuous one, that is, it contains radiations of all frequencies, although the intensity varies with the wave length, being a maximum for a certain wave length and falling off to imperceptibly small values for both very short and very long waves. Curves of this kind can be obtained experimentally for all hot bodies and it is found that the precise shape of the curve varies with the nature of the body and the character of its surface. That is, different bodies heated to the same temperature differ considerably in the extent to which they radiate at the various wave lengths. Now in 1856 Kirchhoff showed that there was a simple relation between the power of a body to emit radiation of any wave length and its power of absorbing radiation of the same kind. Thus, if a certain body at a given temperature radiates twice as strongly at some particular wave length as another body, then it would at the same temperature absorb—i.e. convert again into heat energy —radiation of that wave length twice as strongly. That is, bodies which showed little power of absorbing radiation of a certain frequency would show a correspondingly small emission at that frequency. It follows from this fundamental relation between emissive and absorptive powers of any body that a body which had the property of absorbing all the radiation— of whatever wave length—that fell on it would also have the greatest possible emitting power for all wave lengths. Such a body is called a *perfectly black body* or preferably a full or complete radiator. Although no such body is known, we can obtain something equivalent to it. A small opening made in the wall of any constant temperature enclosure would act like a piece of the surface of a black body since any radiation entering it would be scattered hither and thither from the inside walls and so long as the walls had some power of absorption—even though it were small—for all wave lengths, very little of the radiation entering the aperture would re-emerge. Conversely, it follows that the radiation emitted from such an enclosure through a *small* opening would be in all respects like the radiation which would be emitted from a perfectly black body and would show no trace of the particular properties of the material of the walls.

Physicists have devoted great care to the measurement of the radiation from such cavities maintained at various temperatures. Fig. 239 (full lines) shows the type of curve obtained for two temperatures, T_1 and T_2 ($T_1 > T_2$). These curves are of the greatest importance in the study of radiation from hot bodies since they give the *maximum* radiation that any body can, as a result of the heat motions of its atoms, emit at any temperature and wave length. Most substances.

as the tungsten filament for example, emit much less strongly at all wave lengths than a full radiator at the same temperature. It was realised that it was a problem of fundamental importance to explain why the radiation from a full radiator should have precisely the character shown by the experimental curves. The greatest theoretical physicists of the time struggled with the question, but assuming as they did that the ordinary laws of electricity applied to the motions of the electrons in the atom, they always arrived at results in glaring contradiction to the facts. It was reserved for Planck to show that it was only possible to explain the experimental results, provided it was assumed that whenever an atom emitted or absorbed energy in the form of radiation it did so only in definite amounts or packets at a time. Each of these minimum amounts of energy he called a *quantum* of energy and he showed that the value of the energy quantum for radiation of any frequency was simply proportional to the frequency. Thus, we have the relation

$$E = h\nu$$

where E is the quantum of energy for radiation of frequency ν and h is the universal constant, now known always as Planck's constant. This was a very revolutionary idea and at the time it received strong opposition. Ordinary electrical theory required that an atom should be able to send out or absorb radiation continuously, that is, in amounts differing by any value however small and not, as Planck assumed, only in packets of a definite amount, the value of which was fixed only by the frequency. But all subsequent research has shown in countless ways that Planck had discovered a fundamental fact of nature.

The value of h is $6 \cdot 55 \times 10^{-27}$ erg-sec. This means, for example, that for the yellow light from a sodium flame, the frequency of which is about 509 million million per second, the value of the quantum of energy is about $3 \cdot 33 \times 10^{-12}$ erg. That is, according to this view, the atoms in the flame which are giving off this yellow light do not do so in a steady continuous stream, but emit it in packets or quanta of this size at a time.

In dealing with such minute quantities of energy it has been found convenient to use instead of the erg a special unit called the *electron-volt*. This is defined as the energy transferred to an electron when it moves through a potential difference of 1 volt. Its value is 1.59×10^{-12} erg. Hence the value of the energy quantum for the yellow sodium light may be expressed as 2.1 electron volts. Since the value for any radiation is proportional to the frequency it follows that for X-rays it will be of the order of ten to one hundred thousand electron volts and for γ-rays of the order of some million ; while for radio waves it would be only a thousand millionth of the value for visible light. In Fig. 236 the bottom line gives the energy in electron volts of the quantum for the different frequencies. It is clear that this discontinuity or jerkiness in the exchange of energy between matter and radiation becomes increasingly important the higher the frequency of the radiation.

The Photoelectric Effect.—Planck made his great discovery as a result of very involved mathematical analysis and when one considers how complex a hot solid is, with its atoms jostling one another in a chaotic hurly-burly of motion, it is amazing to think that a fundamental law could be deduced from such a study. Although his theory was received with scepticism, it was not long before it was discovered that there were other phenomena which for the first time received a simple explanation by the use of the same ideas. Nowadays, many experiments could be cited which show in a very simple direct way the truth of Planck's conception of energy quanta. As an example we may mention here the photoelectric effect. If a metal is irradiated with light it is found that, provided the frequency of the light is high enough, electrons are thrown off from the surface. This is the effect on which is based the action of the photoelectric cells which are used to-day in the production of talking pictures, television and in many other applications. The effect was discovered by Hertz in 1888, but it was not until after the development of modern methods of obtaining high vacua and experiments could be made with very clean surfaces in highly evacuated vessels that the fundamental laws of the effect were established. It was then found that these were of a very remarkable and unexpected nature. One would imagine that the more intense the radiation the greater would be the velocity with which the electrons were thrown out from the surface ; and calculations based on ordinary electrical theory lead to the same expectation. But experiment shows that this is not at all the case. Increasing the intensity of the light merely causes a proportionate increase in the *number* of electrons emitted without in any way affecting their velocity. The latter depends on the frequency of the radiation. If this is below a certain definite value, depending on the particular metal used, no electrons whatever are emitted, however intense the radiation is made. If the frequency is raised above this limit, or *threshold frequency* as it is called, electrons are immediately emitted even though the intensity of light is very small. As the frequency of the radiation is increased the energy of the photo-electrons is increased in direct proportion to the difference between the frequency and the threshold value. That is,

$$E = k(\nu - \nu_0) . \quad . \quad . \quad . \quad . \quad (1)$$

where E is the maximum value of the energy of an emitted electron, ν_0 the threshold frequency, ν the actual frequency of the radiation used, and k is a constant.

Einstein in 1905 showed that these facts, although they baffled attempts at explanation on the classical theory, could be very simply understood by an extension of Planck's ideas. The latter had shown that it was necessary to suppose that whenever radiation was emitted or absorbed by matter, the *exchange* must take place in definite packets at a time. Einstein went further and suggested that the energy of the radiation itself existed in such packets or quanta. According to this idea, the energy of the radiation emitted from any source does not spread out in waves over ever-widening surfaces, but is shot out like a shower of bullets. These " atoms" of radiant energy—as we may think of them—are called *photons*. With this view of the nature of light the curious law of the photoelectric effect is easily understood. The electrons in the metal must be ordinarily prevented from leaving it by some force and, hence, to remove an electron from the metal must require a certain amount of work—say **W**—to be done against this restraining force. Suppose that each electron is emitted as the result of the absorption of a single photon ; then it follows from the Principle of the Conservation of energy that

$$\begin{pmatrix} \text{Energy of electron} \\ \text{inside the metal} \end{pmatrix} + \begin{pmatrix} \text{Energy of the} \\ \text{absorbed photon} \end{pmatrix} =$$

$$\begin{pmatrix} \text{Work required} \\ \text{for removal} \\ \text{of electron} \end{pmatrix} + \begin{pmatrix} \text{Energy of} \\ \text{emitted} \\ \text{electron} \end{pmatrix}$$

If the electrons that are emitted all have the same energy, say E_i, inside the metal—and other considerations closely confirm this—we have

$$E_i + h\nu = W + E$$

that is, $E = h\nu - (W - E_i) = h\nu - w$ where $w = W - E_i$. The quantity w depends only on the properties of the metal. If we write $w = h\nu_0$, the equation takes the form

$$E = h(\nu - \nu_0) \quad . \quad . \quad . \quad . \quad . \quad . \quad (2)$$

which is precisely the same as (1) which expresses the experimental results.

According to this theory, the constant k should be equal to h and in 1916 Millikan in America in a remarkable experiment confirmed this prediction. This notion of Einstein was a much more revolutionary idea than Planck's and it was very sceptically received. After all, the wave theory of light had been very successful and this photon idea seemed like a " relapse " to something akin to the long-discarded corpuscular theory of Newton. In many respects it was, although Einstein's " photons " were very different things from the corpuscles imagined by Newton. Subsequent researches have shown that there are many other optical phenomena which are easily explained by the " photon " idea, while the wave theory can give no explanation at all. It turns out that these are nearly all connected with the emission and absorption of light. In fact the whole modern development of the theory of radiation and the structure of matter is based on these fundamental ideas of Planck and Einstein.

Some Facts about Spectra.—Before proceeding further to show how the ideas we have just considered can be applied to explain how atoms emit and absorb light, we must note briefly some of the more important experimental facts about spectra.

It is usual to distinguish two main types : *continuous* and *discontinuous* spectra. We have already met instances of both kinds ; thus the solar spectrum is continuous, containing radiation of all wave lengths within its limits, while the light from the sodium flame containing only certain particular wave lengths is an example of a discontinuous spectrum. The former present in the spectroscope the appearance of a continuous band of colours, as in the rainbow, while the latter give a series of bright lines—images of the slit—separated by dark spaces in which no light occurs. Discontinuous spectra are further subdivided into two types—*line spectra* and *band spectra*. In the latter there are a very great number of lines arranged in very obvious groups within which the lines are so close together that unless the spectroscope has a very high resolving power they do not appear separate, but merge together presenting a band like appearance. In line spectra, on the other hand, the lines do not in general display any obvious regular arrangement. Experiment shows that incandescent solids and liquids give continuous spectra, while discontinuous spectra arise from glowing gases. In the former the molecules are so closely crowded together that they are continuously influencing each other and it is not surprising that the radiation emitted comprises all wave lengths. In the latter, however, the atoms and molecules are on the average much further apart and do not disturb each other's radiation. It has been shown that line spectra originate in atoms and band spectra arise from molecules ; we shall confine ourselves principally to the simplest of these types—the line spectra.

The experimental study of such spectra was begun by Bunsen and Kirchhoff, who in 1860 made a discovery of the greatest significance. They were examining the light from flames in which small quantities of salts of various metals had been introduced and they found that each metal gave its own *characteristic* lines which always occurred in the same place in the spectrum. Thus, sodium salts always gave the same strong yellow line (together with several other much fainter ones) and this occurred in the same place, no matter what the temperature of the flame or the particular salt—chloride, bromide, sulphate, etc.—used. It was clear that this radiation was a characteristic of the sodium atom. Its wave length is found to be always the same. In the same way, lithium always gives an intense line in the red, potassium one in the red and another in the violet, and so on. They concluded that *every different kind of atom had its own characteristic line spectrum* or, as we may put it, each species of atom is like a radio station that can broadcast only on certain definite frequencies. This great discovery at once attracted attention to the study of spectra and now the spectrum of every kind of atom has been mapped and measured with the highest precision. It was at once realised that the spectrum of an element gave a means of *detecting* that element. No one is more certainly recognised by his fingerprints than an element by its spectrum and this method—called spectrum analysis—of detecting the presence of any substance has been thoroughly developed and is very widely employed. It has many special advantages and is extraordinarily sensitive ; for example, a trace of lithium of less than a ten-millionth of a milligram can be detected by its spectrum. But, even more important than this practical application, is the obvious fact that in the spectra of the atoms there must be contained a wealth of information about the *structure* of the atoms. Spectra are, indeed, the language of the atoms and it was early recognised that if this language could be understood it would tell a great deal about how atoms are constructed. This has now been done and nearly all we at present know about atom-building has been obtained from the study of spectra.

The spectra of the various elements differ greatly in complexity. The simplest is given by hydrogen. This has four lines in the visible region, one in the red, one in the blue, one in the blue-violet, and one in the violet. These are usually denoted H_α, H_β, H_γ, H_δ. In addition there are, of course, as for all other atoms, many more in the ultra-violet and infra-red. The next simplest are those of the alkali metals, lithium, sodium, potassium, etc., all of which are strikingly similar to each other. In these, many of the lines are doublets, that is, two very close together (e.g. the well-known D doublet of sodium). The alkaline earths barium, strontium and so on, give still more complex spectra in which triplets occur, that is, close grouping of three lines. An example of a very complex spectrum is provided by that of iron, in which over 5,300 lines have been measured with great accuracy.

At first no particular order or system could be discerned in any of these line spectra, but gradually the patient labours of the spectroscopists were rewarded and regularities were

$$\lambda = 6563 \qquad 4861 \quad 4340 \ 4102 \qquad 3646 \qquad 10^{-8} cms.$$

FIG. 240.

discovered. This was first achieved—as we should expect—for the simplest spectrum, that of hydrogen. In 1885 BALMER showed that the frequencies of the four lines in the visible —together with ten more that had been measured in the near ultra-violet—could be represented by the simple formula

$$\nu = R\left(\frac{1}{2^2} - \frac{1}{n^2}\right)$$

where n is given the values 3, 4, 5 . . . for the various lines, $n = 3$ giving H_α, $n = 4$, H_β, and so on, and R is a constant ($3 \cdot 29.10^{15}$ per sec.) now known as the Rydberg constant. Such a set of lines is called a *series* and it will be seen from Fig. 240 that the lines become closer together as we move towards shorter wave lengths, crowding up to a definite *series limit* $\left(\nu = \dfrac{R}{4}\right)$ in the ultra-violet. Since Balmer's time it has been found that there are several other series of this type in the spectrum of hydrogen, all of which can be represented in a similar manner. Thus there is a series whose frequencies are given by :—

$$\nu = R\left(\frac{1}{1^2} - \frac{1}{n^2}\right), \quad n = 2, 3, 4, \ldots$$

All these lines lie in the ultra violet, crowding up to a series limit at $\nu = R$. They were discovered by LYMAN and the series is named after him. Similarly there are series in the infra-red, given by $R.\left(\frac{1}{3^2} - \frac{1}{n^2}\right), \ n = 4, 5, \ldots$ (Ritz-Paschen) ; $R\left(\frac{1}{4^2} - \frac{1}{n^2}\right), n = 5, 6, \ldots$ (Brackett) ; and so on. In fact, it turns out that the whole spectrum can be represented by the single equation

$$\nu = R\left(\frac{1}{n_1^2} - \frac{1}{n_2^2}\right)$$

where n_1, n_2, are given integral values ; that is, the frequency of every line can be represented as the difference of two members of the sequence $R, \ \dfrac{R}{4}, \ \dfrac{R}{9}, \ \dfrac{R}{16}, \ \ldots \ \dfrac{R}{n^2}, \ \ldots$ These quantities are called the *terms* of the hydrogen spectrum. This leads to a very simple and important way of representing the spectrum by a diagram, as shown in Fig. 241 in which a set of horizontal lines is drawn such that their distances below the line 00′ are proportional to the values of the terms, i.e. R, R/4, R/16. . . . Then the frequency of any line is given by the vertical separation between the corresponding two terms. Thus, the Lyman series is represented in the diagram by the group of vertical lines ending on the lowest term level, the Balmer series by the group ending on the second level and so on, as indicated in the figure. Obviously the number of terms required is far less than the number of lines.

Now it has been found that in many spectra similar series occur and that in every case it is possible to represent all the lines of the spectrum as differences between different members of a set of terms. Of course, in the more complex spectra it is far more difficult to sort out the different series and the separate terms are not given by such a simple expression as in the case of hydrogen. In many cases it is possible to represent the spectrum by means of *four* distinct sequences

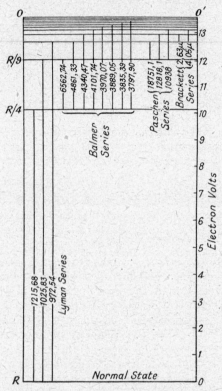

FIG. 241.—Terms (and Energy Level) Diagram for Hydrogen.

of terms (instead of just *one* for hydrogen) and the terms can be expressed in the form $R/(n + \alpha)^2$, where R is the same as before, n takes on a series of integral values and the quantity α has a different value for each of the four sets of terms.

It is usual to denote these four term sequences by the

symbols S, P, D and F.   As an example we give in Fig. 242
a simplified diagram indicating the sets of terms required
for the sodium spectra.   Lines are again drawn (cross-wise
for convenience) connecting those terms whose differences

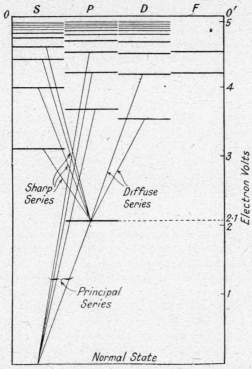

FIG. 242.—Terms (and Energy Level) Diagram for Sodium.

give a line of the spectrum.   It will be noticed that we do
not have a line corresponding to every term difference.
The difference between the lowest S term and the various
P terms gives a series (known as the *principal series*) ; those
between the lowest P term and the higher S terms give another
series (the *sharp series*), while those between the lowest P term

and the higher D terms give yet another series (the *diffuse series*) and so on.

Sources of Light for Spectroscopy. Flame, Arc and Spark Spectra. (Plate IV, *a*, *b*, and *c*).

The position is not quite so simple as indicated in the previous section. In point of fact we find that *each* element can give several quite distinct spectra. In order to explain this, let us first note briefly the various ways in which spectra are produced in the laboratory.

It is usual to distinguish four main methods ; (1) flame, (2) arc, (3) spark, (4) Geissler tube. The first of these we have already noted. With the relatively low temperature of the bunsen flame this is limited to metals which are easily volatilised, such as the alkali metals. By employing flames of higher temperature, e.g. the oxyhydrogen flame—the method can be extended to many other metals. The second and fourth methods will be clear from the description of the arc and Geissler tube given in the section (page 225) on sources of light. In the case of most metals an arc can be obtained between electrodes of the same substance, in which case the arc flame gives principally the spectrum of the pole material while the surrounding gas gives rise, as a rule, to band spectra (from the oxides and nitrides of the substance). For other substances the usual procedure is to use a carbon arc, hollow out the electrodes, and pack these with the material to be examined (as in the flame arcs referred to on page 222). The Geissler tube provides the usual method of examining the spectra of gases ; the tube, filled with the required gas at a low pressure, is connected across an induction coil.

In the third method a spark is produced between electrodes of the required metals by connecting these to the poles of an induction coil. A condenser (such as a Leyden jar) is connected across the spark gap. Without this, the spark obtained is quiet and not very intense, giving mainly the spectrum of the surrounding gas ; but with a suitable condenser the spark becomes a very bright source, rich in radiation characteristic of the electrodes.

Now if the same substance is examined, but these different methods of excitation are used, it is found that different spectra are obtained. Thus, taking sodium as an example, the flame spectrum shows practically only the D-lines, whereas, with a sodium arc we get a spectrum containing many other lines in addition. Again, if we use a spark between two pieces of sodium, we find that certain of the arc lines are weaker or have even disappeared, while certain other lines occur with much-increased intensity ; in addition there are a number of quite new lines. We can thus distinguish the three different kinds of spectra—flame, arc, and spark. In the early days of spectroscopy, many investigations were made of the different spectra of a given element obtained by various methods of excitation. Those lines which were either weak or non-existent in the arc, but appeared strongly in the spark, were called *enhanced lines*. This term is not much used now since, as we shall explain later, modern developments of the theory of light emission have led to a complete understanding of this whole question of the influence of conditions of production on the character of the spectra obtained.

Absorption Spectra.—If light from some source emitting radiation of a continuous range of wave lengths is passed through a layer of some non-opaque material it is often found on examining the transmitted light in a spectroscope, that the spectrum has certain dark regions, showing that the radiation of the corresponding wave lengths has been absorbed. This is called an *absorption* spectrum. Just as for emission spectra, we again find both continuous and line absorption spectra. For solids and liquids the absorption varies with the wave length in a continuous manner, giving spectra crossed by dark bands. The number, position, width and general character, (i.e. sharpness, etc.) depend in a characteristic way on the nature of the absorbing material. A piece of cobalt glass, for example, shows three such bands in the visible region, a broad one at the position 5,300 Å, and two narrower ones near 5,900 Å and 6,500 Å. Plate IV*d* shows an example of the absorption spectrum of a solution.

No substance is transparent for all wave lengths and those

such as glass, quartz, etc., which show no marked absorption in the visible, have absorption regions in the ultra-violet and infra-red. Thus ordinary crown glass begins to absorb strongly at about 3,530 Å in the ultra-violet and at 23,000 Å in the infra-red. The transparency range for quartz is about 1,800–40,000, that of rock salt from 1,750 to 140,000 ; hence the use of these substances in the construction of prisms for investigations of the ultra-violet and infra-red respectively. By altering the composition of glasses, their absorption characteristics can be greatly altered. Thus glasses have been produced which will transmit considerably further into the ultra-violet than ordinary glass, for example, the so-called " Uviol " or " Vita " glasses which are sometimes used for windows ; while others have been made which give much stronger absorption in the infra-red. A particularly interesting example is Wood's glass which absorbs nearly all the visible but transmits about as much in the ultra-violet as ordinary crown glass. This glass is much used in the study of fluorescence.

Since every substance has its own characteristic absorption spectrum, it is possible to use this as a means of identification, just as emission spectra are used. This has given rise to a highly developed technique of absorption spectroscopy, which has been applied to the study of dyes, drugs, oils, glasses, etc., and in many other directions.

In contrast to solids and liquids, gases have absorption spectra with narrow sharp lines ; that is, absorption takes place for certain definite isolated wave lengths. We have already noted an example of such spectra in the Fraunhofer lines. In certain cases gases also show regions of continuous absorption, but it is the sharp lines that constitute their chief characteristic. The frequencies of these lines agree precisely with those of certain of the emission lines of the gas ; it is always found, however, that there are far fewer lines in the absorption spectrum than in the emission spectrum.

Origin of Line Spectra. Bohr's Theory.—Year after year the spectroscopists accumulated vast stores of facts, but although everyone realised that in them a great story lay hidden, no advance towards deciphering their meaning was made until 1913. In that year the long-sought key—the Rosetta stone of the language of the spectra—was found by Niels Bohr, of Copenhagen, and once again it was in a brilliant application of Planck's quantum theory that the way was found. Bohr's arguments were based on the now well-known and widely accepted planetary or nuclear theory of atomic structure which had at that time been recently proposed by Rutherford. According to this theory, an atom can be pictured as consisting of a central positively-charged nucleus—responsible for practically the entire mass of the atom—around which a number of electrons move in various orbits. The charge on the nucleus is Ze where Z is the atomic number and e is the fundamental unit of electric charge ; and since in a neutral atom the total charge must be zero, the number of " planetary " electrons is Z. Now some very simple considerations are sufficient to show that such an atom could not be governed by ordinary mechanical and electrical laws. If it were, it should be steadily radiating energy in the form of waves whose frequencies were those of the electron motions, and, as the atom thereby continuously lost energy, the electrons would spiral in towards the nucleus with increasing frequencies of revolution. Thus, the frequencies of the emitted waves would continuously increase and finally the electrons would collide with the nucleus. Moreover, whenever such an atom collided with another—which happens millions of times per second—it would be bound to have its electron motions entirely altered. It is clear, in fact, that atoms built in this way could not exist, if they obeyed ordinary rules of mechanics. And yet there was very strong evidence for Rutherford's picture. So Bohr cut the Gordian knot by ignoring the ordinary ideas and looked at the whole matter afresh, fixing his mind on Planck's idea and the now well-established *term* principle. We have seen that according to the former whenever an atom emits radiation of frequency ν it does so by emitting a definite quantum or photon of energy equal to $h\nu$. Now since energy is neither created nor destroyed this must be equal to the difference between the energy of the atom before and after the emission.   That is, we can wri..

$$\begin{pmatrix}\text{Energy of}\\ \text{Emitted photon}\end{pmatrix} = \begin{pmatrix}\text{Energy of}\\ \text{atom } before\\ \text{Emission}\end{pmatrix} - \begin{pmatrix}\text{Energy of Atom}\\ after \text{ Emission.}\end{pmatrix}$$

or dividing through by h,

$$\begin{pmatrix}\text{Frequency}\\ \text{of Emitted}\\ \text{photon}\end{pmatrix} = \begin{pmatrix}\dfrac{\text{Energy of}}{\text{Atom before}}\\ \dfrac{\text{Emission}}{h}\end{pmatrix} - \begin{pmatrix}\dfrac{\text{Energy of}}{\text{Atom after}}\\ \dfrac{\text{Emission}}{h}\end{pmatrix} \quad . \quad . (1)$$

That is, we have the frequency expressed as the difference between two quantities, and it suggests itself at once that there must be some connection between this and the fact that the frequency can be expressed as the difference between two terms.   Bohr explained this connection in the following way. He assumed that the atom could only exist in certain states —which he called *Stationary states*. While in one of these states it had a perfectly definite energy and did not radiate at all.   Radiation took place only when the atom changed suddenly from one possible state to another of lower energy and in such a " transition " the frequency v of the radiation emitted was such that the value of the corresponding quantum, i.e. hv, was just equal to the difference between the values of the energy of the atom in the two states.   Absorption of energy, on the other hand, caused a transition of the atom from some stationary state to another of greater energy and hence the atom could only absorb energy in certain definite " quanta " at a time.   Thus, according to Bohr, the various " terms " represented the different values of the energy of the atom corresponding to its possible stationary states.   The state of lowest energy would be the ordinary or *normal* state of the atom, while the others of higher energy are called *excited* states.   The various possible energy values may be denoted E_0, E_1, E_2, etc. . . ., where E_0 is the energy in the normal state and E_1, E_2, . . . the values for the excited states in order of increasing energy.   Thus in Fig. 241 the lowest line corresponds to the normal state with an energy

E_0, the one immediately above to the next possible state with energy E_1, and so on, each line representing what may be called an *energy-level* of the atom. The numbers on the right-hand side give the energies of each state (in electron volts) reckoned from the normal state of the atom as zero. Thus for hydrogen the atom in the lowest excited state has an energy of 10·15 electron-volts more than the normal state. Clearly with these ideas there arises the important problem of dis-covering for any atom how the various stationary states are determined, and of calculating the corresponding values of the energy. Bohr succeeded in doing this *for the simple case of the hydrogen atom* and it will help to make the idea of stationary states clearer if we consider this case a little further.

The Hydrogen Spectrum.—The hydrogen atom consists of a single electron revolving round a far heavier positive nucleus (usually now called a *proton*). Bohr assumed that the electron moved in circular paths or orbits, and further, that only orbits of certain particular sizes were possible. These possible orbits were determined by the requirements that for them the momentum of the electron multiplied by the circum-ference of the orbit must be an exact multiple of Planck's constant, i.e. equal to $n.h$ where n is an integer, called the quantum number of the orbit. This seemed a very curious condition to impose and Bohr could suggest no reason for it, except that it led to the right results. He worked out the values of the energy of the atom for these particular orbits and found they could be expressed in the form

$$E_n = A - \frac{B}{n^2}$$

where E_n is the energy for the nth orbit (i.e. the one for which the product of momentum and circumference $= nh$) and A and B are two constants. He found also that the radii of the different orbits were proportional to n^2. Four of these orbits are shown in Fig. 243. In the normal unexcited state of the atom, the electron moved in the smallest orbit, that for which $n = 1$, while the other values of n gave larger orbits, with greater values of E, corresponding to the various possible

z

excited states. It will be noted that the word *stationary* applied to these various states was not intended to mean that the electron was not moving, but only that while the atom was in any one of them its energy was constant and it did not radiate. Emission of light took place only when the electron suddenly changed its orbit from one of the possible values to another nearer to the nucleus. Thus, if the change or transition was from the $n_2{}^{th}$ orbit to the $n_1{}^{th}$, the difference

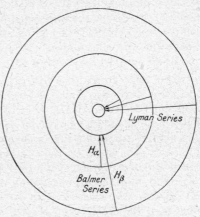

Fig. 243.—Hydrogen Bohr Orbits.

between the energies for these two states was radiated as a photon whose energy $h\nu$ was given by

$$h\nu = \left(A - \frac{B}{n_2{}^2}\right) - \left(A - \frac{B}{n_1{}^2}\right)$$

i.e. $\nu = \dfrac{B}{h}\left(\dfrac{1}{n_1{}^2} - \dfrac{1}{n_2{}^2}\right).$

Now this is, as we have seen, exactly the kind of formula which represents the *experimental results* and the most astonishing thing of all was that the value of $\dfrac{B}{h}$ calculated by Bohr came out precisely equal to the value of R ($3 \cdot 29.10^{15}$) found by the spectroscopists. By putting $n_1 = 1$, and $n_2 = 2, 3, \ldots$ **we** get the lines of the Lyman series ; that is, these arise when the electron suddenly changes from some outer orbit to the innermost. On the other hand, Balmer's series are given by setting $n_1 = 2$, $n_2 = 3$, 4, . . . that is, here the jumps are all from some higher orbit into the second one. Similarly all the other series were explained.

More Complex Atoms.—Bohr's success in explaining the hydrogen spectrum at once commanded attention for his theory. At first great difficulties were encountered in applying it to more complex atoms. In these, there is not just one, but a system of electrons, and Bohr's simple condition for picking out the possible orbits could not be applied. However, the laws governing the movements of electrons within the atom have gradually been discovered, and now quite complex spectra can be completely explained. It is worth noting here that in a large number of cases it has been shown that the " transitions " giving rise to the various lines of the optical spectrum can be regarded as consisting simply of alterations in the orbit of *one* of the electrons. Thus, in the case of sodium, which has eleven electrons, one of these is on the whole further from the nucleus than the other ten, and it is from changes in orbit of this outermost electron that the optical spectrum of sodium arises. It would be out of place to go further into these matters here, but it is interesting to consider various general matters connected with spectra in which Bohr's fundamental idea of definite energy states gives at once a simple explanation.

Absorption Lines.—It is possible on Bohr's Theory to explain very simply why in the absorption line-spectrum of a gas, only certain of the emission lines appear. In a cool gas all the atoms will be in their normal or unexcited state, and, therefore, only those photons can be absorbed whose energies are just sufficient to raise the atom from this normal state into one of its excited states. Hence only those lines of the emission spectrum which arise from transitions back to the normal state will appear in the absorption spectrum. Thus, in the case of sodium, the cool vapour will give an absorption spectrum consisting of the principal series only.

Excitation of Spectra.—Bohr's theory has provided the clue to an understanding of the conditions required for the production of spectra. The atoms can only emit light if they are first excited and for this they must acquire from somewhere the necessary energy. This can happen in various ways, of which we may briefly mention three.

(1) The required energy may be obtained in *collisions* with other atoms. At ordinary temperatures the average kinetic energy of the atoms of a gas is very small (of the order of $\frac{1}{100}$th of an electron-volt) and only a negligible few of them will have kinetic energies much in excess of this. On the other hand, for an atom to pass into an excited state it must receive an amount of energy at least equal to the difference between its normal state and its lowest excited state, and this difference —the minimum excitation energy—is usually of the order of a few electron-volts (10·15 for hydrogen, 2·1 for sodium). Hence at ordinary temperatures an atom cannot obtain from the kinetic energy of any other atom with which it collides sufficient energy to alter its state; all its collisions in such conditions are perfectly elastic. This explains the wonderful stability of the atoms; though they make millions of collisions a second, they are not thereby disturbed from their normal state. However, if the temperature of the gas is gradually raised, their energy of motion increases and eventually a temperature is reached at which a considerable number of the atoms have a kinetic energy equal to, or greater than, the minimum excitation energy. Then some of the collisions will be vigorous enough to raise one of the atoms into the first excited state (of energy E_1), the necessary energy being obtained from the other atom. It then almost immediately emits a photon of energy ($h\nu = E_1 - E_0$) and relapses to its normal state (of energy E_0). That is, the gas will glow with light of just this one frequency. As the temperature is raised still further and more kinetic energy is available at the collisions, atoms will be raised to higher excited states and other lines of the spectrum will appear in the emitted light.

(2) A second method by which atoms may be excited, is by *bombarding them with electrons*. This is the process at work in

sparks, arcs, and in electric discharge lamps such as the sodium, mercury, neon lamps, etc. Many experiments have been done in which electrons of carefully controlled and measured speeds have been made to collide with the atoms of a gas and the resulting light emission studied. Fig. 244 illustrates in a simple form the general idea of these experiments. S is an evacuated glass tube containing a small amount of the gas to be studied. F is a tungsten filament heated by the battery B. As is well known these days, if such a filament is raised to a high temperature, crowds of electrons pour out of its surface. This is, of course, just how the electrons are produced in a " wireless " valve ; in fact the whole arrangement is similar to a 3-electrode valve. G is a

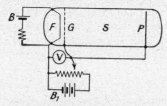

FIG. 244.—Excitation of Spectra by Electron Collision.

metal grid which is connected to another battery B_1 in such a way that it is positively charged relative to F ; that is, an electric field is produced between F and G which accelerates the (negative) electrons towards G. P is a plate connected to G. Most of the electrons on reaching the grid fly through the holes with a velocity which depends on the potential difference between F and G as measured by the voltmeter V. If this is v volts, the energy of the electrons flying through will be v electron-volts. After passing G the electrons are no longer accelerated, since they are moving in the space between G and P which is free from electric forces. The distance between F and G is made small so that very few of the electrons will collide with an atom in this space.

In order to understand what happens let us suppose that the tube contains sodium vapour and let the value of v be slowly increased from zero. So long as v is less than 2·1 volts no light is emitted from the vapour ; the electrons colliding with sodium atoms in the space S have not enough energy to *excite* them and so the collisions are like those of perfectly elastic billiard balls. Immediately, however, the value of v just passes 2·1 volts, we find that light is emitted from the vapour and this light consists simply of the well known D lines. That is, the sodium vapour is giving not its full spectrum but just a single line (or strictly *two* lines very close together). This remarkable result is precisely what we should expect from Bohr's theory. We have seen from Fig. 242 that in order to raise a sodium atom from its normal state to its lowest excited state, it must receive energy equal to 2·1 electron-volts ; it cannot take up less energy than this. Hence, so long as the energy of the electrons remains below this value, they cannot *excite* the atoms at all ; but immediately they attain this value, they can give up in a collision just the amount of energy the atom requires to lift it into its lowest excited level. After this excitation the atom immediately drops back into its normal state, emitting the energy it had gained as a photon of yellow light. As the energy of the colliding electrons is still further increased, they are able to raise the sodium atom into its various other states and hence other lines of the spectrum are emitted. When the value reaches 5·12 volts the complete spectrum is obtained—again as we should expect from the diagram. Experiments of this kind verify in a beautifully direct way Bohr's fundamental ideas.

These considerations have also led to a complete understanding of the relation of flame, arc, and spark spectra. In the flame, far less energy is available for the excitation of the atoms than in the arc, and hence we only obtain a few of the arc lines—namely those corresponding to transitions between the lower excited states. In the spark, on the other hand, the conditions are so much more violent that a considerable proportion of the atoms have one electron completely removed. The positively-charged residue—called an ionised atom—is of course a different structure from an ordinary neutral atom ; but such ionised atoms can exist in certain definite states and hence they will give rise to definite spectra of their own.

It is from ionised atoms that the enhanced lines arise in the spectrum obtained from the spark. We may say that the arc spectrum is derived from a neutral atom, while the spark spectrum arises from an ionised atom. By means of special apparatus it has been found possible to produce sparks so violent that the atoms are not just singly ionised, but are " stripped " of two, three, or more electrons ; each of these doubly, trebly, etc., ionised atoms gives a different spectrum. Thus each atom has a series of spectra, each quite characteristic of it, and it alone. This fact has been of immense value in the study of the temperature of the stars. For instance, if two stars each show lines due to, say, iron, but in one the spark lines are far more intense than in the other, it is reasonable to infer that in the former, conditions are much more violent ; that is, the temperature is higher.

(3) A third way in which atoms may be excited is by absorbing the necessary energy from a beam of light. This so-called *photo-excitation* gives rise to the phenomena of the fluorescence and phosphorescence which we have mentioned earlier in the book. A striking special instance of fluorescence is obtained if we allow a beam of sodium (D) light to fall on a vessel containing sodium vapour at a low pressure. We find that the vapour itself immediately starts emitting light of the same colour. This is easily understood since the photons of the incident light have just the right energy to excite the atoms in the tube into their lowest excited state. Light of any lower frequency would produce no effect. Since in this special case the " fluorescent " light has just the same colour as the exciting light, it is called *resonance radiation*. In the more general case the photons of the exciting light raise the atoms by which they are absorbed into one of their higher levels and they return from this by a series of jumps. Since the photon emitted in each of these must have less energy than that of the " exciting " photon, it is clear (remembering $E = h\nu$) that, in general the *fluorescent light will have a longer wave length* (photons of smaller E) *than the exciting light.* This is

generally found to be the case—and the rule is known as *Stokes' Law*, after Stokes, who first observed it. It is found that there are exceptions to this rule and the reason is not far to seek. Suppose the atom were *already* in an excited state when a photon of the exciting radiation struck it and thereby raised it into a still higher level. If it then passed back into its normal state in a single jump, then the photon emitted would have a greater energy than that absorbed ; that is, the fluorescent light would have a shorter wave length.

There is no essential distinction between phosphorescence and fluorescence, the only difference being that in the former case the excited atoms do not immediately return to their normal state after excitation, so that when the exciting light is cut off, the emission of light from the materials continues for some time after, varying from a fraction of a second to maybe weeks. Such cases of " delayed " return occur as we might expect with solids ; here the excited atoms after absorbing a photon of the incident light are in some way—owing to their interaction with neighbouring atoms—kept in an excited state for some time.

Doppler, Zeeman and Stark Effects.—We have said that every atom radiates light of a perfectly definite and constant set of frequencies. We ought to add that these frequencies can be slightly modified by alterations of the conditions of emission. These changes are very small, but they are of great interest and their investigation has added much to our knowledge. We will consider briefly the three principal causes of such variations.

(1) *Doppler Effect.*—The principle of the effect is well known in the study of sound. If a source of sound, emitting a note of frequency v is moving with a constant velocity V relative to an observer, the latter perceives a sound having a frequency v' differing from v, being greater or less according as the source is moving towards or away from the observer. This acoustical phenomenon was first explained by Doppler and is named after him. But Fizeau showed that the same effect occurs with light. Thus, if source of light is moving relative to the spectroscope the wave length λ' of the radiation observed

in the latter will be slightly different from the value λ it would have if there were no such relative motion. It can be shown that the difference of wave length, $\lambda' - \lambda$ is given approximately by the equation

$$\frac{\lambda' - \lambda}{\lambda} = \frac{V}{c},$$

where V is the velocity of the source resolved along the line joining it to the observer, and c is the velocity of light. λ' will be greater or smaller than λ according as the source is moving away from or toward the observer. It will be seen at once that as c is so great (186,000 miles per second), V must be very large for the change in wave length to be appreciable. It is not surprising, therefore, that we find the most striking instances of this effect in the light from the stars, whose velocities relative to the earth are in many cases very great. When the light from a star is analysed we find in its spectrum the same series of lines with which we are familiar with terrestrial sources. From this we realise that the whole visible universe is built up of the same kinds of atoms as those of which our own earth is formed, and we can obtain from the spectrum of each star information about its constitution. This is an application on a grand scale of spectrum analysis. There is still more information to be had from these stellar spectra. It is found that the various lines do not occur in precisely the same place as they do for the same atoms in a laboratory source; instead, they are all displaced somewhat, either towards the red or the violet end. Everything indicates that we are right in regarding this as an example of a Doppler effect and thus we have a means of obtaining the velocities of the stars relative to the earth. Those that show a " red shift " must be moving away and those with a " violet shift " towards us. By exact measurement the actual velocities can be calculated; for example, we find that Sirius is moving away from us at a speed of 47 km/sec.

There are many beautiful examples of this effect in astrophysics. It is known, for instance, that the sun is rotating and, hence, we should expect that if the light from one edge of the equatorial zone, say, that which is moving towards us, is observed, the Fraunhofer lines would show a slight violet shift, whereas in the light from the opposite extremity there would be a red shift. This is found to be the case and by exact measurements the speed of rotation of this zone of the sun's surface can be calculated. Now the motion of sun-spots gives another way of measuring this speed and it is found that the value calculated in this way agrees with that obtained from the Doppler effect, thus providing a check on the correctness of the theory of the latter. Observations of a similar kind on the Fraunhofer lines in the sun's light reflected from the planets have led to the solution of many problems concerned with their rotation. Again, it is now known that many stars are *double* ones, consisting of two bodies rotating round each other ; in some of these only one of the partners is luminous, in others both are so. Even in the latter case the star always appears as a single one in a telescope, since the components are too close for the highest resolving power (see page 292) to separate them. Our knowledge of their true nature is due to another bit of detective work based on Doppler's principle. In the first case—that with only one component luminous—we find the spectrum lines show a periodic to-and-fro motion, whereas in the other type having both components luminous, each line appears as a doublet, each component moving to and fro, crossing and recrossing the other. It is easy to see that this is precisely what we should expect.

Zeeman Effect.—Nearly a hundred years ago, Faraday, suspecting there must be some relation between magnetism and light, placed a sodium flame between the poles of a strong electromagnet, and observed the D line in the spectroscope, hoping to find it was in some way modified. He failed, however, to observe any alteration ; but years later, in 1896, Zeeman working with a spectroscope of much higher resolving power, succeeded in detecting an effect. He discovered that the magnetic field causes each line of the spectrum to be split into a group of lines very close together. It is found that the effect is different according to the direction in which the light is observed relative to that of the field. Thus, in the simplest case, if the direction of observation is perpendicular to the field (the so-called transverse effect) a group of three lines is obtained, one in the position of the original line, and one at the same frequency difference on each side, whereas the light emitted parallel to the field (the longitudinal effect) shows only two lines, one on each side of the position of the original line, which is here missing. Moreover, each line is polarised in a characteristic way.

An explanation of this particular case—called the normal Zeeman effect—was at once given by the great Dutch physicist Lorentz, and at the time of its discovery formed one of the strongest grounds for the belief that light was due to the motion in the atom of negatively charged particles.

It was soon discovered, however, that in general, far more complex groups of lines are obtained. Thus, with sodium D lines, we find one of them ($\lambda = 5,896.10^{-8}$ cm.) gives a group of four lines, while the other ($\lambda = 5,890.10^{-8}$ cm.) gives a pattern containing six lines. In other cases still more complex groups are found, sometimes containing as many as 16 lines. The particular pattern obtained is always the same for spectral lines of the same series, and this fact has helped greatly in the analysis of the more complex spectra. The pattern is always symmetrical with regard to the original line, and the separation of each line from the normal is proportional to the strength of the field. These more complicated cases were at first quite inexplicable and, hence, they were called the anomalous Zeeman effect. By the application of the ideas of the quantum theory, they have now been completely interpreted.

It is interesting to note that by studying the Zeeman effect observed in the Fraunhofer lines, it has been found possible to obtain information about the magnetic field of the sun.

Stark Effect.—After the discovery of the Zeeman effect, it was natural that the question should be raised as to whether the light emitted from a source placed in an electric field would show any similar effect. After various unsuccessful efforts by others, an effect of this type was discovered in 1913 by Stark, who used very strong fields. Again it was found that each spectral line was split into a group symmetrically arranged on either side of the original position.

Band Spectra of Molecules.—In recent years it has been shown that the same fundamental Quantum principles which are so successful in interpreting the line spectra of atoms can also be used to explain the still more complex band spectra. As we have already noted, experiment shows that these spectra must originate in molecules, and just as, with the quantum theory as guide, the study of line spectra has led to a vast increase in our knowledge of atoms, so the analysis of the band spectra is now proving a powerful means of studying the structure of molecules. It is found that here also the fundamental principles of Bohr hold true. The molecules can exist in certain stationary states only, and in each such state its energy has a definite value ; thus, every type of molecule has its characteristic set of energy levels, and the emission of radiation arises only when the molecule changes from one state to another of lower energy. In the case of molecules, however, there are many more of these levels and the number of possible transitions is accordingly much greater, giving a spectrum with many more lines.

Some idea of the general character of the spectrum of a molecule may be obtained by considering a special case. Let us consider the molecule of hydrogen chloride, HCl. This consists of a hydrogen atom and a chlorine atom joined together, forming a structure which we may compare with a dumb-bell ; the nuclei of the two atoms again account for most of the mass of the molecule and the electrons move round these in various orbits. Now we can conveniently regard the energy of such a molecule as made up of three parts :—(1) it can rotate as a rigid body about an axis perpendicular to the line joining the two nuclei ; this gives a certain rotational energy, E_r ; (2) the two nuclei can vibrate along the line joining them and, hence, there is a definite vibrational energy, E_v ; (3) the system of electrons possesses a certain energy which we may call the electronic energy, E_e. The total energy E of the molecule may thus be expressed as

$$E = E_e + E_v + E_r.$$

According to the general ideas already explained, we should

expect that the electron energy could only have certain definite values $(E_e)_0$, $(E_e)_1$, etc., corresponding to different possible orbital motions, and it turns out that for the other two parts of the energy the same kind of limitation holds, so that each of them can have not just *any* value, but only one of a definite series of values, which we may denote $(E_v)_0$, $(E_v)_1$, . . . and $(E_r)_1$, $(E_r)_2$, . . . etc. Furthermore, experiment shows that the differences between the various values of E_e are much greater (of the order of a few electron-volts) than the differences between different values of E_v (a few tenths of an electron-volt), and these again are considerably greater than the differences between the various possible rotational energies (E_r), (of the order of a few hundredths of an electron-volt). Suppose now that a change of state of the molecule occurs, in which only E_r changes from a higher to a lower value, E_e and E_v remaining unaltered. The energy change is very small and we find that the radiation emitted has a correspondingly low frequency, being in the far infra-red. A group of such lines in this part of the spectrum is actually found and these form the so-called *pure-rotation* part of the spectrum of the molecule. Again, it may happen that a change takes place in which E_e still remains constant, but both E_v and E_r alter. In this case, the energy change is about ten times greater and we obtain a group of lines in the near infra-red ; this part of the radiation from the molecule is called the *rotation-vibration* spectrum. Finally, it may happen that we have changes in which all three components of the energy change their values and in this case, owing to the much greater energy changes involved in alterations of the electron motions, the radiation emitted lies in the visible or even ultra-violet. Since, in this case simultaneous changes in all three parts of the energy may occur, we should expect, and we actually find, very complex groups of lines. These constitute the so-called *electron* bands of the spectrum. We thus see in a general way how the three parts of the complete emission spectrum of a molecule can be understood. The more complex the molecule the more complicated the spectrum, and so far only some of the simpler ones have been completely analysed.

Raman Effect.—In connection with this subject of molecular spectra, it is interesting to mention an effect discovered in 1928 by Raman in India. When a beam of light is passed through a transparent medium—solid, liquid, or gas—it is found that however clear or homogeneous the medium may be, there is always a certain amount of light scattered sideways out of the beam. This effect was studied many years ago by Tyndall and Rayleigh, and we have seen earlier in the book

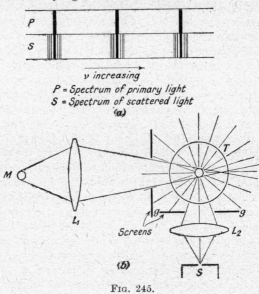

ν increasing
P = Spectrum of primary light
S = Spectrum of scattered light
(a)

(b)

Fig. 245.

how the latter used it to explain the blue colour of the sky. In all this earlier work it was assumed that all the scattered radiation had exactly the same wave length as that of the primary beam. Raman, however, discovered that this is not the case. He showed that if the incident light has a frequency ν, the scattered light, in addition to radiation of the same frequency, contains light of frequencies $\nu \pm \nu_1$, $\nu \pm \nu_2$, . . . The frequencies ν_1, ν_2, . . . are quite independent of the value of ν, and are characteristic of the molecules of the scattering substance ; they are called the Raman spectrum of the molecule (Fig. 245, a). Thus, if the spectrum of the incident light consists of a number of lines, the scattered light has a spectrum consisting of the same lines, each flanked in precisely the same way by a group of close neighbours on either side. These lines of modified wave length—or *Raman lines*—are, of course, very much weaker than the unaltered (or Tyndall) lines, and, moreover, those of smaller frequency are more intense than those of higher frequency.

Raman's experimental arrangement is indicated in Fig. 245, b. Light from a source M—a mercury arc is very convenient—is focused by a lens L_1 on to a tube, T, containing the liquid to be studied. The light scattered laterally is collected by L_2 and focused on the slit, S, of the spectrograph. It is very important that all stray light shall be prevented—by suitably placed screens g—from entering the slit.

It is found that the Raman spectrum is very closely correlated with the infra-red spectrum of the molecule, and since the experimental technique is far easier in the visible than in the infra-red, a vast number of investigations of the Raman effect have already been made and a great deal of information about molecular structure thereby obtained.

The full explanation of the Raman effect again requires the quantum theory and, indeed, it was predicted on the basis of this theory by Smekal, five years before its discovery. The general lines of the interpretation may be stated briefly in this way. If a photon of the incident light strikes a molecule, it may be scattered or deflected off its path into some other direction without loss of energy ; this would give the unmodified or Tyndall scattering. On the other hand, it may be that during the collision of the photon and molecule, the latter is raised into one of its excited states with a higher value of vibrational or rotational energy, the necessary quantum of energy, (say $h\nu_1$) being obtained from the photon, which is thus scattered with a lower energy ($h\nu - h\nu_1$) ; that is, the scattered light has a lower frequency. Again, it may occasionally happen that the photon strikes a molecule which is already in an excited state and that in the scattering process the molecule returns to a lower state giving energy to the photon which then flies on with an energy equal to $h\nu + h\nu_1$; in this case the scattered light would have a higher frequency than the incident light. This latter process is less likely to occur than the previous one and, hence, it is understandable that the Raman lines on the long wave length side should have less intensity than those on the side of shorter wave length.

QUESTIONS. XVII.

1. Give a brief description of common methods used in the examination of spectra.

2. What do you know of the quantum theory ? How does the photoelectric effect support the theory ?

3. Distinguish between continuous and discontinuous spectra.

4. Give a short description of the hydrogen spectrum.

5. What is an absorption spectrum ? Account for the presence of only a limited number of emission lines.

6. What do you know of Bohr's theory ? Of what value is it ?

7. Give an account of one or two methods of producing spectra.

8. How has the Doppler effect been used to identify double stars ?

9. What is the Zeeman effect and how may it be explained ?

10. Distinguish between band and line spectra.

11. What is the Raman effect ? How may it be explained on the quantum theory ?

APPENDIX

Reflection and Refraction.

1. Describe the formation of primary and secondary rainbows. (Trinity Gr.)

2. Two parallel sided plates of glass are cemented together so as to enclose a thin film of air. Show that if the system is immersed in water a ray of light will cease to be transmitted when its angle of incidence on the first glass surface is greater than the critical angle between water and air. How can the principle of total reflection be employed to determine the refractive index of a solid ? (H.C.)

3. Find an expression for the apparent movement of an object when a parallel-sided plate of refracting material is inserted between the object and the eye, the faces of the plate being perpendicular to the line of vision.

Describe some practical method based on this phenomenon for determining the refractive index of a solid. (H.C.)

4. A point object is placed inside a glass sphere of radius r and refractive index μ at a distance r/μ from the centre. Show that all rays from the object which are refracted out of the sphere emerge in a direction which passes through a point on the axis at a distance μr from the centre of the sphere. (Selwyn.)

5. The base of a tank is a horizontal plate of glass 5 cm. thick of refractive index 1·6. On this is a layer of liquid of refractive index 1·5 and of thickness 10 cm., and on this liquid floats a layer of water 10 cm. thick of refractive index 4/3. An observer looking vertically downwards observes a spot on the lower side of the base. What is the apparent position of the spot ?

What would be the difference if the observer's eye were under the surface of the water ? (Trinity Gr.)

353

Lenses and Mirrors.

1. Calculate the focal length of (a) a bi-convex, (b) a concavo-convex lens, the radii of curvature of the faces being 10 cm. and 15 cm. and the refractive index of the material of which it is made being 1·5. (Pembroke.)

2. Two convex lenses each of 20 cm. focal length are set up coaxially 5 cm. apart. An image of a flagstaff 200 m. distant and 10 m. high is formed by the combination. Find the position and size of the image. (H.C.)

3. Show that the focal length of a thin lens can be calculated from a knowledge of the refractive index and the radii of curvature of the two faces.

What will be the focal length in water of a bi-convex lens whose radii of curvature are 10 cm. and 15 cm. ? (Refractive index of water 1·33 ; of glass 1·5.) (H.C.)

4. Find the changes in position and magnification of the image formed by a convex lens as the object moves from an infinite distance up to the lens.

A convex lens of focal length 10 cm. is placed 15 cm. from a concave lens of the same focal length. An object is placed 20 cm. from the convex lens (on the side away from the concave lens). Draw two rays from the object to its final image and determine its position graphically or otherwise. (H.C.)

5. A ray of light from a point on the axis of a thin double convex lens is refracted at the first surface of the lens, internally reflected at the second surface and refracted out again at the first surface. Under what conditions is the final image real ?

Show that if the second surface of the lens is plane and the refractive index of the glass is 1·5, the arrangement is equivalent to a concave mirror of focal length equal to the radius of curvature of the first surface. (Selwyn.)

6. Find an expression for the focal length of a combination of two thin lenses in contact.

A symmetrical convex glass lens, the radii of curvature of which are 3 cm., is situated just below the surface of a tank of water which is 40 cm. deep. An illuminated scratch on the bottom of the tank is viewed vertically downwards through the lens and the water. Where is the image and where should the eye of the observer be placed in order to see it ? The refractive indices of the glass and water may be taken as 3/2 and 4/3 respectively. (H.C.)

7. A metal plate containing an illuminated circular hole is placed at one end of an optical bench and a screen at the other. By means of a convex lens an image of the hole is formed on the screen, the diameter of the image being 2·25 cm. If the lens is moved 20 cm. along the bench an image of the hole again appears on the screen, its diameter being now 1·00 cm. What is the real size of the hole, and how far is it from the screen ? (H.C.)

8. How may a convex lens and a plane mirror be combined to give an image of a pin coincident with the object and (a) erect, (b) inverted ? Give diagrams showing how the image is formed, and explain how the focal length of the lens may be determined in each case. (H.C.)

9. Show that for a very short object the longitudinal magnification produced by a lens is equal to the square of the transverse. (H.C.)

10. A parallel beam of light falls on a double convex lens, the axis being parallel to the beam. After passing through the lens the light falls on a screen whose plane is at right angles to the axis of the lens. Describe carefully the change in the appearance of the screen as the latter is moved from close up to the lens to a great distance from it. What would be the change in the image on the screen if (a) a central patch of the lens, (b) an annulus round the lens, were blocked out ? (Trinity Gr.)

11. A double convex meniscus of air is formed by cementing together two watch glasses of radius r. This is placed in a tank of water at a distance d from the object which is itself in the water. Calculate the position of the image seen (a) by an eye placed in the water, (b) by an eye placed outside the water, the meniscus being a distance l from a plane end of the tank. (Refractive index of water = $\frac{4}{3}$.) (Pembroke.)

12. Show that in the case of a thin lens, (a) all rays nearly parallel to the axis falling on the lens at any given point are equally deviated on passing through, (b) the deviation produced is different for different points on the lens and proportional to the distance of the point from the axis of the lens. Hence, derive the usual formula connecting the focal length of the lens, the radii of curvature of its faces and the refractive index of the material. (St. John's Gr.)

13. A pencil of light diverging from a point on the axis of a thin lens is refracted at the first surface of the lens, reflected at the other surface, and then refracted out. Show that the final

A A*

image will be real except when the distance of the luminous point from the lens is less than

$$\frac{rr'}{2\{\mu r - (\mu - 1)r'\}}$$

where r, r' are the radii of the first and second faces of the lens and μ is the refractive index of the lens material. (St. Catharine's and Selwyn.)

14. Two coaxial thin lenses of focal lengths f_1 and f_2 are mounted at a distance d apart. Find the focal length of the equivalent thin lens. Show how it is possible to construct an achromatic combination from two thin lenses of the same material. (St. Catharine's and Selwyn.)

15. Find an expression relating the position of an object to the position of its image as formed in a single spherical refracting surface. A distant object is focused on the ground-glass screen of a camera when the screen is at a distance of 10 cm. from the lens. If the camera is filled with water of refractive index 1·3, what will be the new distance of the screen from the lens when the object is in focus, assuming that the face of the lens nearest to the screen is convex and has a radius of curvature of 20 cm. ? (St. John's Gr.)

16. What is meant by a caustic curve (or caustic surface) in geometrical optics ? Discuss from this point of view the image of a point object formed by refraction at a plane surface separating a dense from a less dense medium, as well as the images formed when parallel light is incident axially (a) on a spherical, (b) on a parabolic concave mirror. (Pembroke and Queens'.)

17. Discuss the defects of a simple lens when used in optical instruments. (St. Catharine's.)

18. Explain the dispersion produced by a simple lens, and show how the defect may be corrected.

Why is such a correction unnecessary in the case of a simple convex lens used as a magnifying glass held close to the eye ? (H.C.)

19. Explain how two thin lenses in contact are arranged to form an achromatic combination.

Find the focal lengths of thin lenses of flint and crown glass that will give a convergent achromatic combination of focal length 30 cm. (Refractive indices : Flint glass, red 1·644, blue 1·664 ; Crown glass, red 1·514, blue 1·523.) (St. Catharine's and Selwyn.)

20. Discuss briefly two of the principal defects to be found in the image produced by a single lens.

Explain the principle of the " fixed focus " camera. If the lens has a focal length of 20 cm. and a diameter of 4 cm., and if the greatest admissible diameter for the patch of light representing a point image not in focus be 0·02 cm., find the minimum distance from the camera such that all points beyond it to infinity may be in tolerable focus. (St. John's Gr.)

21. A person using spectacles looks over them and is able with one eye to see the moon both directly and also through one of the lenses. The image of the moon is found to be displaced downwards through a distance of one moon diameter. Assuming the moon to subtend an angle of 1° at the eye and the diameter of the spectacle lens to be 3 cm. find the focal length of the lens and explain the defect of vision which it is designed to correct. (St. John's Gr.)

22. What properties should the lens of a camera possess ? Describe in principle how these properties are obtained. Which of them are specially important in the case of the kinematograph camera ? (St. John's Gr.)

23. A watertight camera is provided with a double convex lens having faces of equal radii of curvature, refractive index 1·5 and focal length of 10 cm. It is now immersed in water ($\mu = 1·33$) ; where will the position of the image of a distant object be relative to the lens ? If water were admitted to the body of the camera, what would be the focal length of the lens ? (St. John's Gr.)

Interference.

1. What are the principal characteristics of wave motion ? By considering the refraction of a plane wave at a plane surface show how the laws of refraction of light can be explained on the wave theory. (H.C.)

2. What are the differences between the disturbances which constitute sound and light ? Discuss the evidence in support of your statements. (Trinity Gr.)

3. What are the characteristics of (a) progressive waves and (b) stationary waves ? Show how stationary waves may be produced by the superposition of two trains of progressive waves travelling in opposite directions. How has this phenomenon been applied to the measurement of the velocity of sound ? (Pembroke.)

)

4. Explain the refraction of light on the undulatory theory. Show that the refractive index is the ratio of the velocities of light in the two media. Indicate how the formulæ for the refraction of light by spherical surfaces and by lenses can be obtained on this theory. (Downing.)

5. Apply the principles of the wave theory to find the relation between the focal length of a thin lens, the radii of curvature of the surface and the refractive index of the material.

If a convex lens of focal length 15 cm. made of glass of refractive index 1·52 is totally immersed in a liquid of refractive index 1·35 how will its focal length be affected ? (St. Catharine's and Selwyn.)

6. Discuss Young's arrangement for observing interference fringes. White light from an illuminated slit falls on two narrow slits parallel to the first and to one another and situated 0·05 cm. apart. The interference fringes fall on the slit of a spectroscope parallel to the fringes, situated 1 metre from the two slits and 0·5 cm. to one side of the centre of the fringe system. What will be the appearance of the spectrum ? (St. John's Gr.)

7. Describe Fresnel's method of determining the resultant effect of a plane wave at a point. Plane waves are incident normally upon (a) a circular obstacle, and (b) a circular aperture. Apply Fresnel's method to obtain theoretically the variation of intensity at a point upon the axis in each case as the radius increases from zero. (Pembroke.)

8. A 60° prism is made of glass whose refractive index μ is given by

$$\mu = 1\cdot6074 + \frac{9\cdot36 \times 10^{-11}}{\lambda^2}$$

where λ is the wave length of the light. If light from a mercury arc is passed through the prism at minimum deviation, what will be the angular separation of the yellow and green lines of wave lengths $5\cdot770 \times 10^{-5}$ and $5\cdot461 \times 10^{-5}$ cm. How many lines per centimetre will have to be ruled on a diffraction grating in order to obtain the same angular separation between the mercury yellow and green lines in the first order ? (St. Catharine's and Selwyn.)

9. Explain the formation of Newton's rings between a convex lens and a plane glass plate for monochromatic light. Describe the alteration of the fringe system when a liquid having a refractive index intermediate between that of the lens and that of the plate is introduced into the space between them.

Newton's rings are formed with reflected light of wave length $5,890 \times 10^{-8}$ cm. using a plano-convex lens and a plane glass plate with liquid between them. The diameter of the third bright ring is 2 mm. If the radius of curvature of the curved surface of the lens is 90 cm., find the refractive index of the liquid. (St. Catharine's and Selwyn.)

10. Under suitable conditions two beams of light may combine to produce darkness over limited regions. What are the necessary conditions which must be satisfied if interference fringes are to be produced ? Illustrate your answer by reference to a simple interferometer, such as Fresnel's mirrors.

The interfering sources in a simple interferometer are situated d cm. apart and the fringes produced are observed on a screen D cm. away. Find an expression for the distance between the centres of successive fringes in terms of d and D and hence show that this distance ω is given by

$$\omega = \frac{\lambda}{\phi}$$

where ϕ is the angle subtended at the screen by the two sources and λ is the wave length of the light used. (Downing.)

11. A narrow slit illuminated by monochromatic light, is placed 10 cm. from a bi-prism which has an obtuse angle of $179° 30'$, and is made of glass of refractive index 1·5. Interference fringes are observed in a plane 50 cm. in front of the bi-prism, and it is found that the tenth bright fringe is 6·25 mm. from the central fringe. Calculate the wave length of the light.

A slip of mica of refractive index 1·56 is then placed in contact with one half of the bi-prism and it is found that the central fringe shifts to the place previously occupied by the fourteenth bright fringe. What is the thickness of the mica ? (St. Catharine's and Selwyn.)

12. A thin film is formed between two plane glass plates inclined at a very small angle. Describe exactly how you would measure this angle by an interference method and give the theory of the experiment. (St. Catharine's and Selwyn.)

13. Describe the experimental arrangements you would adopt to view (a) straight sodium fringes, (b) circular sodium fringes, being provided with two half-silvered glass plates and ordinary laboratory apparatus. Describe and explain what would be observed if one of the silver plates were moved slowly in a direction perpendicular to its own plane. (Pembroke.)

14. Give an account of the formation of the colours of thin films. A thin film of air is contained between two parallel faced glass plates, the distance and angle between which can be varied. How would you adjust the plates in order to obtain (a) straight, (b) circular interference fringes ? Describe with the help of diagrams the methods of illumination and of viewing the fringes you would use. (Trinity Gr.)

15. Describe a method of determining the refractive index of a gas. The length of the gas-filled tube of a Jamin refractometer is 20 cm. When the pressure is changed by 50 cm. of mercury, 50 fringes pass the cross wires of the observing telescope. Find the refractive index of the gas for sodium light at a pressure of 76 cm. of mercury and at the temperature of the experiment. You may use the relation $(\mu - 1) = kp$ where p is the density. Mean wave length for sodium D lines = 5,893 Angströms. (St. Catharine's and Selwyn.)

Diffraction.

1. Describe Fresnel's method of dividing a wave front up into zones, and show how it has been applied in the zone plate. (Pembroke.)

2. Describe the physical principles underlying the failure of a photographic lens to produce a point image of a point source, and the methods adopted in the attempts to rectify this defect. (Pembroke.)

3. Describe and explain the distribution of intensity of light on a screen in the neighbourhood of the shadow of a straight edge produced by a point source of illumination. (Pembroke.)

4. Explain the action of the pin-hole camera. Discuss the effect on the image of changing (a) the shape, (b) the size of the aperture. (H.C.)

5. Sunlight passes through a thin flat plate pierced with a number of very small holes of various shapes and sizes. After passing through the plate the light falls on a plane screen parallel to the plate. Describe the appearance of the screen. (Trinity Gr.)

6. Describe and explain the spectra produced by a plane diffraction grating. What would be the effect if the distance between the rulings were (1) very large, (2) very small compared with the wave length ? (Trinity Gr.)

7. Describe exactly how you would use a plane diffraction grating to measure the wave length of the red line in the spectrum of hydrogen. If you used a grating with 6,000 lines to the centi-

metre and a spectrometer reading to one minute, what accuracy would you expect to obtain? (Wave length of H red line = 6.563×10^{-5} cm.) (Selwyn.)

8. When a parallel beam of monochromatic light falls normally on a diffraction grating of m lines per cm. several orders of spectra may be observed, provided the wave length of the light is not too great. What is the limiting value of the wave length if the nth order spectrum is just observable (deviation $= 90°$). Show that by a suitable rotation of the grating it is possible when the latter condition has been realised to reduce the deviation of the nth order spectrum to $60°$. How, and in what circumstances may this change alter the resolving power of the instrument for light of neighbouring wave lengths. (Pembroke and Queens'.)

9. What do you understand by the resolving power of a grating, and upon what factors does this depend?

Two lines in the second order spectrum of a plane grating are just resolved. If the lines are due to light of wave lengths 5,890 and 5,896 A.U., calculate the number of lines in the grating. (Downing.)

Polarisation.

1. Write a short essay on the polarisation of light. (Trinity Gr.)

2. Describe a method of producing a beam of plane polarised light. How would you distinguish between a beam of plane polarised light and a beam of unpolarised light? Is there any other possibility? (Downing.)

3. Elaborate the statement that as far as concerns solid transparent media, Snell's law applies only to amorphous substances and to crystals of the highest type of symmetry. (Pembroke and Queens'.)

4. Describe briefly methods of producing and detecting plane and circularly polarised beams of light. Discuss the interference of light polarised in different planes. (Trinity Gr.)

5. Given a candle and some plane glass plates, how would you obtain plane polarised light? How would you show that it was polarised and what conclusions would you draw from your experiments as to the nature of the disturbance constituting plane polarised light? (Trinity Gr.)

6. What are the grounds for believing that light is a transverse electromagnetic wave motion? (Pembroke.)

Miscellaneous.

1. What is meant by a spectrum ?   Explain the colour of (*a*) the rainbow, (*b*) a thin film of oil on a wet floor.   (St. Catharine's.)

2. What are the factors which affect the diminution in intensity which a parallel beam of white light suffers when passing through the air ?   What advantages are gained by using photographic plates sensitive to light in the infra-red only ?   What would be the characteristics of photographs taken with plates sensitive only to ultra-violet light or of those taken in a thin fog ? (Trinity Gr.)

3. What reasons have we for supposing that X-rays, visible light and ultra-violet and infra-red radiation are essentially similar in nature ?   Compare and contrast briefly their more important properties.   (St. John's Gr.)

4. Employ the wave theory of light to account for the dispersion of light by a transparent prism.   What information about the optical properties of a substance may be gained from measurements relating its refractive index with the wave length it transmits ?   (Pembroke and Queens'.)

5. Give a general account of the solar spectrum and compare the physical properties of the visible and non-visible portions of it.   (H.C.)

6. Describe a method of finding the magnifying power of a telescope experimentally.   Why, for a given size of object glass, is it impossible to distinguish as separate, two points sources which subtend less than a certain angle at the telescope, no matter how the magnifying power is increased ?   (Downing.)

7. Draw a diagram showing the path of rays through a compound microscope from an object point not on the axis when the image is formed coincident with the object at the distance of most distinct vision from the eye.   If this distance is 28 cm., the distance of the object from the objective 4 cm., and the magnifying power of the instrument 14, find the focal length of the lenses. (St. John's Gr.)

8. What effect is produced on the apparent wave length of light waves (*a*) when the source moves and the observer is at rest, (*b*) when the source is at rest and the observer moves.   Discuss some applications of this effect to astronomy and to the broadening of lines emitted from a hot gas.   (Trinity Gr.)

ANSWERS

CHAPTER IV

No. 12. 12 cm. from mirror.
No. 13. 15 cm. from mirror; 7·5 cm. from mirror.
No. 14. 10 cm. and 20 cm.
No. 15. 45 cm. and 22·5 cm. from mirror.
No. 16. Same position as before—image and object coincide.
No. 17. Virtual and erect at 8·57 cm. behind mirror; size 2·57 cm.
No. 18. Object and image coincide.
No. 19. 10·1 cm. behind; 1·56 cm. long. Virtual and erect.

CHAPTER V

No. 2. $\sin\theta = \frac{3}{8}$.
No. 11. $D = 37° 24'$.

CHAPTER VI

No. 8. Size of object 32 cm. Focal length of lens 12 cm.
No. 9. Lens 83·6 cm. or 16·4 cm. from screen.
No. 10. 17·5 cm. in front of lens.
No. 12. Real and inverted, 0·6 cm. from concave lens and 1·8 cm. long.

CHAPTER VII

No. 14. 2·6 cm.

CHAPTER VIII

No. 3. 17·7 cm. approximately.
No. 4. Concave, 200 cm.

CHAPTER XI

No. 5. 45·9 per cent.
No. 6. 10π lumens.
No. 7. $8·3 \cdot 10^5$ candles.

EXAMPLES IN APPENDIX

Reflection and Refraction.

  (5) (*a*) Spot raised 7·71 cm.; (*b*) Spot raised 5·77 cm.

Lenses and Mirrors.

  (1) (*a*) 12 cm.; (*b*) 60 cm. Both convex.

  (2) Position 8·6 cm. from second lens on side remote from object; height 4/7 cm.

  (3) 48 cm.

  (4) Image 10 cm. beyond concave lens.

  (6) Image 12·9 cm. above surface of water. Eye 12·9 + distance of distinct vision (30 cm.) above water.

  (7) Size 1·5 cm., 100 cm. from screen.

 (11) Assuming $\mu = 4/3$, (*a*) Image distance $= 2rd/(2r + d)$ from lens on same side as object; (*b*) Image $\frac{3}{4}$ $(2rl + 2rd + dl)/(2r + d)$.

 (15) 12·97 cm.

 (19) f convex $= 13$ cm. approx; f concave $= 22·94$ cm. Convex lens is crown and concave is flint.

 (20) Approx. 420 cm.

 (21) 86 cm. focal length, concave.

 (23) 15 cm.; 39·1 cm. focal length.

Interference.

  (5) Focal length 62 cm. in liquid.

  (6) Dark line at $\lambda = 0·000050$ cm.

  (8) Angular separation $= 0·343°$; number of lines to cm. $=$ 1923.

  (9) 1·325.

 (11) (*a*) 0·0000455 cm.; (*b*) 0·001136 cm.

 (15) 1·000224.

Diffraction.

  (7) Assuming each setting correct to $\frac{1}{2}$ min. and first order used, accuracy 0·068 per cent.

  (8) Grating set at minimum deviation position. Resolving power increased due to increase in number of lines used and higher order possible.

  (9) 491 lines.

Miscellaneous.

  (7) Focal lengths 3·08 cm., 8·75 cm.

INDEX OF NAMES

INDEX OF SUBJECT MATTER